Mental Health and

Urban Social Policy

Leonard J. Duhl & *Robert L. Leopold*

EDITORS

WITH THE ASSISTANCE OF

Martha Crossen Gillmor

MENTAL HEALTH AND URBAN SOCIAL POLICY

A Casebook of
Community Actions

Jossey-Bass Inc., Publishers
615 Montgomery Street · San Francisco · 1968

MENTAL HEALTH AND URBAN SOCIAL POLICY
A Casebook of Community Actions
Leonard J. Duhl and Robert L. Leopold, Editors

Jossey-Bass, Inc., Publishers
615 Montgomery Street
San Francisco, California 94111

Library of Congress Catalog Card Number: 68-54942

Printed in the United States of America
by York Composition Company, Inc.
York, Pennsylvania

FIRST EDITION

681011

THE JOSSEY-BASS
BEHAVIORAL SCIENCE SERIES

General Editors

WILLIAM E. HENRY, *University of Chicago*

NEVITT SANFORD, *Stanford University and
Wright Institute, Berkeley*

Foreword

Donald A. Schon

ORGANIZATION FOR SOCIAL AND TECHNICAL INNOVATION
CAMBRIDGE, MASSACHUSETTS

The last two presidential administrations have brought to attention what might be called the problem of public learning. Broadly, how do we, as a society, learn from our deliberate efforts to effect orderly social change? More narrowly, how do we learn from our attempts to use federally sponsored programs to carry out the intent of social legislation?

Federal programs of social reform or social change—such as the community mental health center program whose history Leonard Duhl and Robert Leopold sketch in their introduction to this book— tend to fall into a pattern.

There is the conception of a new program that has somehow come into good currency. It responds to the inadequacy of old institutions, to demands for form, or to a sense of crisis. It embodies new ideas, based usually on very limited experience. It is generally clearer in abstract formulation than in application. Not infrequently, it contains the seeds of contradiction, embodying conflicting positions whose compromise permitted passage of the legislation.

Under the new legislation, a sum of money is made available—substantial in itself but considerably below the amount judged essential to an adequate national program.

Administration of these funds rests with a central federal agency.

This agency solicits proposals for local programs on a national basis. In general, local agents "propose" and federal agents "dispose." Guidelines for programs are developed and communicated. Control over local proposals and programs takes the form of the use of the "carrots and sticks" provided by federal funds.

The central office is usually sparsely funded. It is unable to devote much effort to training or technical assistance for those who are to receive funds.

In such a process, how is public learning to occur? How are those charged with central administration, and those engaged in carrying out local programs, to learn about the variety of program designs that have been attempted, and their consequences? How is learning to be generated about the concrete meaning of new legislation, its meaning in application? How are realistic program models that suggest options for local action to be developed? How is there to be developed a documented basis for consultation and technical assistance to local groups?

Mental Health and Urban Social Policy has a number of audiences and objectives. On one level, it is broadly concerned with community mental health service and with the many issues affecting its success or failure. The case histories presented cover a broad range of cultural situations, foreign and domestic, rural and urban, white and Negro, poor and middle class. It represents, therefore, a cross-cultural discussion of community mental health. But its major impact, it seems to me, will be on those concerned in various ways with the development of community mental health centers under the legislation of 1963.

Duhl and Leopold make a contribution to public learning about the process of implementing this legislation by bringing together firsthand accounts of the development of community mental health programs and of endeavors in community psychiatry that throw light on the problems of such programs.

Four main strategies or models emerge from these case histories, each raising its own issues of special concern:

(1) *An outreach or extension of existing psychiatric practice, aimed at populations for whom treatment has been relatively inaccessi-*

ble. This model underlies Leopold's story of a community-oriented private practice. Here the principal concerns are with community acceptance of the utility of psychiatric service, with the problems of relations with existing medical facilities, and with approaches to the shortage of psychiatric manpower.

(2) *Efforts at secondary prevention, whose purpose is to identify mentally ill individuals before their illness has reached crisis proportions.* The rationale for such a program is spelled out in the paper by Henrik Blum and Samuel Susselman. Concerns are with the problems of identifying signals that "flag" mental illness, with systems of information and referral, and with relations to sources of treatment.

(3) *Programs aimed at influencing the mental health climate of a community, through consultation to key institutions such as courts, schools, and other service agencies.* Leopold discusses this model in describing his Philadelphia group practice. Problems tend to relate to the process of consultation itself, to the gaining of entry into relevant agencies, and to determination of the effectiveness of the psychiatric input.

(4) *Programs in which the unit of treatment shifts from individual or family to the community itself, and from the mental illness of individuals to the sickness of communities.* In such programs, the psychiatrist's interventions relate somehow to treatment of the community itself. The account of Sheldon Schiff and Sheppard Kellam comes closest to this model and, understandably, issues of power and political action move from the background to the center of the stage.

The models are by no means mutually exclusive. A particular account may touch on several at once. But they are worth distinguishing because of the significantly different problems they pose for mental health professionals and because of the different goals they represent.

The present book of case histories is, to my knowledge, the first to discuss these issues in any detail and to provide a varied background of documented experience against which public learning about the community mental health center movement can proceed.

As such, it deserves attention.

Preface

*H*undreds of people have been directly and indirectly involved in the preparation of *Mental Health and Urban Social Policy.* Colleagues in psychiatry and in related fields contributed ideas, questioned and criticized our concepts, and suggested new approaches to the papers as well as to the pertinent activities in which we and the authors have been involved. This book is, thus, only one product of a vast network of interchanges among colleagues and friends to whom we express our appreciation. Special thanks go to the group known to themselves as the Space Cadets. They have given both the intellectual and the free-floating support that only the best of friends can supply, and they have been truly sustaining figures in our lives.

We reviewed more than forty-three potential contributions for this book. Some were solicited, others arrived unsought. Some were not used because they did not illustrate the points we were trying to make, and some of those included have been edited and revised. We regret we could not include them all, for each in its own way had much to teach.

Our gratitude and a special dedication go to Robert Hanna Felix, the great master of mental health work, psychiatry, and politics —a teacher who has incomparably led the way. Many of us learned from him much that we know about the problems of the emotionally disturbed in our society—in his role as teacher and as director of the National Institute of Mental Health, and through his impact on his colleagues.

We gratefully acknowledge the editorial assistance of Dorothy S. Kuhn, particularly in her editing of Chapters Two, Three, and Fifteen. Finally to our families, staffs, assistants, and secretaries—Dorothy Cole, Phyllis Krotonsky, Helen Gichner, Marilyn O'Rourke, and Anne Galvin—our thanks.

Berkeley
Philadelphia
New York
September 1968

LEONARD J. DUHL
ROBERT L. LEOPOLD
MARTHA CROSSEN GILLMOR

Contents

The Authors

M. N. Beck, M.D., Department of Health, Division of Mental Health, Charlottetown, Prince Edward Island, Canada

Henrik Blum, M.D., M.P.H., clinical professor of community health planning, School of Public Health, University of California, Berkeley

Daniel DeSole, M.D., Department of Psychiatry, Veterans Administration Hospital, Albany, New York

Leonard J. Duhl, M.D., professor of urban social planning and public health, University of California, Berkeley

Frank Hladky, M.D., director, Tulsa Psychiatric Foundation, Tulsa, Oklahoma

William P. Hurder, M.D., superintendent, Adler Zone Center, University of Illinois; acting director, Institute for Research on Exceptional Children

Jack H. Kahn, M.D., D.P.M., psychiatric adviser, Borough of Newham, London

Robert L. Kahn, Ph.D., associate professor of psychology, Department of Psychiatry, University of Chicago

Sheppard Kellam, M.D., co-director, Woodlawn Mental Health Center, Chicago; associate professor of psychiatry, University of Chicago

Serge Lebovici, M.D., Ancien Médecin Assistant des Hôpitaux de Paris

Robert L. Leopold, M.D., associate professor of clinical psychiatry and director, Division of Community Psychiatry, University of Pennsylvania; director, West Philadelphia Mental Health Consortium

Lester M. Libo, Ph.D., associate professor and director, Behavioral Science Program, Department of Psychiatry, University of New Mexico School of Medicine

Seymour Perlin, M.D., professor of psychiatry, Johns Hopkins University School of Medicine; director of clinical care and training, Henry Phipps Psychiatric Clinic, Johns Hopkins Hospital

Sheldon Schiff, M.D., co-director, Woodlawn Mental Health Center, Chicago; associate professor of psychiatry, University of Chicago

William F. Sears, M.D., adjunct professor, Department of Psychiatry, University of New Mexico School of Medicine

Leon N. Shapiro, M.D., associate professor, Department of Psychiatry, Tufts University School of Medicine

Philip Singer, Ph.D., social affairs officer, Social Development Division, United Nations

Samuel Susselman, M.D., associate clinical professor of psychiatry, University of California School of Medicine; supervising psychiatrist, children's service, Langley Porter Neuropsychiatric Institute, San Francisco

Edward M. Swietnicki, B.S., staff reporter and columnist, *Knickerbocker News*, Albany, New York

This book was prepared between 1960 and 1968, the years which saw the creation of a national mental health program and the eruption of a new urban politics. In national decision making, these two developments stand for a new set of values—values that take into account as never before the voices of the young, the dispossessed, and the alienated; values that ask not for "solutions," but for a rational and flexible *process* for coping with the problems of an ever-changing and turbulent society.

The meaning of our book and its very reason for being depended on the appearance in our national life of those values and on the hope and the promise they offer.

Thus, we dedicate this book to John F. Kennedy and Robert F. Kennedy who so brilliantly symbolize the values, and so valiantly led the way, in the two highly relevant developments that characterized the years of this book's preparation.

Mental Health and

Urban Social Policy

Mental Health and
Political Process

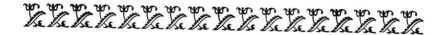

Leonard J. Duhl
UNIVERSITY OF CALIFORNIA, BERKELEY

Robert L. Leopold
UNIVERSITY OF PENNSYLVANIA AND
WEST PHILADELPHIA MENTAL HEALTH CONSORTIUM

Introduction

Psychiatrists, psychologists, psychiatric social workers (all mental health professionals, in fact), in attempting to cure the mentally ill, are concerned not merely with individuals, but with society as well. In the past ten to fifteen years, psychiatrists have begun to recognize the relationship of disease to society. They have begun to move from the concept of single causality to a more comprehensive, ecological approach to mental health. Their concern with human behavior has moved them toward broader sociobiologic concerns. Disease is a socially defined condition, and mental health must be conceived of as a social problem. The etiology of mental health can be looked for not in single factors, but rather in the permutations and combinations of multiple, interacting factors ranging from individual biological differences to environmental changes to the interactive relationships among individuals.

Psychiatry's new orientations are toward the psychopharmacological and biophysical, toward the rediscovery that the hospital is an institution with a sociology of its own, and most recently toward community mental health, a movement that reflects concern for preventive, emergency, and parapsychiatric services in coping with mental disease.

These new orientations have affected the entire mental health

3

profession—its decision-making processes and the ways in which it causes, affects, defines, and corrects the behavior of its patients. As a result, the profession has expanded its attempts to influence "the system," from the individual system to the ecological system. This expansion has not been abrupt; it has been, rather, a gradual and continuing change from concern with individuals to concern with community health.

The purpose of this introduction is to show how these new orientations have changed the mental health community. By chronicling the activities of the National Institute of Mental Health (NIMH) and of several mental health professionals, we hope to demonstrate how (1) one's political actions are determined by his "system-conception," (2) how pressures upon that system may cause it to change, and the scope of one's activities to change accordingly, and (3) how such changes in system-conceptions are brought about by change agents.

Such changes in systems are never completed, since change induces more change.

A mental health professional who elects to perform the role of change agent in society insofar as he deals with a social concern—a specific problem or situation that he wants to correct or change—may perform many different functions and fulfill many different roles. Understand, he is not working in the clinical, one-to-one relationship. If his goal then is to help construct a social system that produces mentally healthy individuals, he must first accept that he is not in a position to construct a totally new, ideal social system. He must take on an existing social system, decide what in that system must be changed in order to produce a socially desirable result, persuade a majority that his decision is valid on empirical, moral, and legal grounds, and find ways to involve large segments of the affected population in bringing about the changes he is advocating. He is not a politician, in other words, but much of his function is nonetheless political.

Such a role requires that he undertake action to persuade a majority to support his decision, and to involve people in implementing his ideas. This, by any definition, is political action. In most cases, there are a number of political actions he may take. Which one he chooses depends on the *system* in which he sees himself operating and his *conception* of what choices are available to him within that system. From this system-conception he determines his long-range goals and immediate objectives.

Political activity leading to change must thus be examined in the context of the systems in which agents of change see themselves to be operating. In the field of mental health, as in most other fields, it is neither standard nor uniform. Rather, each change agent comports himself politically in response to his own set of ideas and is influenced by the pressures brought to bear upon him by those whose system-conceptions are different. Change takes place as a consequence of the interactions of these change agents. Politics is a process of accommodation —of conciliation and reconciliation—between competing interests determined by varying system-conceptions.

The recent history of the mental health field demonstrates this process of interaction between system-conceptions and the changes that result. But to describe some of the political decision-making and issues in the field of mental health is to violate a prevailing taboo. Public exposure of the undiscussable process of mental health politics is just as disquieting as exposure of an individual's private world. It is even more so when the unwritten rules and procedures are revealed by someone who is a part of the mental health field. That there exist among the mental health professionals tendencies toward political behavior that are similar to those engaged in by professionals of other fields is not easily acknowledged. Most mental health professionals prefer to regard the mental health problems of medicine, psychiatry, and human reform as nonpolitical in nature.

This seems especially so within the NIMH. In this most ideal of worlds, science seemingly reigns supreme and politics is reduced to a minimum. And indeed, when one is deeply preoccupied with the problems of therapy, of working in a clinic or hospital, or of processing research grant applications, one may not be aware of the political processes going on around this well-protected field. Yet politics affects its very existence.

These political processes have varied in degree and nature according to the mental health professionals' concept of the system in which they operate. Until recently, mental health professionals, at least on the national level, conceived of their sphere of operation very narrowly. As long as the budget of the National Institute of Mental Health was of a size that could be considered infinitesimal when compared to the heavily budgeted programs in other institutes and agencies, there was in the mental health world a sense of political purity and isolation from the political process.

In the last few years however, the growth of public concern with mental health and the enlargement of the NIMH operations have expanded the horizons of mental health professionals working at the national level. As a result their political activities have increased and several different system-conceptions have emerged. Today there are within the mental health field a number of different and often competing schools of thought as to what the scope of mental health activities should be.

The concepts of community mental health have been changing constantly, and the changes have accelerated as social pressures, generated by international and internal crises, have impinged upon these concepts. Arising out of a social demand for psychiatric treatment for broader segments of the population, a movement that was once considered the exclusive concern of the psychiatric profession has expanded, within the past ten years, to include issues that fall within the academic domains of psychology, sociology, anthropology, social work, and nursing, among the professions, and—perhaps most significant— within the province of the political process itself. A brief review of the history of the National Institute of Mental Health may be the best method of demonstrating how these changes of conceptualization have come about, and of showing what relationship they have to the political system.

The founders of NIMH in 1946 were Public Health Service officers who had matured in the atmosphere of World War II psychiatric success. Most were products of classical psychiatric backgrounds who conceived of the Institute's function as primary support of the study of mental illness. These founders—along with a small nucleus in Congress, the National Committee Against Mental Illness, a few state mental health directors and mental health professionals—constituted the bases of power in the national mental health program.

The participants in this small network tended to define the field of mental health very narrowly. Their concerns were primarily with the field itself—the hospitals, administration of clinics, and expansion of research. Their conception of the mental health system did not extend to broader considerations, such as a high priority concern with the prevention of mental illness in a total community.

As long as this network and the financial resources available to it remained small, the internal policies of the mental health movement were determined according to a set of conceptions held in common by a small number of strategically placed people. Their power was based primarily on their positions, the respect of their professional colleagues, and the similarity of their conceptions to those of the few friends of psychiatry and mental health outside the professional field. They were able to determine the allocation of mental health resources with a fair degree of freedom because they were unencumbered by the politics of compromise created by competing conceptions of what the system should be and how it should function. They were able to stand more or less clear of "politics" and fight on the issues of science, theory, and human concern.

This should not suggest, however, that agreements, collaborations, and reinforcing systems did not exist. The very structure of the NIMH boards of review and study sections and the National Advisory Mental Health Council insured that the allocation of mental health program funds was in part determined by political decisions. In the late 1940's and early 1950's, these decisions were made by a very few persons in close collaboration: a few congressmen, the state directors, the American Psychiatric Association, the National Committee Against Mental Illness, the NAMH, and the NIMH. But they were made by men who shared essentially the same system-conception. In their perceptions of mental health problems and of how much additional money was needed they differed only in emphasis, not in philosophy. Because they were so relatively small a group, because their budget was small, and because their system-conceptions were similar, their political bartering did not extend beyond their own closed system. Though they participated in political bartering among themselves, they did not engage competing disciplines or enter the larger political arena of national big-money politics. They were politically self-isolated.

This isolation from mundane politics was never true of state systems. The budgets of state mental health divisions have been among the largest of all state human-service programs. One mental health program has almost 80,000 currently budgeted positions and is the state's largest bureaucracy both in budget and number of employees.

When any program acquires a sizeable budget and establishes itself in a community, it becomes a target of the bartering procedures for funds and power within that community's government. Those involved in the program find themselves forced by the pressures of big money to expand their conception of the system in which their program operates. As their program becomes an important resource of the community, their interests become intrinsically related to the politics of that community. This expansion of concern requires broadening the system-conception of the program's professionals and increases the number of people concerned with and therefore a part of that system.

Because of large budgets, those concerned with state programs have been for a long time intimately aware of the politics of mental health. They have learned that the presence of a mental hospital or even a clinical program in a community can be—in terms of the jobs and money it brings to the area and the resulting economic and political repercussions—equivalent to defense industry. Their battles, which on the surface have seemed to stem from a concern for program, have been, underneath, a fight for power. Programmatic issues have forced them into playing the political planning game for the much bigger stakes involved in land utilization, control of jobs, and allocation of resources within a state.

Between 1946 and 1954, the concerns of the national mental health community began to enlarge so as to bring it more directly into the arena of big-money politics. As the result of changes instituted in part by mental health professionals and in part by interested professionals outside the mental health field, NIMH expanded its concerns into the realms of other social sciences and entered the arena of big funding. The politics of the real world became increasingly important, and—relatively speaking—the politics of mental health less so.

This expansion of the system-conception of mental health was a product of two kinds of pressures—those created by the new concerns of mental health professionals with other social sciences, and those created by the growth of lay interest in mental health. Both of these changes brought pressures to bear on the mental health world, causing its members to expand their system-conceptions. Simultaneously, both changes broadened the field of mental health to include laymen and members of related disciplines. As a result, the scope of mental health programs was enlarged, and the structure of decision-making on mental health problems became much more complex.

The changes were also due to certain key figures who began to push for a broader professional outlook. These people introduced new ideas as to the scope of mental health practices, ideas that forced mental health politicians to redefine their systems and to undertake political action to maintain or extend their interests. Power figures in psychiatry were pushing to revamp psychiatry—especially mental hospitals and mental hospital systems. There were additional pressures from people entering the field of community health, from proponents of the concept of the open hospital, from groups of physicians studying the epidemiology of the poverty-sickness-poverty cycle in the cities.

Psychiatrists became involved in programs dealing with delinquency, accidents, alcoholism, and a host of areas that no more than thirty years ago would have been thought to be on the extreme periphery of psychiatry.

As a result of these pressures, the professional focus of NIMH, even in its early days, expanded from the comparatively narrow study of mental illness to the broader subject matter of mental health. The Institute began to support not only clinical psychologists but all psychologists and soon became the largest supporter, next to the Department of Defense, of behavioral science in the United States. Its area of concern broadened to include basic biological research, sociology, psychology and even urban studies—all, of course, related in some way to a mental health context.

After Congress established the Joint Commission on Mental Health and Mental Illness in 1955, the budget of NIMH expanded from $18 million in 1954 to over $300 million by 1966 to cover the program costs of its expanded concerns. NIMH had become involved in delinquency studies, in the Mobilization for Youth program of the Ford Foundation, and in the President's Committee on Juvenile Delinquency. It had begun to undertake a wide range of research studies in areas not really in mental illness per se, and had become a supporter not merely of psychiatry but of all social science.

At the same time there was pressure on the mental health system from people outside the field who were becoming increasingly concerned with mental health. As psychiatrists became more involved with the total community, their vocabulary and philosophy were adopted by the public. The psychiatrist's perception of problems relating to human behavior became increasingly incorporated into general knowledge. Though the number of people dealing directly with the psychiatrist did not increase markedly, the world of mental health became known to the layman.

The growth of lay interest not only increased public demands upon mental health professionals, but expanded the system of mental health to include new segments of the population. The need for a larger budget created by these pressures forced NIMH and the mental health field to enter the political process of getting a larger budget—to organize their forces and enter the broader political arenas of Congress, the state legislatures, the world of businesses and corporations. In other words, pressures on the conception of mental health concerns changed that system so as to require mental health professionals to enter the larger political process.

The complexities introduced into the mental health world by this expansion can be demonstrated by two examples—the controversy as to whether mental retardation or mental illness should be the priority concern of mental health, and the movement to establish community mental health centers. A brief summary of the disagreements and political activities surrounding the issue will illustrate how greatly the system of mental health has expanded and how political its activities have become as a result.

Psychiatry has been moving toward a broader sociobiologic concern with human behavior and a community orientation. This movement, however, has been neither smooth nor uncontroversial. The movement from hospital orientation to patient orientation, recognition of the possibilities for working with environment factors, increased interest in the biologic aspects of mental illness and a sociopsychological concern with family and the broader community have emerged amid strong controversy as to what the proper focus of mental health work should be. Prevailing conceptions have been challenged by the introduction of new focuses and ideas. Psychiatrists have been required to adapt their concept of man from an individual one to an ecological one, to revise their conceptions of key institutions and services, and to acquire expertise in social science disciplines other than their own.

The differences of opinion as to what the scope of psychiatric concern should be were brought to public attention by the activities of the Joint Commission on Mental Health and Mental Illness. The issue was raised initially in determining the composition of the Joint Commission. Should it be established as a psychiatrists' organization or should it include representatives of other disciplines? The decision that its board should represent the full range of organizations from nursing associations to social welfare groups set the stage for the more significant dispute over what the Commission's recommendations for future NIMH activities should be.

Despite pressure from NIMH for a man more representative of the entire health field, a psychiatrist was selected as the Commission's chairman. NIMH had envisioned the work of the Commission as a broad evaluation of the psychiatric system by outsiders and an investigation of community mental health problems. Other forces, however, conceived of the Commission's work more narrowly as a psychiatric report by psychiatrists with a stress on the problems of mental illness.

What is seen from the Commission's preliminary reports and the public reactions to its final report, however, is that while the Commission was mainly concerned with mental illness in the state systems, its staff and outside sources were concerned with the broader problems of mental illness in the community. The final report of the Commission reflected its board's narrow construction of NIMH responsibilities. The report was hospital-oriented; it proposed to enlarge state mental health programs; and it implied that to plan for the prevention of mental illness was a useless exercise. It stimulated a heated response from community-oriented psychiatrists at NIMH and elsewhere.

In response to the Joint Commission's report, the mental health professionals involved in the newer areas of NIMH research united to stress the need to include public health programs among the Institute's activities. They joined forces with the proponents of research in mental retardation and psychopharmacology to push for a community mental health center program and a concern for total services to the total community. They emphasized the need for a community mental health center to tie together all activities related to public health, including the hospital. But they left open as an option the possibility that a hospital itself could be a community mental health center.

The Community Mental Health Center Act of 1963 represented a compromise between the hospital orientation of the Joint Commission's report and the comprehensive community program urged by the community-oriented members of the mental health world. The community mental health centers established under this act reflected the expansion of the mental health world's system-conception to include non-mental-illness concerns, but continued to rely upon psychiatry as the ruling discipline for the centers.

The discrepancies in the way these community mental health centers operate today reveal the continuing differences in the system-conceptions of their administrators. All too often, these centers are merely extensions of the former state hospital systems—staffed by state workers and operating as mental health clinics; or else they are clinics expanded more in name than in service. They represent the expanded world of psychiatry and its new community orientation, but the psychiatrist is still the kingpin in their operation.

A few of them, however, represent a still more expanded system. They operate as broader institutions concerned with the total community—working out linkages with the poverty program, the welfare departments—in brief, with all the formal and informal community agencies concerned with human services. Staffed by people with a community therapist orientation, these centers reflect an emerging awareness that treatment and prevention of mental illness are social problems involving many factors that cannot be controlled or manipulated within the patient-doctor relationship alone.

The community mental health center controversy demonstrates how the mental health field has become increasingly embroiled in the politics surrounding the allocation of resources. Becoming part of the broader decision-making apparatus has required its professionals to make new judgments, choices, and decisions based on issues that are non-psychiatric. The broadening of psychiatric concerns to include all areas has led them to an overlapping of interests, preoccupations, and the lines of the professions and organizations, and to a greater involvement in the informal political processes of our society.

Pressures are created by the attempt of society to determine the place of psychiatry in achieving today's social goals. When society tries to deal rationally with its problems and begins to ask for cost accounting and program budgeting, it has to set values on its programs. Choices have to be made between spending tax monies on individual psychiatric treatment or on consultation or, indeed, on housing.

A tendency arises to move toward the designation of a role for each discipline despite the confusion related to overlapping of concerns and functions. Funds and manpower are limited. Priorities must be set, and these pressures force us to adapt an operations research approach to the planning process.

Indeed, the attention now given to developing social indicators in statistical analysis of programs, the pressures for commonality of language in various sectors, and the linking of computer systems in welfare and health sectors to those in physical planning, are only precursors of a drive toward a rational assignment of roles.

But human beings do not always behave rationally. Those with current bases of power, that is, the old professionals in the old institutions, are hardly willing to give up their power; and indeed why should they? Power is gained at an extremely high cost. Once one's territory, either geographic or functional, has been won, one does not easily relinquish it. Instead one fights with it, and as the stakes become higher, the battles get more vicious, and the back-room concerns of allocating resources become more critical.

In such political arenas the cast of critical characters becomes larger, regardless of whether one is protecting one's vital categorical concerns and territory, or trying to create a new, more rational approach.

As we follow the involvement of the mental health field in the political arena we see NIMH becoming more and more deeply concerned with congressional committees, federal agencies, the White House and the Bureau of the Budget, and state programs becoming involved in coordination activities, in a variety of programs in the governors' offices and, indeed, in the battles of the cities. One has the sudden feeling that he no longer has the power to determine his own destiny, and that forces far beyond his control in the total society are beginning to reform professions and institutions in such a manner that the professionals are losing hold. Thus, the consumer, the other professions and, indeed, everyone concerned with the human arena, have joined the mental health profession's battle.

But those concerned with allocating resources have become even more heavily involved in the process. On the national level, the final planning and decision-making apparatus is Congress, for it is here that the ultimate playing out of the power struggle occurs, the battles for resource allocation are joined, and the decisions reached. The decisions emerging from the Senate Committee on Reorganization, the struggles around the Department of Housing and Urban Development, the concerns about the poverty program, and the evolving manpower activities of the Labor Department are radically changing the world of the mental health professional.

One can accept this broadening of structure in several ways. One can continue to battle for his own arena and, by mobilizing power behind it, defend his territory to the utmost. One may also be able to negotiate from one power base with another for the biggest cut of the pie.

But there is an alternative strategy, especially if one is concerned with the problem and not with the organization or the profession. For then one can become concerned with achieving the totality of program required to meet the needs of our society through whatever means he can mobilize.

This strategy requires a different approach to the problem. It requires those involved in the mental health program on whatever level—federal, state or local—to understand the breadth of the problem and to become deeply involved in its total politics. It means making alliances within the social structure so that one can influence political decisions.

Such a strategy also requires that the mental health professional stretch his imagination to embrace the concept of a national mental health effort through an evolution of programs all the way across the board in every government agency. For not all programs affecting the mental health of a community are ones that should be treated by psychiatry. Mental health problems in our communities are presently being treated through the whole operation of social agencies as well as through a vast number of other channels. Not every patient who is found through these other channels to have an emotional disturbance needs psychiatric care. He may need instead the services of another institution treating psychiatric conditions by a variety of nonpsychiatric means.

The development of comprehensive community programs, then, is really a much more important step toward curing mental illness than the expansion of mental health studies would be. NIMH, when it broadened its program between 1946 and 1954, began an expansion of its system-conception to include the concept of comprehensive care. The Office of Vocational Rehabilitation made a similar attempt in its support of rehabilitation programs; the welfare administration, the Children's Bureau, the horizontally designed poverty program, and the Department of Housing and Urban Development and the Model Cities Program have also made attempts at programming in this broader system.

But social problems cannot be solved by any one organization, whether headed by psychiatrists, social workers, or educators. The reason why this larger system is so conceptually different from the other two and so difficult to implement with programs is that its goal is not that any one program have a larger impact, but rather that all programs together have a greater impact. NIMH has not made the final step away from psychiatric concerns into that broad strategy for mental health that recognizes this difference and acknowledges that a dollar's worth of effort in low-income housing may pay off more than a dollar invested in psychiatric treatment.

To operate in the larger system of mental health concerns one must deal with the total society rather than with the individual's emotional problem as the key to restoring mental health. For the individual's mental health is formed by the total society in which he exists. If you cure a mentally ill patient from a low-income background in a hospital, you must then return him to the poverty community. If he goes back to the poverty community, conditions in the community can undo everything that you have done. It is therefore the total society that needs a mental health treatment program and, almost more important than what you do in individual psychiatric treatment is how you treat the total environment. One concerned with the larger system must seek to build up the skills and directions of the total community —of general doctors and teachers and workers.

To operate in the broader system, then, the psychiatrist must return to the ecological model of man. He must become concerned with developmental processes rather than disease—with preventive mechanisms rather than symptom treatments. He must no longer operate merely through the traditional mental health institutions, but through the many key institutions and services in society that affect the way people learn to cope with stress and that can offer the possibility of learning new techniques of adapting to crisis. He must look at the total environment and decide where the best points of intervention are.

This means that at least some of the persons in the mental health field need a new sort of training, that people must be recruited who have skills quite different from those originally considered basic to successful psychiatric training. It also means that the society itself must be educated so that those human values that promote mental health begin to exert pressure in the decision-making process. And this means that mental health personnel genuinely interested in community mental health potentials must themselves define their own value systems—and sometimes, to revise them.

Here we will return to more concrete discussion—again turning to historical developments. The Community Mental Health Act and its staffing provisions were formulated out of a basic philosophy that psychiatric and related services could be administered in an integrated fashion, so that prevention, treatment, long-term care, after-care, and return to the community could become, in a sense, one continuous process. The assumption underlying this philosophy was that, if services could be so integrated, high-risk members of the community, whether patients or potential patients, would not get lost, somewhere along the line, to the same isolation and helplessness that had originally helped to produce the illness or the probability of illness. This philosophy also assumed that the system of mental health care was a known system, with well-defined boundaries, composed of a series of federal, state, and local organizations—themselves part of a vertical network of institutions and personnel—which, if properly organized, could provide this totality of services. For psychiatry itself, this was a major step forward, in that it proposed, within the structure of the community health center concept, to organize a set of disparate institutions into a more effective system. Only when some moves in this direction had been taken did the psychiatrists begin to discover the political realities involved—that no established bureaucracy was going to accept without a fight the suggestion that any of its autonomy be surrendered.

But events began to move very swiftly after the passage of the Community Mental Health Act, and within only a few years it was obvious that even the apparently innovative and startling proposals evolving out of the assumptions just described were no longer relevant to the real situation in the nation. Let us use, as our best example, the situation the journalists have so colorfully labeled "the crisis of the cities." Euphemisms aside, let us look at the mental health problems of the inner cities—of the urban underprivileged minority groups, Negro, Puerto Rican, and Mexican, who largely populate the inner cities.

Without question, the state hospitals—like the prisons—are populated predominantly by the poor and by the minority group members. If you restrict yourself to psychiatric concepts, you look for the etiology of schizophrenia in an attempt to understand the disease. But, as the riots in the cities have begun to teach us, mental diseases, regardless of diagnostic label, are symptoms of a deeper disease. That disease lies in the social and economic system that puts so many stresses on these groups that disproportionately high percentages of them break down severely enough to require hospitalization. Such socioeconomic causal factors are not within the province of traditional psychiatry.

But community mental health programs, if conceived as programs for prevention as well as treatment, must be prepared to engage with the social system in such a way as to modify these stresses and build into the community not only treatment but also social and political skills that will teach the dispossessed how to use the political process to ameliorate their own conditions. They must, in other words, be prepared to teach the slum dweller how to master his own environment and how to develop a sense of autonomy.

No community mental health group can engage in such a program without becoming involved in a cooperative way with poverty programs, the Model Cities Program, programs for job training, any and all agencies that affect, adversely or positively, the community's self-perception and its powers of political adaptation. It means, too, that the community health agency must involve itself in a gradual process of institutional change, so that other, related agencies, like the Welfare Department, alter their own self-perceptions in the direction of treating their clients like citizens instead of like wayward charges. And most of all, it means that the mental health agency must engage itself with the community, so that it does not simply ossify into another bureaucratic structure telling the community how it ought to behave, but instead enters into a partnership with the community (as indeed the Model Cities Program officially demands), so that the agency is responsive to the needs of the community as the community perceives them—not as a consulting sociologist who spends a week studying the community decides the priorities should be determined.

Legitimate questions here are "What is the psychiatrist's role in such a program? Does he belong in it at all?" He does. The need for direct and indirect treatment will of course persist, since neither social scientists nor medical scientists can be expected to come up with a prescription for eliminating social and individual pathology. But the psychiatrist must coordinate his role, perhaps more thoroughly than anyone, with the other skilled professionals in the total community mental health program. He can be the ideal mediator among the groups, including the community groups, that must constantly find viable ways to function together. But in order to perform this role the psychiatrist must be willing to forego the position of authority that his professional status has accustomed him to assume. Not every psychiatrist is able to do this (as some of the case histories to follow will demonstrate). It thus becomes important that the psychiatric curriculum be modified to include training in community psychiatry—that, as we said earlier, we recruit people with new kinds of skills.

What we must be prepared to recognize is that commitment to the concept of community mental health agencies in this new context is a commitment to the idea of orderly social change—and if social change is to be orderly, the time to make such a commitment operational is now.

Evolution of
a Casebook

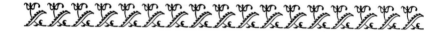

Robert L. Leopold

UNIVERSITY OF PENNSYLVANIA AND
WEST PHILADELPHIA MENTAL HEALTH CONSORTIUM

Leonard J. Duhl

UNIVERSITY OF CALIFORNIA, BERKELEY

I

Efforts to manage the problems of mental illness and to promote mental health on the basis of community responsibility are not new. But even in communities with highly developed services, individual agencies tend to operate in isolation. As a result, most cities had—and have —gaps in services, duplication of effort, and waste of money—this in the face of acute shortages of both personnel and money. This fragmentation of services leads to disruption in the lives of patients, who must wander from agency to agency seeking the kind of service they need. Cutting across all other considerations, this isolation can mean not only isolation from other mental health agencies but also from other kinds of community services and agencies—a denial, in effect, of the relationship between mental health problems *per se* and other social and medical problems. Even more than the middle-class patient, who may have the social skills to find his way around the system in times of personal crisis, this situation produces almost insurmountable barriers for the undereducated, socioeconomically deprived populations of the urban slums, who are under the additional handicap of not being able to formulate their needs in ways that the agencies find "acceptable."

On October 31, 1963, the Eighty-eighth Congress of the United States enacted Public Law 88-164, the "Mental Retardation Facilities and Community Mental Health Centers Construction Act of 1963," which offered states the use of federal matching funds of $150 million over a three-year period to construct comprehensive community health centers. In May 1964, regulations ordered in that legislation were issued, setting forth the requirements to be met if the states were to qualify for federal funds in creating state systems of community mental health planning.

The passage of Public Law 88-164 indicated that there has finally been some recognition of our contemporary social crisis: that mental hospital rates are continuing to rise; that retarded and psychotic children have little or no access to treatment: that research on prevention is a major necessity. And the law envisioned mental health centers that would provide a full range of services for *all* patients rather than for special groups only; that would provide them in a coordinated program in the patient's community; that would relate these services to other community services that have a bearing on mental health; and that would concern themselves with a full program of prevention designed according to a mental health model.

As psychiatrists who had been concerned with community mental health issues for a long period of time, we felt that it would be informative to see what had evolved as community mental health centers began to develop. Aware of the manpower shortage in psychiatry and related mental health professions, and aware that different communities would adopt different approaches, we decided to attempt to survey as many programs as possible, asking the contributors to describe as candidly as they were able not only what they considered to be their successes but also their failures; and to evaluate, as best they could, the reasons for failures, any mistaken assumptions, or misconceptions with which they might have approached their planning, and the kinds of obstacles they encountered in attempting to implement their plans. Our concern was with process—with the processes involved in the psychiatrist's adaptation to a different role, with community responses to this new approach, and with what techniques might have been developed for dealing with the resistances we knew would be encountered.

We assumed that although programs would differ, we would be able to discern some threads that would be generally applicable in community mental health planning. And we were convinced that a frank appraisal of errors in approach and execution would be of genuine teaching value to persons planning to enter the field. Thus, the chapters are extremely diverse. They include success stories, descriptions of highly innovative techniques that evolved out of an individual's sensitive perceptions of his own community, generous descriptions of programs that failed because their administrators had failed to develop such perceptions, programs that succeeded because they were established in cultures that were much more accepting of the entire concept of community responsibility for health and mental health care.

Let us trace some of the threads we were able to separate out of these chapters. The first, and most striking, is the concept of consultation. This concept, as all the illustrations demonstrate, was at first a product of necessity: the necessity forced upon a profession suffering a severe shortage of trained personnel.

Drs. Samuel Susselman and Henrik Blum, in Contra Costa County, California (Chapter Two), were working in a large, scattered community in which no psychiatric services had existed. They were forced to rely on extremely limited manpower while introducing new services and making old services more useful. Their solution was to extend the psychiatric consultation model considerably, so that the psychiatrist could serve as consultant to key workers in all the social service agencies established in the community. The major problem the psychiatrist faced in this situation was that of establishing non-threatening relationships with a variety of personnel in a number of different fields, and the authors have been candid about the stumbling blocks they encountered in setting up such relationships, and particularly about their own original misperceptions of their roles. To have attempted to provide direct psychiatric service with minimal personnel would have been useless; the only road toward broadening and modernizing services was that of educating agency personnel to more informed ways of using their capacities for insight, in the eventual direction of developing in-service training programs for nonpsychiatric agency people.

Like Drs. Susselman and Blum, Drs. William F. Sears and Lester M. Libo in New Mexico (Chapter Four) and Dr. William P. Hurder in the southeast United States (Chapter Five) were serving scattered, small-town populations. Faced with limited personnel, low budgets, and the additional problem of populations unsophisticated about or even hostile to mental health concepts, they too relied upon the consultation model. In New Mexico, Drs. Sears and Libo decided to use nonmedical personnel as consultants if candidates could meet certain criteria of training and experience and could work well with the personnel of the existing social agencies in the community. Here, we encounter a precursor of a model that was to develop later, particularly in the large urban centers—the training of local nonprofessional health and mental health community workers. In New Mexico, the program directors utilized their resources, which differed considerably from locale to locale, in an extremely flexible manner, adapting their program wherever necessary in order to meet the differing local needs.

Dr. Hurder's chapter describes small programs in three distinctly different kinds of communities. What we found most striking was his ability to identify and work with the power structure in each of these communities, and to adapt his approach so that he was able to provide important services within social contexts acceptable to each. These programs were not labeled mental health services. For example, where the program could best get community sanction by being called a medical program, the psychiatrist never identified himself as such, but retained his medical identification. As "the doctor," he aroused no anxiety among the psychiatric patients and their families, for whom the definition of "mental illness" would have been unacceptable.

We have discussed these chapters at some length because we feel they are important models and are apt to remain so for some time. It is hardly likely that statewide, coordinated, adequate services for both urban and rural areas are going to develop very rapidly. At this point, the emphasis in the United States is much more heavily on urban needs, because the urban crisis poses a sharper threat to the stability of the society. Although mental health problems abound outside the cities, psychiatrists interested in practicing community psychiatry in rural or small-town settings will have to rely on their capacities for ingenuity and innovation if they are to strengthen whatever resources exist in such areas.

In one respect or another, all the case histories presented here use the consultation model. One of the lessons one can derive from these experiences is that the psychiatrist, while he may serve as mediator or as consultant, is still most effective when he retains his identification as psychiatrist. He may sometimes have to alter his traditional role and techniques in order to be effective, but his ability to alter role as the situation requires it lies in the particular skills he has acquired in the course of psychiatric training. As psychiatric consultant, he is leaving the decision-making process in the hands of those who consider it their province, but his psychiatric identification and the expertise associated with it make it possible for him to influence the decision-makers in the direction of rational solutions. Particularly so long as the manpower shortage continues, the consultation model will remain a pragmatic necessity. But, more important, where the psychiatrist functions as teacher, mediator, interpreter, he is most likely to be able to effect those attitude changes in agency operations that will in time lead to genuine institutional change. This is a theme we will return to later.

One consultation model included in this volume was deliberately selected to contrast to evolving patterns of community mental health concepts. Dr. Leon Shapiro (Chapter Thirteen) acted as a consultant in the traditional sense. He served one agency: the courts. But in the process of acting as consultant to the judges, he was able to expand his function from that of providing an advisory service for judges to that of working with the entire penal system—the courts, the parole system, the personnel of the prisons, and the prisoners themselves. Taking the correctional system as a given, he was able to create a special community psychiatric program and to provide in a very sophisticated fashion for some of the needs of all his "clients." This more familiar form of consultation has the drawback of serving only a selected population, and unless it is somehow linked into the larger system of human services, it is inevitably narrow and limited.

It is easy to see, even among the cases already mentioned, that differences in culture patterns in different regions of the United States impose on planners for comprehensive community mental health the requirement that they take into account the attitudes and perceptions of the communities they propose to serve. This fact is more vividly demonstrated by the three case histories drawn from other countries.

In Chapter Ten, for example, Dr. Serge Lebovici, a child psychiatrist, describes his program in the Thirteenth Arrondissement of Paris.

In France, the tradition of child psychiatry and of psychiatry in general is one of pyramidal hierarchy. The professor of psychiatry in Paris is *the* psychiatrist for all of France. The attitudes and values of this kind of psychiatry get transfused into every program within the country. The basic orientation of French psychiatry is anti-analytical, biological, Kraepelinian, with little concern for either social program or for the dynamics and understanding that arise out of psychoanalytic insight.

Dr. Serge Lebovici came out of the psychoanalytic field, with experience of people like Dr. Sivadon who had already started a community program in Paris. Dr. Lebovici then developed an innovative group, trying to put into practice his own concept of some of the developmental problems of child psychiatry. He sought to understand the problems of the child in the family and the community and attempted to break the grip of the hierarchical psychiatric establishment in Paris and in France.

His must be considered a revolutionary attempt, one that highlights an important issue for us: community psychiatry can take only several steps beyond what currently exists; it cannot aim for a completely radical departure from the existing system. Dr. Lebovici was successful because he drew on the reservoir of the small number of psychoanalysts in France and also on the experience that came out of the *Educateurs* and the people outside the psychiatric tradition who have been working with children in France. Thus, although he was breaking with the French psychiatric tradition, he could find allies and support in other, equally acceptable, national traditions.

The community mental health program reported in Chapter Eleven, by Dr. Jack H. Kahn, represents the other end of the spectrum. Given a society in which the preconditions for the successful operation of an integrated community mental health program already exist, putting one into action does not involve overcoming established prejudices. In England, the idea of community responsibility for the total population is already built into the culture. Other attitudes, such as a willingness to keep the mental patient in the community as long as possible, the willingness of general practitioners to treat psychiatric patients, and the esteem offered by public service, all go to create a climate in which integrated services are considered rational, economic planning. Dr. Kahn had the further advantage of returning to a community where he knew all the doctors, the nurses, the key figures with whom he had to work, so he never faced the problem of establishing communication and building up mutual confidence.

Since the culture of England allows for government provision of a number of services, all of which could be co-opted, in a sense, by the community mental health program when circumstances required it, Dr. Kahn did not face the bureaucratic sensitivity and obstructionism described in other chapters, and was able to restrict his mental health program to mental health needs. If the poverty program in the United States really develops along the lines originally conceived for it, and provides adequate services in nonmedical areas, the psychiatrist in community mental health will also be able to stay in the medical field. If the poverty program fails to develop, the community mental health program will be forced to take over some of these services if it is to have any preventive function at all.

On Prince Edward Island, Dr. M. N. Beck (Chapter Twelve) occupied an equally enviable position. Here the cultural preconditions were not identical to those in London, but resembled them in many ways. And again, the author had the advantage of knowing his own community and how to function in it. But a separate aspect of Dr. Beck's experience is a vivid demonstration of another thread that runs through all these cases—the need to establish ties to the power structure of the community. In Dr. Beck's case, he was a part of that power structure, and thus particularly well equipped to bargain with it. However, such networks of communication must be established not only with the power structure but with the community residents to be served, for the community mental health program must have the sanction of all the groups in it.

We have commented, although not systematically, on some of the chapters already discussed in terms of the program director's ability to establish working relationships with key figures in the community and to perceive the needs of the community as the community perceived them. In a program serving a small population, this problem may never prove too acute. It may be easy to identify the key members of the power structure, and easy to establish communication with persons in the community who are fully capable of defining the community's felt needs, simply because they themselves are key figures in informal communicational networks.

Dr. Frank Hladky (Chapter Seven) reports on an attempted comprehensive community health program in just such a community. The program collapsed after several years of effort, and Dr. Hladky, analyzing this breakdown retrospectively, attributes it almost entirely to the failure of the group attempting to establish the service to make contact with the community, either haphazardly or systematically. His final evaluation suggests that had such contacts been made and maintained in a systematic and self-conscious fashion, the program might have had a perfectly good chance to succeed.

In Chapter Eight, whose authors are anonymous, for reasons that will become apparent, we see an example of well-intentioned planners, whose plans, looked at objectively, were, indeed, perfectly intelligent and designed to meet genuine community needs on a broad basis.

The authors of Chapter Eight are anonymous because they have written in detail about a situation that could not be described unless it were sufficiently disguised. In this mythical city of Northeast, the possibility of establishing a comprehensive community mental health services existed in fact, and the idea had the support of some of the key medical and political figures on the scene. It probably still has. The political pressures the authors describe no doubt also existed and still exist. But what is equally clear is that the planners tangled with community processes they did not understand and with political realities to which they could not or would not reconcile themselves. In failing to adapt to these local realities, they lost crucial support. But this ability to work within an entrenched structure is critical to the success of innovative planning. Once the planner has established his credentials within the community, he may be able to move toward the institutional changes that shift the political pressures in the direction of support for his program. Even so, these authors recognized what too many community mental health planners still fail to recognize—that some mental health goals can be achieved only if programs move out into the areas usually assigned to the poverty programs.

Drs. Sheppard Kellam and Sheldon Schiff, in Woodlawn, Chicago (Chapter Six), selected their arena for operations on the basis of a consideration that was finally recognized on the federal level only with the passage of the poverty program legislation and the Model Cities legislation—fullest possible community participation. They were determined in advance to get community acceptance and community participation in their planning, and it took them some years to find a place where such preconditions could be met. The place happened to be one of the worst of Chicago's Negro slums. When the Chicago Board of Health offered Woodlawn the opportunity to have a community mental health center, the authors gave priority to establishing ties with the local community power coalition, a group whose members were not necessarily completely compatible, but one in which all concerned would have a voice in deciding what services the community needed and would accept. (However, there are situations in which no such coalition exists, and the incoming psychiatrist must find ways to mobilize this community support and participation.) Although the directors of the center made mistakes—possibly in faulty response to deliberate testing from the community—they refused to abandon their first principle: the responsibility of the center to the perceived needs of the community. Clearly, their persistence finally convinced the residents of Woodlawn of their sincerity.

Perhaps the first major test of this sincerity was Drs. Kellam and Schiff's willingness to institute their initial program with first-graders, in an attempt to solve a problem to which the community assigned its highest priority—the school dropout rate. Neither Dr. Kellam nor Dr. Schiff had originally considered beginning their efforts here, but they responded immediately not only to the community's demand but to their own realization that the assignment was an extremely realistic one.

Their experience highlights the importance, in any new community mental health effort, of selecting as a point of entrance into the community a service the community wants and sanctions, regardless of what conventional psychiatric assumptions might lead the observer to believe the community needs.

Chapter Nine, by Drs. Seymour Perlin and Robert L. Kahn, is somewhat outside the original framework of this volume, in that it does not describe process so much as it describes another element vital to effective community mental health planning—that of choosing populations to be served in such a way as to set up researchable situations for later evaluation. The system of catchment areas developed by these authors at Montefiore Hospital has been adopted widely throughout the country. For, with the growth of community mental health planning and the current moves in the direction of providing comprehensive community health services, under the Model Cities program, the need for research becomes more apparent, not only in the early planning stages but at every later stage. Only with sufficient experience and refined evaluation will replicable and reliable models be established.

The authors laid the foundation for a community mental health program in the Bronx, but they left Montefiore before it had had time to get embedded into the community. Later, Montefiore became part of the Albert Einstein College of Medicine complex, which transferred its community mental health efforts to Lincoln Hospital, under the direction of Dr. Harris B. Peck.

The final chapter of this volume represents, for its author, the fruits of the many lessons learned in the course of compiling this casebook. It describes only the initial stages of a program whose director has been able to draw on the experiences of all the contributors to this volume as well as of those of many other psychiatrists throughout the country. The West Philadelphia Communty Mental Health Consortium, which he directs, will hopefully be able to bypass many of the blind alleys illuminated by other centers' wrong turnings, and take advantage of the more successful techniques pioneered by more fortunate or more provident innovators. Nevertheless, and significantly, his chapter closes on a series of unanswered questions and unresolved problems, proclaiming the contention that social planning is an open-ended process, requiring constant trial and error, evaluation, reorganization of priorities, and reassessment of problems. This is particularly true of the large centers operating in or being planned for urban ghetto areas.

It is precisely in these areas, where the need is greatest, that the services have been the poorest, the manpower least available, and the needs least perceived.

Origins and Progress of a Mental Health Program

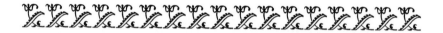

Samuel Susselman

THE LANGLEY PORTER NEUROPSYCHIATRIC INSTITUTE

Henrik Blum

UNIVERSITY OF CALIFORNIA, BERKELEY

II

Contra Costa County is one of the San Francisco Bay Area's nine counties. The Berkeley hills hide most of the county from San Francisco, so that only its tip is visible on a clear day. Located on this tip is the city of Richmond which, during World War II, grew proportionately faster than any city in the United States—from 23,000 in 1940 to 120,000 in 1948—largely because of the war-born shipyards located within its boundaries. At the end of the war, Richmond contained nearly half of the county's population. The rest of the county is made up of small cities, commuter suburbs, and rural areas.

New settlers remained after the war; temporary housing accommodations deteriorated into near-slums; by late 1964, urbanization of the rural valleys had swelled the county population to about 500,000. These rapid changes brought problems that were and are being met by the county's agencies.

INITIAL CONCEPT

Shortly after World War II, four of these agencies—Social Welfare, Probation, Schools, and Health—decided to develop further their

33

capacity for dealing with problems of children. Their staff of social workers, psychologists, and medical personnel lacked only a psychiatrist to complement the traditional team for psychiatric work with children. It was hoped that a child guidance clinic could eventually be developed. In 1948, Mental Health Act funds made it possible to employ a psychiatrist for three hours of psychiatric time per week.

The committee delegated to plan the program soon realized that these hours would be used most fruitfully with the agency workers, whose activities affected many, rather than with one or a few families, and in indirect rather than direct service to patients and clients. The members of the committee had arrived at this conclusion independently, and their agreement to this decision was unanimous. The psychiatrist (Dr. Susselman), whose concept of psychiatric consultation was an outgrowth of his training in child psychiatry at the Langley-Porter Neuropsychiatric Institute, was also in full agreement with this conclusion.

For professional personnel, a successful conference resulted in insights, relief of anxiety, and often in positive shifts in a worker's activity; these results were constructive not only for personnel but also for their patients and clients. If county agency personnel, in a community without psychiatric services, could thus be helped, many people for whom there was no direct psychiatric service would be helped indirectly.

Psychiatric practice in a clinic setting will point up the similarities between family interactions and those of agency personnel, particularly with regard to the use and misuse of authority; it will uncover the ubiquitous involvements of therapists with themselves and others, so like workers' involvements; and it will show the tendency of individuals at moments of conflict to reveal matters about themselves while talking of others, so characteristic of parents speaking about a child or each other.

Other learning experiences are reinforced in the course of consultation; for example, the importance of precise implementation of such concepts as "limits" and "function" and the significance of unwarranted missed appointments, tardiness, unpaid fees, and so on. Careful inquiry into the details of a problem, whether a clinical one or an agency problem, is essential. Frequently, as a consultant asks for a definition of agency policy and limits of function, base lines can be re-established for that worker who is overextending himself and client.

With this concurrence that consultation might be the most effective procedure, a psychiatric program[1] was initiated. It was regarded as a program of education for agency personnel (a sort of in-service program), which would lay the foundation for a child guidance clinic. The program was considered experimental because neither the agency personnel nor the psychiatrist was certain about its methods and efficacy.

During the first nine months (September 1948 to July 1949) the four participating agencies met with the psychiatrist for a three-hour period every fourth week. In the relatively smaller county of 1948, it was possible to meet with an entire agency. Often members from the other participating agencies attended, usually around a common problem. Sometimes guests from other agencies not committed to the program were invited to learn about the project.

At the end of nine months, each agency evaluated the program in writing. They agreed, generally, on the following:

> An important contribution of the present service has been the feeling of reassurance and support that the psychiatrist has given individual workers. The reassurance is related to certain specifics: the informal, free way in which the session is conducted; the knowledge that the case presented will not be criticized; that the worker can feel free to present her mistakes as well as her successes, since the focus of the discussion will be on the worker-client relationship. Because of this feeling of relaxed freedom in the sessions, workers feel that they have gained considerable understanding of their own motivations in their professional relationships, giving them increased objectivity and relief from anxieties that may have been blocking movement in their cases.
>
> One of the valuable results of the program has been the closer cooperation and joint planning of the four county agencies. The county has no council of social agencies, no social service exchange and no social service directory. Although an amicable interagency working relationship has been developed over the years there are many problems that need clarification; functions need to be defined, a division of labor decided upon, and a multitude of problems discussed from time to time.
>
> In the absence of a council of agencies to meet this need,

---

[1] "Psychiatric program" was a misnomer; see later discussion.

getting together was usually brought about by a crisis or a particularly pressing issue.

The mental health project brought the four agencies together for a common purpose. The meetings of the supervisory heads have provided a vehicle for broader cooperation and understanding of each other's problems and functions. Workers and supervisors have participated in other agencies' clinic sessions when cases that were of mutual concern were discussed.

Knowing other agencies better has resulted in each agency being able to coordinate interagency referrals and to make the best of community resources for all clients.

Some weaknesses in the procedure followed this year have been observed and it is hoped that with additional time next year some of these problems can be corrected.

The chief difficulty has resulted from the lack of opportunity for individual workers to meet with the psychiatrist after the meetings to work through problems raised by group discussions. In spite of every precaution, some workers were traumatized and unresolved at the end of a session. There was no opportunity to clarify the situation with the psychiatrist until a month later, if at all, because of insufficient time. Some of these situations were clarified through supervisory conferences, but this does not meet the worker's needs in all cases. Plans for next year include arrangements for working on this problem.

The large size of the groups has presented a problem in some situations. Some cases presented did not touch on an area of experience for the entire group and were not of vital concern to all. Some workers at times were reluctant to discuss their real feelings in the large group. Smaller groups will probably solve part of this problem.

Scattered through the reports of individual agencies were statements reflecting the attitudes of some of the workers:

Some reactions have been extremely negative, some extremely positive, and many a healthy combination of the two. In general, the reaction has been positive. To find that a psychiatrist is an ordinary human being who readily admits he does not have all the answers was at the same time disarming and reassuring to the group. In response to the continuing desire of many workers for concrete advice, directions and suggestions and for specific bits of information, the psychiatrist did a good job of trying to help people relate their "knowledge" and "themselves" to each other . . . emphasis was placed on the impossibility of refer-

ring everyone with problems to a psychiatrist and workers were
encouraged to try their own skills. . . .

℀ *DIRECTIONS OF EVOLUTION* ℀

In the fall of 1949, nine months after the program started, the
county hospital joined the four agencies and, like them, subordinated
its needs for direct service to patients to the training aspects of the program. Psychiatric time was increased to twelve hours per week, since
each agency requested three-hour weekly consultations. The agencies
endorsed the county hospital's offer to pay for the psychiatrist from
its pool of consultation funds. As Mental Health Act monies were progressively withdrawn, finally ceasing in 1952, the county hospital assumed the total cost of the program. The psychiatrist was invited to
join the medical staff of the hospital and the title *Chief of the Contra
Costa County Hospital Psychiatric Service* was added to that of *Psychiatric Consultant to the Contra Costa County Mental Health Program.*

At the end of the second year another evaluation was made by
the agencies. Excerpts from this, the last one in writing, follow.

Many problems were solved through the psychiatrist's and
the group's help in analyzing the worker's function, the limits of
his responsibilities and clarification of his feelings. . . .

Help was given to many staff members in working out
situations that involved their relationships with coworkers and
superiors. This was frequently done in the group and often in
private conference with the psychiatrist. . . .

Local school administrators and teachers have been helped
to solve the following types of problems: (1) handling of individual pupils, (2) relationships with parents, (3) relationships
between administrators and teachers, (4) relationships between
administrators and boards of trustees. . . .

Over a period of two years all county social agencies have
shared in a common philosophy through their contacts with the
psychiatrist.

It is the opinion of the entire group that the psychiatrist's
method of dealing with the emotional responses of the workers is
far more effective than if he were to do the traditional type of
psychiatric case consultation.

Our present appreciation has quite a different quality
from last year in that it seems based on an emotional acceptance. . . .

One worker stated that she has been "freed" from having to follow her "book-learning" and has developed a better understanding of the relationship between theory and practice. She also claims that she is better able to analyze her own feelings on the development of a given situation. At times when she is confused as to how to proceed, and the thought occurs to her that she would like to discuss it with the psychiatrist, she stops to think what he might say and finds her own solution. Accordingly, there are a number of instances in which she would have turned to him last year that she now can handle alone and independently.

Another worker pointed out that she had been helped to more fully and emotionally accept the right of the individual to make his own plans and to progress at his own pace and consequently has become more objective in her dealings with her clients. Another worker pointed out that the psychiatrist has helped us define our relationship with other county departments and to delineate our special function.

From probation department came the following:

There has been a definite growth in the care and comfort with which probation work is carried out. Various inter- and intra-agency problems of long standing have been clarified. The following topics are illustrative of the type of matters taken up with the consultant: casework with the adult sex offender; establishing proper limits on behavior; the role of the probation officer in investigating crimes; casework in an authoritative setting; the effect of insecurity on job performance.

Between 1950 and 1952, the Civil Service Department and two new junior colleges were added to the program. The Richmond City Health Department became a member agency until it was absorbed by the County Health Department in 1954. On the whole, the consultation effort continued to be popular, perhaps as much because of the agencies' commitment and enthusiasm and their determination to make it succeed as because of the quality of the consultation alone.

All views were not this laudatory. Excerpts from a report by the nursing director of the Health Department, who had administrative responsibility in the psychiatric program for her agency for about two years (until the present Health Officer was appointed in 1950), are given with her permission. This very instructive document, written several years after the program started, contains forthright dissent and honest statements about the effect of the program on her own attitudes as they fluctuated from time to time. While the psychiatrist considered her an important benefactor from the program, her report indicates, if one reads between the lines, what was accomplished, together with some of the impedances to the program as it was evolved. It raises the problem of how her objectives could have been met.

When I came to Contra Costa County I built a home, went to work for the Health Department, and I became involved in a psychiatric experimentation—all at the same time. My evaluation may be tinged by these factors.

One morning, the Health Officer told me that the psychiatrist was here, and no one else seemed to be, so would I sit in on the meeting and see what it was all about. Thus I inherited a "psychiatric" program. I thought I needed the whole deal about as much as I needed two heads—but it was mine. Later on at an administrative meeting (no administrators—I was still staff) I found out that we had latched on to some mental health funds and we were going to spend some of ours to get theirs.

I was given no direction as to what I was to do with the psychiatrist, but the four agencies sent representatives to a meeting and we fumbled around with the problem. As I was far more interested in developing a nursing program in the county, I am sure I was a "permissive participant." The whole deal seemed slightly out of focus, it seemed to me. We had more urgent administrative problems, I thought. No one enlightened me —in fact, no one else in the department seemed to be involved, so I turned the matter over to the nurses.

We planned nothing—the nurses just met with the psychiatrist and discussed their problems. Listening to them, I thought they were administrative, not psychiatric. Occasionally (the county was growing) I thought I had more important things to do than go to the meetings. This was a matter that the psychiatrist and I never agreed on. In fact, he was considerably annoyed at my attitude and we had some sessions around this. I very distinctly felt he was putting pressure on me to promote *his* program because of his interest and involvement in it, not because I thought it was important. I was resentful that he put this pressure on me personally, rather than take this matter up with Administration.

Contra Costa County was really growing now and the nurses were aware that there were an increasing number of other agency workers involved in the same problem families that they were. We began to schedule meetings of caseworkers, sometimes involving all agencies. These meetings were held primarily to clarify function in the family but through them we began to know other agency programs. This was productive, I thought, and the nurses seemed to agree. I also felt we could have planned these meetings and arrived at the same conclusions without the psychiatrist there, except that we didn't do it unless we set aside this time. However, I do feel there was a constructive movement during these meetings. To what extent the previous meetings with the psychiatrist had helped I am not sure, but at least we began examining why we disliked certain agencies, certain people and certain programs. I think the nurses became more aware of their own contributions to the confusions—and, seeing this, they could prevent further contributions.

Whether or not our psychiatric sessions had anything to do with it, staff morale was high. This was observed and commented on many times outside of the agency. Most frustrations were handled easily and without friction.

We shifted our attack slightly during the next year and most of our discussions were around problem cases carried by nursing—*or maybe,* cases carried by problem nursing.

Each year we had long discussions of "How are we going to use the psychiatrist's time?" The problem was eternal.

Many experiments were tried with both the numbers and the composition of the groups who participated in the consultation meetings. These experiments were dictated by various factors. The agencies were growing in size, and meeting with a whole agency was too cumbersome for fruitful, free interchange. New workers, with their need for review of already understood concepts, detracted from the spontaneity and enjoyment of discussion and robbed it of the freshness of new discoveries. It was also expensive and time-consuming for agency personnel from Martinez, the county seat, to meet in the Richmond branch office, the population center. It became more feasible and efficient to meet separately with each branch office and with each branch unit that had specialized functions, for example, Social Service units like Adoptions, Child Welfare, Old Age Assistance, Aid to Needy Children, General Assistance. The Probation Department requested separate consultation for its adult and juvenile units, detention staff, and for its psychologist, who in turn became a roving consultant for his agency.

HIERARCHY OF CONSULTATION

In all agencies, conferences were held with a supervisor alone or with a supervisor and the worker involved with a particular problem. Each agency thus arranged for its use of psychiatric time individually, seeking a very flexible program while moving in the direction of smaller groups and greater group specialization.

In general, it was found that a supervisor who benefited from a conference was more effective with his unit, while one who did not resolve a dilemma often impeded a worker who might himself have a clear idea as to how to proceed. That this could occur was strikingly illustrated after one meeting and discussion, when a worker expressed his readiness to proceed with a case, giving the impression of having resolved an impasse. At the next monthly meeting of this unit he presented the same case, at certain moments in the discussion glancing at a woman near the psychiatrist but outside his visual periphery. Nothing was being settled. After the meeting the psychiatrist chatted with the woman toward whom the worker had glanced. This verbal interchange seemed spontaneous and took but a few moments—as though both persons knew that only a brief discussion was enough. The psychiatrist learned that he was talking to the worker's supervisor and spoke of his feeling that the conference had failed to clarify matters. She agreed and made a few pertinent comments that she had not expressed in the conference. The later work with the case proceeded well. It is important to know where each individual stands in the hierarchical organization. The supervisor holds the key to the progress of a case. If she is clear, she can help the worker; if she is not, even the clear worker might be made uncertain.

One result of such observations was that the Department of Social Service experimented for some years with consultation for a group of supervisors, although this agency still continued with other unit conferences attended by workers and supervisors. For the same reason, consultation was held in several agencies with groups of administrators (where the supervisory hierarchy or philosophy was not as clearly established).

Again, the report of the Public Health Nursing director was illuminating:

Administration then began to use the psychiatrist. This was more in my line and I began to use these meetings administratively. By expressing insecurity, hostility, or lack of comprehension, I repeatedly presented problems that impeded my program. By the group and the psychiatrist working to clear up my hostility, insecurity, and so on, the problem was brought out in the open and could be administratively dealt with to the satisfaction of all of us. This had a slight drawback, I think—it became apparent to some that I was the only one on the whole staff who had problems, which in itself is a problem.

From these and other related experiments with other agencies grew the concept that the most effective use of limited consultation time for any one agency was discussion with individuals as high up in the agency as would be willing to participate, and with as small a group of these individuals as possible—preferably, with one person. The nursing director commented wryly on the fate of this concept: "The psychiatrist has always said that the farther up he can work in the hierarchy the more successful he will be. This year he is back where he started, working with nursing."

Eventually, however, the concept was implemented elsewhere to the extent that monthly individual meetings were held with the heads of most of the participating agencies. Here, in addition to difficult cases, various problems were discussed, especially those problems that went on among agency personnel, horizontally and vertically, as well as across agency boundaries.

Another development with the involvement of agency heads was their appearance on the mental health planning committee, gradually replacing those of their subordinates who pioneered the program. The committee came to consist solely of the heads of the county agencies involved in the program, together with the Chief of Special Services for the County School Department, who accompanied the Superintendent of Schools, and the head counsellor of a junior college who was brought by his Administrative Chief. The County Administrator attended several conferences. Meetings with the psychiatrist were held each month, and various agenda were tried. Eventually these meetings served to air the problems of the program and to plan for it.

The loss of several of the original planning committee members was felt keenly, especially when the discussions took on other colorings and when the program began to change direction. However, because the change was consistent with the concept of working with individuals as high up in the hierarchy as possible, the psychiatrist felt it was inevitable. Only later did he identify what caused his vague uneasiness. In his desire to interest and involve hierarchical heads, he had neglected to note that another hierarchy existed within every agency, which could best be termed the hierarchy of clarity about certain issues. This is not meant to imply superior clarity on all issues. Despite the importance of supervisors in the progress of a case, an administrative subordinate might contribute significantly to the clarification of the thinking of his superior. The county heads, involved in the psychiatric program, repeatedly demonstrated their capacity to accept such contributions by their subordinates—the ongoing program was one example of this capacity. It was unfortunate that this later stage did not include the continuing participation of those individuals who pioneered the program and whose continuing counsel would have proved valuable.[2]

℀ EXPANSION OF PSYCHIATRIC SERVICES ℀

By 1952, when the program was four years old and the amount of psychiatric time was still twelve hours per week, a psychiatrist who had recently settled in the county was added. He devoted twelve more hours per week to the program, spending seven at the county hospital with patients and the hospital residents. In 1954, a third psychiatrist was recruited and employed for twenty hours per week. The psychiatrists met weekly to integrate their work. The increased psychiatric time was absorbed by the hospital, which by then had built a new psychiatric ward as part of its expansion program. The amount of time devoted to actual agency consultation for the entire county remained about the same.

The new ward increased the number of psychiatric beds from eight to twenty-six. Although these beds were not filled immediately, the expanded capacity permitted more flexibility in dealing with patients: it was less imperative to discharge or transfer patients to a state hospital in order to make beds available for emergencies, and more efficient use of the ward could be planned. This was the only psychiatric inpatient facility in the county, which by then numbered about 340,000 people. Until psychiatrists found time to spend with them, these patients had been seen by residents who, under supervision, cared for all the hospital patients. The residents were capable of meeting most medical and surgical needs, but rarely had even a minimal

[2] William Stegeman, Hazel Bearss, Harlan Lewis, John Davis, Gladys Kayes.

amount of training or experience with psychiatric patients. Now every psychiatric patient who presented a problem to the residents and medical staff could be seen by a psychiatrist.

With the assignment of a block of psychiatric time to the ward and to direct service to patients, referrals from the rest of the hospital and from agencies were encouraged. Closed ward service expanded and outpatient service began. Most of the outpatients were referred for diagnostic work-up, but in reality the evaluation constituted a brief treatment service. Usually some acute problem was resolved or some workable plan was evolved. In a very few instances outpatients were seen regularly for weekly interviews when the psychiatrist felt this to be indicated. The evolving policy permitted this freedom.

Several results grew from the establishment of direct service to patients, results that had an important bearing on future planning. One was that referring a case, discussing the findings with the psychiatrist, and working out a plan became an important learning experience for the agency worker. The second result was that the psychiatrists were in a position to meet the need of the Health Department to develop its own mental health program.

A third development was the gradual realization that the direct work with patients and with matters concerning them, such as liaison with community agencies, was the psychiatric program. That part of the program in which the psychiatrist did not work directly with patients was the mental health program. By this definition, the original program had been a mental health program, and not a psychiatric one. The mental health program might do well without the services of a psychiatrist, because it began to clear up his thinking about past events. The director of the county hospital had taken the position that the program at its outset was a medical program, since a psychiatrist was a physician. This view was never debated, even though consultation was regarded as primarily educative by most. As a result of this new discrimination, it was simpler to separate objectives and ways of working in a known field, such as psychiatric work with patients, from the experimental and untried efforts in the mental health part of the program. For in this program the methods were less proven and tried, and included lectures, films, dissemination of literature, group meetings of various kinds, and so on. Psychiatric consultation was one of these methods and played a significant role in the county. Nevertheless, consultation by members of other disciplines is not to be excluded, nor should any new procedure that promises to be useful.

Fourthly, the original goal of developing a child guidance clinic had shifted towards evolving a program shaped to a variety of specific needs as they were now being expressed and as they could be met by available personnel.

With the increased number of psychiatrists, some were appointed to the Lunsey Commission to replace at least one of the two general practitioners in decisions regarding commitment of persons to a state hospital. The presence of a psychiatric specialist was regarded as a much-needed improvement.

Finally, because of the vitality of the emerging program all psychiatrists who settled in the county were invited to join the county hospital staff at regular consultant fees.[3] This invitation was also intended to encourage new psychiatrists, especially recent graduates, to settle in the county by providing them with paid work while they developed their private practice. It was hoped that most of them would continue their association with the program indefinitely. Thus, there was a further increase in psychiatrists while, at the same time, a setting was provided that contributed toward integrating their work and attitudes with those of the better acquainted psychiatrists. The one important drawback of the plan became apparent when six part-time psychiatrists were employed in 1956. It was difficult and costly to the county for the psychiatrists to meet with each other on a continuing basis. Conse-

---

[3] While the psychiatrist received $35.00 for three hours at the outset, in reality each visit to the county took five hours, since the commuting from San Francisco was one hour each way. The additional two hours and the cost of transportation for each three-hour session were never issues, not even during the period when he visited the county four mornings per week.

The cost of his services was low compared to the fee then current for the time of private psychiatrists. However, it was high compared to the fee paid to the county hospital's medical consultants and to the added psychiatrists, namely, $25.00 per morning (or three hours). In addition, the $15.00 per hour (exclusive of the time and cost of travel) took on other meanings, at least to the psychiatrist, as the amount of time devoted to the county increased. His salary for only twelve hours was more than was paid the other psychiatrists and approached the salary of his employers, who put in a minimum of forty hours (many county department heads voluntarily and because of the demands of their jobs often worked evenings and weekends). While these comparisons might have occurred only to the psychiatrist and might have played no part in the thinking of the county officials who employed him, he felt it would have been useful, if only for himself, had he initiated a frank discussion of these issues. Instead, he chose to reduce his time progressively, ostensibly to accommodate the cast of new psychiatrists.

quently, for a year they met for an hour on their own time following the monthly meeting of the county hospital medical staff, hardly sufficient time to discuss accumulated problems.

The psychiatrist recognized as soon as direct service began to grow that a coordinator was necessary to process referrals and to tie up loose ends of the program, especially with the presence of several part-time psychiatrists and more in prospect. This premature proposal was not accepted at the time. An effort made to refer patients through regular medical social service channels proved to be premature, too. As a result referrals were made directly to the psychiatrist on duty until a more expanded program was achieved some time after the psychiatrist was no longer connected with the program.

Discussions with department heads, either individually in scheduled interviews or collectively in the monthly Mental Health Committee meetings, were an important experience, as these meetings went on concurrently with consultation meetings at all levels in practically every agency. It was instructive to notice the timing of and attitude toward the same subject matter at various hierarchical levels: for example, the acceptance of certain policies handed down from a director, the gaps in communication up and down the hierarchical line, the tendency for subordinates to keep touchy subjects alive when they had long been settled at higher levels, the banding together of units vs. units, of agencies vs. other agencies, and of groups of agencies vs. groups of other agencies (all of which could be reduced to involvements of individuals), unwitting sabotage, and so on.

All these are negative examples because these were almost exclusively the problems discussed with the psychiatrist. However, at times the psychiatrist had the opportunity to watch new ideas unfold and he was often impressed by the imaginative and creative capabilities of many, especially by their spontaneous expression of psychiatric insights, some of which the psychiatrist had acquired laboriously. This is to say nothing about what he learned from his consultees.

Discussions with agency heads made the psychiatrist realize that the directors had, over the years, come to regard their own agencies as containing within their structure a built-in in-service training program through their supervisor-worker organization. This concept, in most instances, was explicitly stated, understood, and implemented through individual and unit interviews; that is, worker with supervisor,

supervisor with regional director, regional director and any combination of these, as situations dictated.

As a result the psychiatrist realized that things had shifted—that each agency could take new and individual steps to develop its own teaching program rather than depend upon psychiatric consultation as its main in-service teaching method. Coincidentally, each department was beginning to explore its own ways of solving problems, short of psychiatric consultation. For instance, the Social Welfare Department had employed a university professor from the School of Social Welfare to teach a course to supervisors. The Director of Social Welfare was formulating ideas to provide in-service training to college graduates without social work training and to teach them casework concepts on the job, since there were then few applicants for social work jobs. Discussions went on continually with the School of Social Welfare in an attempt to find ways to share and integrate the experience of the agency with the academic program offered by the school. The Probation Department and the School Department were similarly planning for in-service training.

In short, departments were developing and growing as was the knowledge in their respective disciplines. Even though the directors did not realize some of their ideas in practice, their thinking was in the direction of less rather than more psychiatric consultation. The psychiatrist recognized with the agency personnel the importance of this trend (in some instances he was the one to voice it), and discussed with them his own emerging question about the place of a psychiatric consultant in an agency whose function was not primarily psychiatric. If they needed consultants, why could they not get them from members of their own disciplines? However, he felt that in most instances, the know-how existed within the agency and that the organizations were geared to educate themselves with the aid of the nearby educational institutions.

At about this time the Health Department was reformulating its thinking regarding mental health, having tried various ways of working with the psychiatrist. Meetings had been held with nurses, with supervisors, and with administrators. One supervising nurse with considerable nursing and administrative background had just returned from a year's study of mental health. In her supervised field work she had interviewed psychiatric patients. She wished to set up in the nursing department a program of mental health, which she would supervise. The Director of the Health Department had meanwhile explored, in staff discussions, the feasibility of public health nurses providing services to patients released from the psychiatric ward of the county hospital after recovery from an acute psychotic episode. He proposed that nurses start by interviewing suicidal patients who were ready for discharge from the hospital and were willing to be followed by a public health nurse after their return home. The nurse was to interview the patient each week on a home visit.

The psychiatrist saw value in the idea since the nurse would have an opportunity to interview patients more frequently than usual and to receive some form of supervision. In addition it soon became apparent that the nurses, in the course of being introduced to patients by the psychiatrist, were learning a good deal about interviewing. They learned about the careful, considerate preparation for transfer of the patient to them and about the importance of explaining clearly to the patient and of offering him choices without attempt to coerce or influence his choice. Other benefits accrued from this direct service. Workers in the various agencies, in the process of referring a case or discussing findings about their referred patient with the psychiatrist, were making gains, too, that somehow differed from what they received from psychiatric consultation. This was the kind of experience the psychiatrist had recognized as important while as a fellow in child psychiatry he was formulating his ideas. All this helped stimulate his thinking about the value of direct service and the conferences with agency workers about the patient versus indirect service (that is, consultation) as an in-service training device for county workers.

By 1956, the inpatient service grew to equal, in census, the medical service, which until then had been the busiest in the hospital. The ward was used to house patients who caused problems in management in the jail, the juvenile home, and the rest of the hospital; they were kept for short stays until some crisis was resolved. Requests for outpatient service increased.

While the program was showing this robust growth, the psychiatrist felt that an important element was slipping away. Monthly one-hour meetings gave scant time to work out many of the problems encountered by six psychiatrists, let alone to develop fresh ideas that could spread because of their validity. Involved as he was in a philosophy of consultation that was not generally shared by the psychiatric staff, he hesitated to relinquish his own consultation efforts and supervise the work of the other psychiatrists in the reduced time he was now devoting to the county. Instead, he sought ways to increase the effectiveness of his consultation through the formulation that had long guided him, namely, working with the highest and the fewest in the hierarchical order as the best use of scarce psychiatric time for any one agency. If he could work more concentratedly with such individuals, what they learned could trickle down through their built-in supervisory systems.

Consequently, he advanced the idea that an individual from each agency, preferably a department head or his assistant, be assigned to the psychiatric service half-time for a period of six months or a year. A program similar to a field placement of psychiatric social work students could be arranged with the main emphasis on interviewing psychiatric patients, under the supervision of a psychiatrist. Most of the executive members of the agencies, the potential candidates, had had postgraduate training and successful, highly responsible work experience. They would be expected to learn as rapidly and as efficiently as less well prepared graduate social work students. Supplemental reading could be assigned and formal classroom work could perhaps be provided.

The detailed planning of such a program was deferred while the merits of the suggestion were considered. The idea was intriguing in itself and as the logical extrapolation of the concept that the most efficient form of indirect service is through the most concentrated direct service to individuals in positions of wide influence.

Yet the concept was also disquieting to the psychiatrist and posed an important question, for he saw that the most concentrated direct training service in the field of psychiatry and mental health was that received by the psychiatrist himself. Had his been thorough enough he might not have departed in critical moments from the stated credo and would have therefore correctly related his contribution to mental health to that of other community workers among whom the psychiatrist would now be counted.

In retrospect, the proper move seems clear: to consolidate and strengthen the psychiatric service, to coordinate the work of all part-time psychiatrists around clinic services; particularly, to devise a supervisory system with its inherent in-service training, as was customary for all agencies connected with the program, and along with the other

psychiatrists increase the efficacy of all services, including consultation. The county leaders with their progressiveness and imagination
might have found ways to develop and keep this emerging service even
if the psychiatrists took costly time to learn together. Many benefits
might have resulted. A psychiatric service or agency, so integrated,
would have demonstrated that the psychiatrist's principal contribution
to mental health was his devoted and efficient service to patients, just
as the devoted and efficient discharge of work responsibilities of every
agency worker is his contribution to mental health. Such attention to
designated work by its very nature coordinates the available resources
of the county to maximum efficiency around the problem to be solved.
Thus the pool of mental health problems lessens, for such endeavor *is*
mental health in its most fundamental sense, and what remains in the
pool can be studied collaboratively by all county agencies, with the
psychiatric service playing an important supplemental role rather than
a chief one.

But this is all in retrospect. Not only was the psychiatrist not
ready to head up such a psychiatric program, but his interests and
commitments were leaning toward clinical research and teaching. In
July 1956, about eight years after the program began, he resigned to
devote more time to the Children's Service of the Langley Porter Neuropsychiatric Institute.

In 1957, the Short-Doyle Act for Community Mental Health
Services[4] offered Contra Costa the opportunity to significantly extend
its mental health activities. After some jockeying, the program was
formally placed in the county hospital where previous mental health
budgets had been centralized, a decision that occasioned misgivings
among several psychiatrists who felt that a separate psychiatrically run
agency would be best. Public health and many lay groups questioned
whether either psychiatric or general medical therapy environments
would permit enough program flexibility or stimulate the community's
understanding. In retrospect, it can be seen that probably the most
pertinent misgivings were those expressed by the county hospital director, who felt that the very rapidity of the growth of mental health

---

[4] An Act passed by the 1957 California Legislature, which, under the
general supervision of the State Department of Mental Hygiene, established
matching reimbursement for local mental health services in five general categories—inpatient, outpatient, rehabilitation, information (education), and consultation to community groups and agencies.

services would rob the program of its vitality to explore, react, and reconstruct its activities. In spite of these evidences of general anxiety and awareness, the most-likely-to-succeed solution to the problems, which will be discussed shortly, was never broached.

The program psychiatrists and county hospital director wanted to expand cautiously so as to lose no ground; the public health officer and community groups took the position that active participation in the statewide extension of programs would more rapidly fill the personnel and service void, and that enlarged field experience even in the hands of relatively inexperienced persons would offer more to the community in the long run. The latter view prevailed.

The new program brought with it a legislatively-specified, essentially lay board that would supposedly make policy, but the law made no particular mandatory provision for what no one clearly foresaw as necessary; namely, a means and method for maintaining even a minuscule machinery for study, research, and intellectual exchange. In this potential vacuum, the county hospital director who was appointed to direct the county Short-Doyle program attempted to encourage what had become the traditional monthly sessions of department heads and chief psychiatrist in order to retain the thinking and steering body. However, no encouragement was given to the psychiatrists to extend the exploratory and study aspects of their own work as they, with full-time psychiatric leadership, were about to take over the main responsibilities for program direction under county hospital and lay board policy makers.

The interested nonpsychiatric agencies continued to spearhead and maintain the pressure for the original community goals, which were essentially based on beliefs described by Blum and Ketterer:[5]

1. Emotionally disturbed persons brought to an agency's attention are often in a phase of exacerbation and have passed through a prior phase in which the illness was less severe or fixed, but nevertheless under way.

2. It should be easier to reach such persons therapeutically at a time when their illness is less fixed, when they and others in their environment are less pessimistic in attitude. Presumably, at this time they can be assisted with a lesser expenditure of limited psychiatric resources.

3. It should be possible to provide many persons in the

[5] Blum, H. L., and W. A. Ketterer, "A Health Department's Activities in Mental Health," *Public Health Reports*, 73:7, July 1958.

early stages of their disturbances with a supportive relationship through their contact with workers who are not psychiatrists but are employed by agencies whose work unveils emotional implications. If these workers are well indoctrinated in psychiatric principles and can work with psychiatric guidance, they should be able to accomplish a great deal. These "caretaker persons" may exist in or out of agencies or organizations. Those in agencies should be easier to mobilize.

4. It should be possible to utilize the services of a high proportion of professional people such as school guidance workers, probation caseworkers, social welfare workers, medical social workers, public health nurses, teachers, and others. This group numbers about one per cent of the general population and two per cent of the adult population and has a large number of public contacts as well as some psychological orientation.

5. It might be possible to transmit continuously a significant amount of psychiatric understanding and working know-how from the psychiatrist to these field workers. This would probably be most successful if the information were mediated by another small but strategically placed group of workers who are equipped with significant psychiatric skills. These are the psychologists, psychiatric public health nurses, and psychiatric social workers.

Restated, the field worker in a supportive relationship with many disturbed persons would work closely with skilled intermediaries who in turn would deal directly with the psychiatrist. In this way the limited services of a psychiatrist could be extended through many professional workers or "caretakers" to a great number of their contacts. We have called this the "trickle down" approach.

At about this time the countywide as well as the broad national dissemination of information and concern about emotional ills created an understandable, unavoidable, and undeniably justified pressure for increased direct therapy services. The county staff additions under the Short-Doyle Act continued to be direct service-oriented persons while the original more venturesome and community-oriented psychiatric influences retreated under the excessive time demands of the growing program. Interestingly, the state Short-Doyle program rapidly became community-oriented in the broadest possible interpretation of the Act.

Some satisfaction was being generated generally from agency and community ability to get a modicum of patient therapy to those poorer patients eligible for county hospital care and to some few others accepted there at part and full pay. In addition, as the county program attracted part-time people there was an increasing availability of private psychiatry and psychologic counseling. However, the concern with and exploration of the professional worker's role in the exciting new endeavor continued to erode. Equally misleading and also tending to obscure need for professional growth was the implicitly accepted notion that all psychiatrists understood the issues and goals of community psychiatry (mental health as we define it) and would therefore be concerned with the analysis and elaboration of the processes involved. The activities that did not, but might have, taken place are perhaps best illustrated by Caplan in his analysis of what could be learned by a psychiatrist doing community work.[6]

The senior author felt the need for continuing growth as critical to his profession and returned to a private practice and teaching environment. The junior author could never quite accept the position that growth might take place only in an academic psychiatric environment but never faced the issue that if it were to do so in the community setting, time must still be set aside for study and contemplation if the program experiences were to be profitably utilized in the continuing extensions into a new field. No time was ever reserved for the many new participant psychiatric workers to consider the implications of their work. Meetings with operating agency heads and key workers, which had clearly influenced and shaped earlier thinking as much as any academic environment could, became less frequent and lost content. This tendency was probably promoted both by the knowledge that more of the direct, skilled, patient services were being provided and by a sense of futility among some department heads as they watched the formally established and growing program harden its shell into traditional one-to-one psychotherapy.

The steady decrease of community orientation for most newly recruited professionals in the growing service and the reduction in their exchange and indoctrination time resulted in their ignoring community concerns. Finally, the mutual lack of comprehension produced cleavages that are still very manifest.

Instead of any clear attempt to restore the older, more profitable joint venturing, the junior author and others tried to supply the missing community education, promotion, and program-oriented

[6] Caplan, G., *Principles of Preventive Psychiatry*, New York: Basic Books, 1964.

agency consultation partly by using two of the health department personnel who were paid also through the county Short-Doyle program. The key shared person, a health educator, was in a low status position and was not a mental health expert. The Short-Doyle demand to stick to direct service and the health department pull to encourage community concerns and understanding created difficulties for him that he was unable to resolve because he had neither the position nor the authority.

Out of such adversity the heretofore badly floundering community mental health association began to flower and offer leadership. With support from the health department and a minority of the community's psychiatrists, the association, with other kindred spirits, without county Short-Doyle support or approval, pioneered in just a few years the introduction of many services; it forced county Short-Doyle and community attention on the need for services for teenagers, suicides, and the mentally retarded; it initiated programs for college student volunteers for classes of severely disturbed children, visiting programs at the state hospital, return-home planning for hospitalized cases, private day care, friendly visitors, special team evaluations of epileptics and of children who were not developing properly, and classes for emotionally disturbed and educationally handicapped in public schools.

With or without full blown success many of these small voluntary efforts seem to have served both clients and caretakers well and remain firmly embedded in the social community. But nowhere in the professional community has there been a renaissance of the old forum in which experiences were examined and new concepts formulated out of them. In fact, although citizen resoluteness forced county Short-Doyle policy changes, its very imaginativeness seemed to cause a further diminution of the spontaneous innovativeness from the professional community.

The confusions of the expanding front finally have now cleared enough for us to perceive that the fault did not lie primarily in the rapid growth, with skills under the influence of a single therapy-oriented agency utilizing recently matriculated experts. Rather, the unperceived withdrawal of the academic, laboratory type, learning-teaching environment plunged each new county Short-Doyle specialized worker into a set of chores whose dimensions were perhaps too carefully delineated during and for his training.

By contrast, the elements of community concern have maintained a relatively free forum through the mental health association, in spite of the austerity era of community concern at the county Short-Doyle level. The association has been strengthened by exploration and experience and is now less in awe of degrees and officialdom as it sees its own inspirations belatedly accepted and acknowledged. The essentially lay groups have also won several local and state policy and legislative battles by judicious joining of forces. This would be the first time in our county that any groups tagged as "mental health" have been able to work together effectively.

These events have provided for many of us restoration of faith in an aroused public's pluralistic but reconcilable views. It also confirms some beliefs that the greatest influences currently stimulating professional psychiatric thinking are lay dissatisfactions with the roles professionals carve out for themselves as they provide services originally brought into being by the laity, who continue to pay for them and benefit—or suffer—from them.

Truly concerned professional and humanitanian psychiatrists can not help but become involved in and promote community psychiatry (mental health) if they do a sincere job with their clients. For the psychiatrist cannot by himself re-create each of his patients and must more often look to providing crisis assistance and thereby client growth. Psychiatrists must become aware of the need for certain social or supportive institutions and furthermore must help create them. Equally, they must realize that destructive local or socially massive environments create highly hostile, dependent, escapist personalities that would not be able to respond to psychotherapy, even if it were available. Victims of overwhelming deprivation cannot be made "normal" through the medium of psychotherapy in the unchanged and often inescapable environments such as racial ghettos invaded and surrounded by the flamboyant slogans of freedom, equality, opportunity, and wealth.

Community Oriented Private Psychiatric Practice

Robert L. Leopold

UNIVERSITY OF PENNSYLVANIA AND
WEST PHILADELPHIA MENTAL HEALTH CONSORTIUM

III

XXXXXXXXXXXXXXXXXXXXXX

This case history concerns a community mental health program that developed within the framework of a private group practice conducted by four psychiatrists. The program was not the result of planning. Rather, in the early phases of its growth, serendipity played a significant part. These beginnings were modest enough. Typically, a member of our four-man group would be asked to fill some community need and would respond, primarily because the requested service corresponded to a special interest of his own. Such activities soon led him to discover new areas of interest. Meanwhile, his response had called the community's attention to his availability, so that it would request additional services. As he became further involved, his range of interests broadened and deepened and requests for services increased. Soon there was too much for one man to do; other members had to be involved. Thus the special interests of the entire group flourished and expanded; and, concurrently, requests for service came more and more frequently.

Soon a few simple involvements in community service had grown into a complex mass of activities. At some point in our history, the group began to see that in order to handle these activities adequately and still maintain the traditional functions of the practice, there would have to be formal planning for disbursement of time and energy. Gradually, a structure of sorts took shape, but still we did not think of the structure as a "program." Yet, in retrospect, it is clear that by practicing as a group, we were able to render a fairly wide range of community services while remaining essentially private practitioners.

Working in partnership with Dr. Josgre C. Yaskin, and under the sponsorship of the Philadelphia Psychoanalytic Institute's Extension Division, I began early in practice to conduct lectures and seminars for ministers and rabbis, for management and supervisory personnel from industry, for nurses, and for attorneys. Subjects were drawn from areas considered pertinent and useful in these diverse occupations, such as dynamic psychology, the fundamentals of psychoanalysis, counseling techniques, and interpersonal relationships. Thus, quite early in my professional career, I had an opportuntiy to branch out from private practice into the general community by way of sharing some psychoanalytic insights with certain community "caretakers."

By 1954, the numerous activities of this private practice made it desirable to add a third physician, Dr. Harold Dillon. He came to the practice from a post as assistant clinical director of a major voluntary mental hospital in the area. In addition, he was conducting a neurological and psychiatric consultation service he had started about two years before in a small general hospital in Stroudsburg, Pennsylvania, about 100 miles from Philadelphia.

In 1955, Dr. Yaskin, the senior member and founder of the practice, died. Harold Dillon and I, as partners, continued the office much as it had operated previously. But the demands on our time became overwhelming; soon it was apparent that we needed additional manpower. In time, two other psychiatrists, Arnold Sadwin and M. Lawrence Spoont, joined us. Both had considerable neurologic experience, and were advanced candidates in psychoanalytic training. In addition, Spoont had been, for two years during his military service, in charge of an army community psychiatry unit and came to our practice with a deep interest in community work and considerable preparation for moving in this direction.

❧ *EVOLVED PRACTICE* ❧

Our office, by 1960, was conducted by four men, three of whom were partners and one an associate. Ages ranged from the late thirties to the late forties. Our major base was in the private practice of psychiatry and neurology. From this base, we were able to develop a broader range of community services, in both clinical and nonclinical areas, than appears to be possible under the usual circumstances of private practice.

The unusual circumstance that made this possible was *group practice*. Here, group practice refers not simply to an association of doctors who share office space and other facilities for convenience and economy, but, more basically, to a sharing of tasks and responsibilities. This pattern of dividing work was established early in the history of the practice, and it was not difficult to extend this pattern to meet the additional demands created by our community activities.

By its very nature, psychiatry is not usually seen as lending itself to a sharing of its clinical obligations except in rather limited circumstances, for example, in some aspects of institutional patient care. Neurology allows considerably more latitude for an interchange of tasks and responsibilities among several therapists, usually without discomfort for either patient or therapists. In fact, neurology originally provided the *raison d'être* of this group practice. Nevertheless, with experience we found that the work could be shared in certain areas of our psychiatric practice. Some psychotic patients and some patients with psychosomatic illnesses actually seem to benefit from relationships with several therapists. Also, there are certain neurotic patients in psychotherapy who, in the absence of their own therapists, can be given support by other therapists, sometimes even with positive advantages for the patients. In addition, any member of the group can handle an emergency patient for a short time until it is decided which member will be the most satisfactory long-term therapist, and where he can fit the patient into his schedule.

Whatever the circumstances that made possible our community services, certain concepts remained central to our operation. We believe that rendering medical care is the primary task of the physician; that to function effectively in nonclinical as well as clinical areas, he must remain solidly entrenched in his medical identification; and that his medical identification continues valid only as long as he continues to renew himself as a clinician. Thus every member of this practice, regardless of his commitments in nonclinical areas, was also actively involved in the private office and hospital care of neurologic and psychiatric patients and in traditional university teaching obligations and outpatient clinic responsibilities.

AMERICAN FRIENDS SERVICE
AND PEACE CORPS

Our work with the American Friends Service Committee typifies the way in which the practice grew in other and less traditional directions through a combination of almost fortuituous circumstances, serendipity, and the demonstration of our availability for responding to needs. The AFSC is a philanthropic agency that concerns itself, among its many activities, with efforts to build peaceful relations between peoples of different cultures. The field programs it maintains in countries all over the world are a major element in these efforts.

The group acted as psychiatric consultants in the selection, training, and field support of workers in these programs; as psychiatric consultants at various levels in the overall administration of the agency; and as traditional clinical psychiatrists and medical consultants in the agency's medical program, devoting some four to six hours a week to the agency on a limited fee-for-service basis. But since we were deeply concerned with its work and its goals, our preoccupation with its needs extended well beyond these hours.

The personnel secretary of the agency requested my consultation initially (1958) in connection with a relatively simple need. I was asked to help with the selection of field workers, primarily by identifying psychologically unsuitable applicants. Although I knew almost nothing about the organizational structure and operation of the AFSC, I did happen to know a little about the AFSC philosophy. Furthermore, my teaching experiences with groups of people from industry had given me a considerable interest in the selection interview.

At first, the agency viewed my services in the selection process with little enthusiasm. But it was not too long before I interviewed an applicant who seemed dangerously close to a severe depression.

Although I recommended that he be rejected, he was accepted. Just before he and his wife were to leave for overseas, the depression in fact materialized, and the man had to be released from service. This incident legitimated the psychiatrist's role in the selection process, and, subsequently, more faith was placed in my contributions.

Meanwhile, my interest intensified in the work of the agency as a whole, and in the selection process in particular. Comparatively few psychotic or prepsychotic applicants were presenting themselves; rather, I was commenting with increasing frequency on the psychological qualifications of relatively healthy applicants. These comments now began to receive some consideration from the agency. But they were necessarily quite general and of limited value. I had too little knowledge of actual field jobs to be able to evaluate with any assurance a particular individual's psychological assets for a particular job. It seemed to me that talks with field workers on completion of their assignments would be helpful. Permission was granted to conduct termination of service interviews. Not only did these interviews provide me with useful information with respect to the selection process, but they appeared to be helpful to the returning worker as an integrative experience. Also, they were a valuable source of feedback information for the agency about its field work. Of course, data of this kind are converted to the form of general conclusions before release to the agency so that individual confidentiality will be protected.

The importance of first-hand information from the field now became increasingly apparent. The agency accordingly decided to make it possible for me to make personal visits to the field. These field trips added to my knowledge of the foreign cultures the agency deals with. They sharpened my perception of my own cultural bias and helped me to manage it more effectively. Thus I was helped further to understand the psychological strains of the work for which I interviewed applicants and to evaluate more sensitively the applicants' assets for coping with them.

During this evolution in role, the agency was becoming more acutely aware of other needs with respect to the psychological aspects of its field work. In some cases, it felt that these needs were not being dealt with effectively. Possibly the presence of a psychiatric consultant who was interested in the agency's work helped to stimulate this awareness. Eventually I was asked to participate in the pre-departure orientation of field workers by helping them to prepare psychologically for their new circumstances. The agency also asked me to assist in adding a psychological dimension to their program of support for field workers. My field trips, of course, were valuable in efforts to develop these training and support programs realistically.

By the time I was making field trips for the agency, the demands on my time had increased enough to make it necessary to involve other members of our group in the agency's work. Their interest and enthusiasm soon matched mine.

Our growing involvement in the selection, training and support aspects of the agency's field work inevitably brought us into extensive contacts with administrative processes throughout the agency. Again, perhaps our presence stimulated awareness on the agency's part of certain psychological needs arising in these processes; and again, we were available and interested in any case, so that we were soon being called on for consultation in connection with many problems concerned with organizational and interpersonal relationships.

Whatever service we performed for this agency, we insisted that we remain consultants to the personnel secretary. No matter who requested a consultation, we responded only after she had been informed of the request and sanctioned the proposed service. Thus we retained the sanction usually conferred on the physician in nonmedical circles, and at the same time, had the obviously valuable sanction of a responsible and highly respected figure in the organizational structure. By adhering rigidly to this policy, we minimized any potential feeling of threat that "the psychiatrist" might be hovering about without appropriate authorization and perhaps for questionable purposes.

Furthermore, by maintaining contact with her, we were assured of good communication with her, and through her with the agency. Communication between the group office and the AFSC office was frequent and continuing—by telephone, mail, and personal visits. We tried to respond to the communicated needs of the agency quickly and willingly. For example, when a crisis of the most profound and tragic significance in a Friends' installation abroad was reported to our office, the day's commitments were rearranged immediately so that I could spend the afternoon and part of the evening with the staff at headquarters. When such needs arose (fortunately, they were rare), our roles required us to respond to them even at personal inconvenience and cost if our usefulness to the agency was not to be severely limited.

We also believed that we must keep pace with *all* pertinent agency needs and respond to them even if they are not communicated, but rather are felt. In nearly all organizational work, it is likely that some needs will become apparent to the consultant before they are perceived by the organization. Thus, on a field trip to Mexico, I saw certain needs in the agency's medical program and was able to bring them to the attention of responsible staff members. This response to felt needs eventually catalyzed some appropriate changes.

The needs in Mexico and the response to them were, in fact, part of a chain of events evolving out of a hiatus that had developed in the medical services available to the organization. Following the Mexico episode, the organization asked us, on a temporary basis, to take some of the responsibility for strengthening its medical program. Certainly our training and experience as psychiatrists had not prepared us to deal with the problems of a medical program demanding knowledge of tropical medicine, preventive medicine and immunology. But our office did have sufficient acquaintance with the local medical community to be helpful as a resource for establishing contacts with suitable professional personnel.

The AFSC work required so rapid and so frequent a shifting of roles that we sometimes seemed to be functioning in several roles at the same time; such a situation required a great deal of flexibility, not only with respect to shifts in role but also with respect to differing views and beliefs. We had to learn to be on guard lest a tendency to think of ourselves as "AFSC people" might beguile us into forgetting that we were consultants with no responsibility for operations.

Our involvement in the Peace Corps came about in similar circumstances. In its initial stages of development, the Peace Corps consulted the AFSC because of the striking similarities between the latter's work and the proposed new program. Subsequently, the AFSC personnel secretary asked me to accompany her to an early planning session (1961) of the Peace Corps Selection Division. Following the session, I was asked, and agreed, to help with the psychiatric aspects of the Peace Corps selection program so that the selection experiences of the AFSC could be utilized in meeting the relevant needs of the younger agency.

It seemed at first that my Peace Corps assignment would require only small and occasional allotments of time, on a consultative basis. But, amid the inevitable confusion that attends the initial organizing phases of a new and experimental agency, there was a great deal of work to be done and an acute shortage of professional manpower to do it.

For approximately the next year and a half, various administrative as well as consultative functions were undertaken. Over this period, I spent one or more days a week in Washington, countless hours on the telephone with Peace Corps staff, and many days at training sites throughout the country and at overseas Peace Corps installations. For about half of the period, Peace Corps was still requiring a psychiatric examination for every trainee, a policy that underwent a radical change after February 1962.[1] Hence, most of my Peace Corps time before that date was devoted to trying to find enough psychiatrists to handle this prodigious task, to helping orient these psychiatrists to their work, to arranging time-and-place schedules for the examinations, and generally to supervising the psychiatric component of the selection process.

But somehow, amid all this hectic activity, time was found for the purely consultative role in selection that had been planned. This time was spent in helping to establish psychiatric criteria for selection, to delineate procedures for psychiatric evaluation, and to search for ways of dealing with the psychiatric manpower shortage.

Despite preoccupation with selection, consultation of another kind was beginning to evolve during those early months. Mainly, we explored the possibility of using psychiatrists in areas other than selection—for example, in training and overseas support. Then, in February 1962, the entire Peace Corps psychiatric program was reconstructed. The mandatory psychiatric interview for every trainee was eliminated. Psychiatric manpower was now released for other purposes. After that, with the backing of other interested personnel, both psychiatric and nonpsychiatric, many of the plans formulated tentatively in the earlier talks became realities. Roles developed for psychiatrists in the training and support programs as well as in selection; moreover, psychiatrists began to be used as consultants at various levels of the overall operation of the Peace Corps.[2]

[1] Leopold, R. L., and L. J. Duhl, "The Peace Corps: A Historical Note on a New Challenge to Psychiatry," *The Journal of Nervous and Mental Disease,* 137:1–3, July 1963.

[2] Leopold and Duhl, *op. cit.;* Leopold and Duhl, "New Frontiers in Psychiatry: The Peace Corps," *Psychiatric Studies and Projects,* 2, January

The new psychiatric program, with its infinitely broader utilization of psychiatric manpower, created vastly more complicated administrative problems than the old. Dr. Leonard Duhl had set aside time for Peace Corps work equivalent to my allotment. During the balance of the eighteen-month period I have referred to, he and I together tried to administer the new program. But consultative functions continued and multiplied—now not only in selection, but also in training and support, and at various levels of overall operation. Soon it was apparent that there was simply too much work for two part-time psychiatrists. Two other part-time psychiatrists were enrolled for work in Washington, and eventually, in June 1962, a full-time chief psychiatrist was appointed.

I was able gradually to relinquish my administrative duties and return to my initial role of consultant. Trips to Washington, to training sites, and to overseas installations, and telephone calls continued, but became less frequent, and usually were more for consultative work than administrative purposes.

Needless to say, a psychiatrist practicing alone would have had difficulty making available on short notice the amount of time the Peace Corps required, to say nothing of the continuing and expanding AFSC commitment. Even if I could have done it on my own, teaching and other organizational responsibilities, as well as the needs of private practice, would have suffered immeasurably. But the members of the group simply rearranged or increased their work loads according to the time this work required. Throughout all these developments, we continued to maintain a firm footing in private practice.

But it is not surprising in this kind of practice that other members of the group should themselves become involved in Peace Corps work. The younger men participated in some psychiatric interviewing during the early Peace Corps days when the individual psychiatric interview for each trainee was mandatory. Harold Dillon became one of the early training site psychiatrists.

The opportunities we had in the AFSC and Peace Corps work for evaluation of essentially healthy people helped us arrive at concepts of normal psychological functioning, which have been valuable not only in everyday clinical practice but also in our teaching programs, particularly with graduate students in internal medicine, and

1964; and Duhl, Leopold, and J. T. English, "A Mental Health Program for the Peace Corps," *Human Organization, 23*:131–136, Summer 1964.

in helping psychiatric residents to understand that the world is not populated entirely with sick people.

Our involvement with the agencies at various levels of operation has enlarged our knowledge of organizational structure and functioning, and particularly has sharpened our understanding of social systems and the functioning of individuals in relation to their social systems. All this has been valuable in conceptualizing the problems of individuals as social beings, adding not only to our resources in clinical practice and teaching, but to those available for handling many kinds of organizational relationships.

One of the most significant professional rewards, in the context of this book, rests in the fact that the agencies' mental health activities, of themselves, constitute community mental health programs. As such, we believe they provide promising models for preventive psychiatry and for an economical utilization of scarce professional mental health manpower. We feel that much of the practical experience we gained in working with these agencies can be useful wherever and whenever we are asked to help with other community health programs.

℣ UNION HEALTH CENTER ℣

Our work with the Union Health Center (operated by the International Ladies Garment Workers Union) was another area of the practice that began with a fortuitous contact in the community. This contact, our interest, and our availability were prime factors in the development of a well-defined program combining elements of private practice and community service.

Some years ago, Dr. Samuel C. Stein, the Union Health Center's medical director, and assistant professor of medicine at the Division of Graduate Medicine of the University of Pennsylvania, told me that the Center needed some consultants in neurology and psychiatry. He said the Center could not afford the going fees, but asked if our office would undertake this responsibility at reduced rates as a community service. We agreed to do so, and established a basic fee of ten dollars a visit, which remains in effect today.

Patients were referred to us for neurological or psychiatric evaluation after they had been examined at the UHC. Our reports were sent to the medical director. He would then order tests or institute treatment at the Center in accordance with our suggestions. However, certain neurological patients had to be hospitalized for more definite diagnosis, and in some instances, for treatment; and certain psychiatric patients required specialist psychiatric treatment. With the consent of UHC (which was virtually automatic), these patients then became private patients of the group. Fees for services to them were not paid by the UHC, but by the ILGWU insurance program to which nearly all Center patients belonged. Follow-up care after hospitalization was provided either in the office of the group or at the UHC, depending on the patient's wishes, geographical location, and financial status. Normally, we saw about six to eight new UHC patients each month.

Some of the group members were available to Dr. Stein for informal consultation on the activities of the UHC as a group medical care organization. At one point, the Center formed a committee of its consultants, which met regularly. One of our associates was quite active and apparently helpful.

The work with the Center brought our group into contact with patients from a socioeconomic stratum different from that of the usual private psychiatric caseload. It particularly increased our understanding of the medical and social problems of a group of older people, that is, retired workers. Thus we were helped to perceive some of the bias imposed on us by our own subculture, and to make some initial efforts to free ourselves from its restrictions.

MEDICOLEGAL WORK

In a metropolitan area such as ours, industrial and motor accident rates are high. Many of the injured have psychiatric and neurological difficulties, and the demand for expert opinion is enormous. We were called on for this kind of work continuously from the time we began to practice. In responding, we made no distinction between the kinds of examination made for plaintiff or defendant, and reports submitted are entirely medical in nature.

For a time, the requests for evaluation and testimony threatened to overwhelm our practice. About 1958, we began to limit the intake sharply (at considerable financial sacrifice, incidentally). We were determined not to let medicolegal work become the major preoccupation of the office.

Nevertheless, a certain amount of such work must be accepted as a community obligation. This also applies to evaluation and testimony in criminal and other court matters. A discussion of the complexities and difficulties besetting the relationships between law and medicine is hardly pertinent here. But it is not outside the scope of this book to point out that the lag between psychiatry and the law is a major community concern, and that psychiatrists who turn their backs entirely on medicolegal work do not diminish the lag. Only by engaging in such work can they familiarize themselves with its inherent problems sufficiently to be in a position to participate in remedial efforts. Furthermore, if conscientious and concerned psychiatrists refuse all medicolegal work, they encourage exploitation of the field by those whose motivation and interest lie elsewhere than in rendering impartial testimony. The community can only be damaged thereby.

The work has other interesting social and community aspects. It sometimes happens that evaluation of an accident victim leads to his becoming a patient in psychotherapy. Often the person is one who ordinarily would not come into treatment because his is a level of society where the pathways to psychiatric treatment are almost unknown. Thus here again the psychiatrist is able to extend his professional resources further into the community than is ordinarily possible in private practice, and we ourselves benefit professionally from contact with patients whose subculture differs markedly from that of the majority of private psychiatric patients.

Furthermore, our medicolegal work provided us, in the records of persons we evaluated in cases of accidental injury, with one of our largest reservoirs of data for research and writing. Thus we were able to study, and to report from time to time, on the post-traumatic psychological states in general,[3] and, in particular, on the psychological manifestations of whiplash injury,[4] and of concussion in children.[5] An especially interesting project concerned the short-term and long-term

[3] Leopold, R. L., "Management of Post-Traumatic Neuroses," in J. H. Nodine, *Psychosomatic Medicine,* Philadelphia: Lea and Febiger, 1962; and Leopold and H. Dillon, "Psycho-anatomy of a Disaster: A Long Term Study of Post-Traumatic Neuroses in Survivors of a Marine Explosion," *The American Journal of Psychiatry, 119:*913–921, April 1963.

[4] Leopold, R. L., and H. Dillon, "Psychiatric Considerations in Whiplash Injuries of the Neck," *The Pennsylvania Medical Journal, 63:*385–389, March 1960.

[5] Dillon, H., and R. L. Leopold, "Children and Post-Concussion Syndrome," *The Journal of the American Medical Association, 175:*86–92, January 14, 1961.

psychological sequelae of a maritime disaster, when we were asked by a firm of maritime attorneys to examine at various intervals the survivors of a tanker explosion not far from Philadelphia. In most cases, our initial examination took place within a matter of days following the accident. We had the unusual opportunity of reporting the immediate psychological effects on thirty-six survivors of disaster, and the long-term effects on thirty-four of these, whom we saw from three and one-half to four and one-half years after the accident.[6]

We were asked by the same firm to assist in evaluating the survivors of four subsequent marine disasters, again on a continuing basis over several years. Using these cases for research, we hoped to formulate various theses concerning the post-traumatic psychological states. We believed that the victim of post-traumatic psychological damage frequently is misunderstood, poorly managed, and much maligned, and there was, we felt, an inescapable obligation to the community to present findings and to argue for a more informed approach to his problems. We were particularly interested in the possibility of forestalling long-term psychological damage following accidents by means of immediate psychotherapeutic measures. This interest brought our investigation quite specifically into the realm of preventive psychiatry.

🜨 TEACHING IN THE COMMUNITY 🜨

I have already mentioned some early opportunities for community teaching sponsored by the Philadelphia Psychoanalytic Institute's Extension Division. Contacts made then led to subsequent requests from local business groups for similar courses. Thus, for example, I conducted two series of seminars for the Women's Personnel Group of Philadelphia, the first in general techniques of interviewing, the second in the psychodynamics and techniques of counseling interviewing.

Work of this kind suggests such a considerable potential for wider dissemination of psychiatric knowledge and insight in the community that a few details would seem pertinent here. The second WPG course was perhaps richer and more interesting than others. The six-

---

[6] Leopold, R. L., and H. Dillon, "Psycho-anatomy of a Disaster: A Long Term Study of Post-Traumatic Neuroses in Survivors of a Marine Explosion," *The American Journal of Psychiatry, 119*:913–921, April 1963.

teen participants, all personnel officers, came from twelve business organizations (representing such varied enterprises as banking, manufacturing, oil refining and distribution, publishing, insurance, and retailing). At each of six ninety-minute sessions, one woman presented a case history from her counseling experience as a basis for a discussion of general principles. The main function of the psychiatrist here was not that of a company consultant, but of an educator. Various recommendations were made in the course of the case discussions; they were sometimes used as guides in working toward individual solutions, but they were purely incidental to the learning process, and not offered as solutions in themselves. There was no attempt even to touch on the whole range of psychiatric concepts suggested by the cases. Rather, within the framework of an outline of personality development and ego functioning presented early in the course, an effort was made to sample judiciously the kinds of understanding of feeling that could be helpful in occupational relationships. The participants thus had an opportunity to enlarge their resources for dealing with problems encountered in counseling.

Later, with the assistance of M. Lawrence Spoont, I presented seminars on the mentally disturbed employee for the Industrial Relations Association of Philadelphia; both Harold Dillon and I conducted seminars on the emotional aspects of industrial problems for annual institutes of industrial medical officers.

Other educational commitments outside the university and hospital milieu included speaking engagements, particularly in the area of mental health promotion in the general community. For example, Harold Dillon lectured for local county medical societies, and I gave a number of lectures for the American Academy of Religion and Mental Health.

𝕏 HOW WE DO IT 𝕏

From a financial point of view, the firm base of this office in private group practice made possible our commitments to social psychiatry and community health work. Each member was able to make a very adequate living, and no one was dependent on any one source for his income. There are no rewards for working harder than anyone else, for bringing "more business" into the office. Knowing that his income will continue notwithstanding, each member feels free, within reasonable limitations, to become involved in his community concerns to an extent that is not limited by the hourly fee an organization may pay him for his services; and again, within reason, he need not calculate in terms of dollars lost to the office the time he uses for research and writing, or in teaching for which the compensation, if any, is relatively poor.

As far as availability of time is concerned, the group arrangement made it possible for each member to assume some community responsibilities—each in accordance with his own special interest. Each member knew, with rational qualifications, that other members of the group would increase or rearrange their workloads to free necessary time for his activities. The very existence of this assumption, of course, depended on like-mindedness about the importance of community service. It would be hypocritical, however, to suggest or to imply that all of us always saw eye to eye on the worth or pertinence of each member's particular interest or commitment at any given moment. Furthermore, there is no "boss" to say what anyone may or may not do. Thus it is essential that members of a group such as this communicate, freely and often, what they are doing or planning to do, so that they may arrive at some kind of consensus as to which interests should be pursued and which abandoned, and may arrange time allotments carefully and with regard for the convenience and the capabilities of each member.

Communication, then, is vital in such an operation. In busy schedules, time must be deliberately allocated for meetings of the whole group.

But while time must be planned carefully, it must be kept flexible. The needs of organizations, like those of individuals, do not always present themselves according to schedule; responses often must be immediate, particularly in a time of crisis. Thus group members must be pliable in their attitudes toward time schedules, and willing to make unexpected changes.

Obviously, the interests and abilities of all members cannot be identical: here, too, there must be pliability and a willingness to take on unaccustomed tasks frequently, and often on short notice. It follows that there must be, within the group, a continuing exchange of orientation to each other's tasks. The techniques of consultation must be utilized freely, although rather informally, so that the undertaking of an added responsibility becomes a real learning experience.

Thus each member is constantly adding to his inventory of professional skills and increasing his capacity for interchanging responsibilities quickly and executing them with little or no supervision.

Those psychiatrists who wish to enjoy the rewards of community service from a base in private practice need not wait necessarily for a program to happen: they can plan for it. Certainly, significant elements in any program's development will be fortuitous circumstances and availability for response to community needs. Nevertheless, interested readers could initiate deliberate and specific planning so that these elements may be utilized to the greatest possible advantage, both for the community and for themselves.

Consultation in Areas
Without Psychiatric Facilities

William F. Sears and Lester M. Libo
UNIVERSITY OF NEW MEXICO SCHOOL OF MEDICINE

IV

Providing mental health services to scattered populations in large, sparsely populated areas is a problem that faces many states and countries. The few available professional workers must be used strategically in programs that usually involve innovative approaches in services and in manpower use. The mental health program in New Mexico[1] emphasizes community development through locally-based consultant services in developing and sustaining services that fit the characteristics and readiness of the "underdeveloped" area. The state is divided into districts, and in each of these multi-county areas there is a lone consultant, who is a senior professional worker from psychology, social work, or mental health nursing. The district consultant helps the community define its needs and resources, provides liaison between local help-seeking and state-level facilities, conducts public information and education programs, offers case consultation, gives in-service training

[1] This project was supported by MH-286, a Mental Health Project Grant, National Institute of Mental Health. Other participants in the project were: Charles Griffith, Ph.D., cultural anthropologist (evaluation); and the following district consultants: George Gliva, M.S.W., social worker; C. Elizabeth Madore, M.A., nurse; Eugene Mariani, Ph.D., psychologist; and Robert Fortier, Ph.D., psychologist.

for the community's own workers in public health, welfare, education, law enforcement, medicine, religion, recreation, government, and voluntary service, and helps the community develop additional facilities.

The psychiatrist in this program functions as an itinerant consultant to the districts. His role is one of support to the local programs, including mainly case consultation, in-service training, and liaison with local medical practitioners and associations. His position is an unusual one—there were no other psychiatrists in the three districts he served, nor in the state headquarters of the mental health program (the state director is a psychologist). Furthermore, the psychiatrist functions in a consultant, not clinical, role.

This program, entitled "Mental Health Consultation in Underdeveloped Areas," was under the auspices of the New Mexico Department of Public Health, and was begun in 1959. Though the demonstration was completed in 1963, the format has been continued and has been adopted by other state institutions and agencies as New Mexico's approach to serving its scattered population centers.

DISTRICT CONSULTANTS

Selected areas of the state were identified by local and state leaders as being interested, needful, and ready for a concentrated effort in community mental health. One well-qualified nonmedical mental health representative was placed in each of these areas in the role of a "community mental health consultant." This consultant was based in the local public health department and lived in and served a three- to four-county district. This approach is similar to that of the Agricultural Extension Service, with its County Agents. The idea of a lone resource person in mental health who lived and worked in the local district, and the definition of his role as a consultant rather than a practitioner, was quite similar to the idea of the County "Ag" Agent, whose function was to help other farmers rather than take over the farming of the land himself.

In contrast to a clinic program, the caseload of the district consultant is his consultees, the other help-giving workers in the community: the public health nurses, welfare workers, physicians, clergymen, school administrators, guidance counselors, teachers, recreation leaders, judges, probation officers, and civic leaders. His task is not to carry individual cases. Rather, he must mobilize, coordinate, and help to expand, if necessary, the community's resources toward constructive mental health goals, both for individuals in distress and for agency programs. The consultant helps individuals with emotional problems to reach sources of assistance, both specialized and general, with a minimum of delay, and he adds to the skills of strategic community service workers in dealing with clients' problems. He also helps the community assess its needs and facilities, and helps to plan, improve, and expand those programs that have mental health meaning.

In order to carry out these functions with a high degree of professional competence, it was recognized that the community mental health consultant had to be a well-trained representative of his profession, someone to whom the community could turn with trust and respect. Since there were no clinics, mental hospitals, psychiatrists, training centers, or other sources of professional supervision or inspiration nearby, the community mental health consultant had to be a professionally mature, highly motivated person capable of functioning independently.

Personnel standards, therefore, were set quite high for these positions. The psychologist had to have a Ph.D., with a specialization in clinical psychology and five years of experience, including community work. The social worker had to have a master's degree, with five years of experience in psychiatric social work and community organization. The nurse mental health consultant had to have a master's degree, with specialization in public health–mental health consultation, plus five years of experience.

The program was fortunate in obtaining well-qualified representatives of these three disciplines. Each could function on diagnostic and therapeutic roles, could do well in the community organization and education aspects of mental health programs, and could direct his efforts toward prevention and promotion, as well as clinical care.

In two districts, the consultant was a clinical psychologist; in another district, a social worker; and in the fourth, a nurse mental health consultant.

THE PSYCHIATRIST

The project, staffed by nonmedical mental health representatives, was designed to have psychiatric consultation provided by a part-time psychiatrist who visited each of the districts one day each month. Because he is a private pilot who owns his own airplane, he could make these trips with a minimum of travel time and fatigue.

One of the roles of the psychiatrist was to assist the district mental health consultant with case conferences, which were attended by representatives of the community's care-givers. The district mental health consultant and the psychiatrist in this way provided leadership in getting the community to participate in demonstrations of an extended team approach to data-gathering, problem-solving, and care-giving services.

Over the four-year period of the demonstration project, many workshops were provided for teachers, police officers, and other strategic groups. The psychiatrist served as one of the resource persons for these activities.

During the early months of the program, the psychiatrist would frequently assist the district mental health consultant with interpretations of the program to the community. Many of his contacts were with local practitioners of medicine. These were sometimes done on an individual basis in which the psychiatrist would interpret the role of the full-time, locally-based, district mental health consultant, provide initial liaison between the consultant and a local practitioner of medicine, and demonstrate program operation by assisting with appropriate consultation both to the physician and to other care-givers who had a legitimate involvement with a particular case. On other occasions, the psychiatrist attended local medical society meetings and described and interpreted the program.

A considerable amount of the psychiatrist's time and effort was devoted to providing a supportive "ear" for the district mental health consultant, who, being the lone mental health worker in a large area, would often feel the need for professional collaboration and companionship. Together, the psychiatrist and the district mental health worker reviewed the responses that the mental health worker had encountered from individuals and groups within the community, and attention was given both to the district mental health worker's feelings and to plans of action for dealing with specific problems. The psychiatrist devoted time to both general and specific aspects of program development and to a review, with the district mental health worker, of his roles and activities within the community.

Between monthly visits to the districts, the psychiatrist was consulted by long-distance telephone regarding specific professional problems that the district mental health consultant encountered and wished to discuss.

Later in the project, the psychiatrist shared with the district mental health consultant the task of program planning for work to follow completion of the formal project. For example, in one district a new project for selecting, training, and giving ongoing support to indigenous, nontraditional mental health workers evolved and is currently in progress. In another district, a research and service project for treatment of Navajo problem drinkers was formulated and is currently operational.

The psychiatrist had no administrative authority over the district mental health consultant. Therefore, the district mental health consultant was not forced to see the psychiatrist as his employer or supervisor. This permitted the psychiatrist to focus on the local community mental health worker's program and feelings without need for concern about administrative duties.

The psychiatrist did not at any time develop a patient case load of his own. (There was not a single case during this four-year period that might be considered as the psychiatrist's "personal treatment case.") His "case load" was, instead, the three district mental health consultants and their consultees. (There were four districts, but in one district another psychiatrist was available and served as the psychiatric consultant.) This made the role of the psychiatrist in this program unlike that of many visiting psychiatrists in more traditional settings, in which a series of appointments are set up for him in order that he might "hold clinic."

✯ PHILOSOPHY AND METHODS ✯

Chief among the guiding principles of the mental health consultation program was the conviction that, ultimately, mental health could most effectively be promoted and mental illness most effectively be treated in the environment in which they existed: that is, in a community of families, schools, churches, social agencies, employment resources, recreation centers, health services, and the like.

Furthermore, unless the total community was involved in dealing with mental health problems, the primary mental health professionals themselves could neither stem the tide through treatment nor decrease its origins through prevention. Related professionals would have to be enlisted, and community responsibility would have to be increased. The mental health worker would be fighting a losing battle if he were to be used only as a dumping ground for society's rejects, without the community doing its share in continuing to work with disturbed persons at all levels of care and to try to prevent the continuing production of emotional disorders in the population.

This program emphasized the importance of community caregiving resources and provided a format for their most effective and coordinated utilization. The program philosophy recognized that both the restorative and the disruptive aspects of family and community life exist simultaneously at any given point in time. The forces that may tip the scales one way or another are found throughout the fabric of family and community living. Mental health and mental illness, therefore, are both a product and a responsibility of the total community, not just the responsibility of professional mental health workers. Slicing up responsibilities for the mental health of a community into "professional-type" or "citizen-type" compartments would be unwarranted dismemberment of the community.

Thus, the program was community-oriented with the objective of making maximum use of existing local resources and developing new ones through local action. Community development of mental health resources, broadly defined, was the prime activity of the program.

Such a format was broad enough in its philosophy to include and utilize a wide variety of care-givers and yet it was at all times goal-directed and practical. The approach tended to move care-givers away from more traditional and at times somewhat encapsulated methods of providing services and invited a philosophy of "let the one who can best give service do so without becoming tied up in jurisdictional entanglements." This program format in many instances permitted service by individuals, professional and nonprofessional, that could not or would not have occurred within the framework of more traditional agency and program structures. It not only permitted better and more meaningful coordination of services within the community, but also permitted and fostered more effective working relationships with specialized resources outside of the community such as the state hospitals, correctional institutions, medical specialists, and others.

℣ FACTORS AFFECTING OPERATION ℣

With the initiation of this project, thirteen of New Mexico's outlying communities had, for the first time, the sustained interest of professional mental health workers in their midst. Before this program began, there were no full-time trained professionals from any of the mental health disciplines in public care-giving or consultation positions in these thirteen New Mexico communities. Even at the state level, there were no trained psychiatrists in full-time public employment. (In 1959, the New Mexico State Hospital, for example, had no full-time formally-trained psychiatrists on its staff. Two psychiatrists in private practice spent one day each week at the hospital as consultants. One of these psychiatrists became the psychiatric consultant for the new community mental health project. At that time the state had a total of only seventeen psychiatrists, all in private practice, and all but four of them lived in Albuquerque, a city not involved in the districts to be served by the project. These districts were all quite distant— three to six hours driving time—from the state's centers of professional practice and public resources in mental health.)

It is important to emphasize that there was a virtual absence of professionals in the state who were employed full time in public mental health programs and had an investment in any other treatment approach that might be philosophically or administratively opposed to this new project. This new program did not have to compete with any other formalized community mental health program. This project, for the first time, put sustained effort and manpower over a period of four years into communities where very little effort was being expended, from either local or state-level resources.

Opposition was encountered in only a few areas. It came from a heterogeneous collection of people, including other professional care-givers, a very limited number of individuals in state and local government, and several members of conservative political action groups.

Jurisdictional Problems. Some of the communities' sanctioned care-givers were threatened by the appearance of a mental health professional. They feared the new consultant would usurp their prerogatives and positions of influence within the community structure. The attitudes of strong-willed individuals in positions of authority in agencies or institutions or private practice in many instances determined receptivity to the mental health consultation program. Receptive individuals could and did expedite the use of consultation services in the domain of their authority. Those who were threatened by or disagreed with the program's philosophy and services could and did effectively block access to the program. In three communities, three welfare department administrators tried to influence their staffs and the community at large in their reception of the program. Two were wholly negative toward the program but with different outcomes. In one community, the welfare director effectively prohibited her staff from utilizing the consultant's services with the explanation that "we don't want to be sued for tampering with peoples' emotional problems." In another community, a welfare representative informed her workers that they were to have nothing to do with the district consultant. Even though this welfare official was in a position of authority, many of her local caseworkers ignored her prohibition and worked closely with the mental health consultant. In a third community, the welfare director was receptive to the consultant and involved him in welfare department programs from the start: as a case consultant, in-service trainer, and adviser in program planning. The welfare director's receptivity and satisfaction with the consultant's contributions to her program were transmitted widely throughout the community. As a community "old timer" herself, her evaluation of the consultant carried substantial weight in important professional and social circles in the town.

In some communities, conducting mental health education and training programs and providing organizational consultation to some of the care-giving agencies was inhibited by the reluctance of certain other "middle-level" mental-health-related professionals, such as social workers or guidance counselors, to accept the consultants as "teachers" for themselves or their staffs. The implication that the district mental health consultants had greater professional stature was too threatening to them. The consultants generally found greater cooperation and willingness to be "trained" by or consulted with from people and agencies at opposite ends of the scale: highly qualified professionals in top institutional and agency positions and subprofessional workers whose duties brought them into contact with the most disturbed individuals.

Criticism. Some professional clinical workers expressed concern about the spectres of substandard or untried professional practice and about involvement of nonpsychiatric personnel in community mental health roles. During one group discussion of the program by physicians, one psychiatrist frequently referred to the district mental health consultants as "nonprofessionals" and warned of the dangers of "medically untrained people becoming involved with areas of illness that should be handled only by psychiatrists." Another psychiatrist pointed out that the project approach was vague, ill-defined, and not proven to be helpful or even safe. He likened the project to an effort to "take the temperature of an unknown beast with an unmarked thermometer."

At the community level, some private practitioners of medicine expressed concern over the medical-legal aspects of having nonmedical people become involved in sharing medical information and in planning for total care of the patient.

Resistance. The Division of Mental Health of the New Mexico Department of Public Health was the sponsoring agency for this program. Soon after the program was introduced into one community, the psychiatric consultant was scheduled to speak to a local association. Shortly before the meeting, a physician in the community called the psychiatrist and aired his anger with the local health department (especially as it related to the health department's activities with chest x-rays and diabetes control, which allegedly were not coordinated with the local medical society). He emphasized the degree of antagonism felt by local physicians toward the health department, implied that there would be a "showdown" with the health department because of its unacceptable behavior to the local medical community, and ended his conversation by saying that he would hate to see a colleague and personal friend "get hurt." Much later this same physician went out of his way to support the mental health program in the state when a group of very conservative physicians were attacking all federally supported programs, including the mental health project. Meeting with this physician several times, discussing the project with him, encouraging him to collaborate with the district consultant, and especially, assisting him with some of his own patients were at least in part responsible for his change in feelings and actions.

Extremist Groups. Almost from the beginning, the mental health consultation program was attacked by a variety of extremist groups in New Mexico. The antagonism toward mental health seemed based on the extremists' perception of the mind as the last bastion of individual integrity and mental health activities as a concentrated, subversive attack on that remaining fortress. The primary charge focused upon psychiatry and psychology as alien systems of thought, which undermined the basic beliefs and sentiments of the American way of life. Mental health practice was not seen as a humanely helpful resource but rather as a foreign system that threatens to brainwash patriotic Americans to accept anti-American values. Furthermore, *community* mental health represents the dangerous tentacles of this conspiracy reaching into every school, church, courtroom, and home to spread the evil. Case finding is not reaching out a helping hand to a troubled individual or family; it is only the means of identifying and incarcerating (for brainwashing) patriots who oppose this and other subversive movements. School testing and counseling services are not a helpful adjunct to the overall educational process; rather, these services have been surreptitiously installed in school systems to corrupt young minds by an un-American ideology regarding parent-child relations, attitudes toward authority, treatment of deviates, peer group relations, attitudes toward sexual behavior, and so on. In this regard, there is a profound hiatus between the extremists' normative view of the world (the "ought-to-be" dimension) and conditions as they are. In extremists' thinking, an existing condition that does not conform immediately to their normative standards is inherently suspect, if not blatantly subversive. Theirs is a universe of absolutes, of incorruptible truth versus despicable untruth. There is no room for ambiguity or relativism in their ideology.

For example, one of the district mental health consultants, in describing to a community leader what kinds of work a consultant does, stated the well-known fact that expectant mothers are often ambivalent in their feelings about their children. Feelings of irritation and resentment are often mixed in with feelings of love, he explained. Counseling and group discussions with a mental health consultant can therefore be reassuring. The consultant's purpose, of course, was that of anticipatory guidance; he wanted to indicate the normality of ambivalence and to help prepare the women to handle their feelings of guilt if they should happen to sense resentment in themselves. The consultant was being analytical, descriptive, and accepting of the world "as is."

The community leader's reaction was swift and critical. "Do you think that a public employee should be paid, out of tax funds, to teach mothers to hate their children?" he demanded at a public hearing on the mental health budget request. The consultant was charged with the sin of undermining maternal love by inculcating alien, subversive thoughts into the women who would never have thought of hatred toward their children. In that community's value system, decent women naturally loved their children; if they did not (and the community had ample evidence of deprived children), it was because the women were evil. In other words, the community's reaction was a normative one, the world of "should be." The consultant's scientific remarks, as interpreted by the community leader, became an invidious threat to basic community values. The community leader proceeded to criticize the consultant publicly and to some extent swayed community opinion against him.

A segment of conservative New Mexicans argue that the clockwork of human affairs is a process of natural selection in which people are sorted out automatically into their appropriate places in this world. Things are as they should be—even for the sufferer—but, if they are not, it is because some meddler has been tampering with the natural course of events. One conservative argument of long standing against "intervention and assistance" is the belief that sustained work with needy individuals inevitably creates continuing dependency on such services, rather than the restoration of such individuals to effective social functioning. Professionals in social service endeavors are then accused of "make-work" activities to perpetuate their own unnecessary positions. The use of the word "need" in agency reports is criticized particularly in this regard.

Community Support. Local community support was expressed through two administrative structures. The more formal structures were the county government, represented by the elected county commissioners, the local school system, and the district court. Support from these sources was in the form of appropriated funds for the itemized positions in the county health department budget for mental health personnel, or budgeted contributions to the health department for mental health services rendered. The other source of community support came in the form of contributions, usually in rather small amounts, from individuals, civic groups, and local organizations. The mental health association in one community, for example, contributed $100 per year to the program; in another, $1100.

In another small community, an organization of parents of retarded children desired a local facility for their trainable children who could not enter public school. (The public school system provided special education classes for educable retardates only and there were no local resources for the trainable retardates.) Prior to the availability of a community mental health consultant, the parents' group devoted much of its energies to obtaining state legislation that would provide the desired facilities in the public schools. As the district mental health consultant began working with this group, he was able to help them provide the desired facility for themselves without waiting for enabling state legislation. This group of parents worked out an arrangement with the local school system for classroom facilities. Then it initiated a fund-raising campaign in order that its own special education teacher could be hired. A local automobile dealer donated a used car and the parents' group quite successfully sponsored a drawing and sold a large number of "chances" for this used automobile. This event gained widespread publicity in the community and the drawing for the used automobile became a much anticipated event.

The community resident who won the car expressed his delight in winning and then returned the automobile to the parents' group. They repeated the fund-raising effort with this used automobile and in short order provided their trainable retardates with a special education teacher.

In general, funding through local governmental agencies proved to be rather inconsistent. Newly initiated local service programs were frequently the first to be cut during periods of financial stress, and new mental health programs were no exception. The public schools were more consistent contributors in the few communities where they were initially involved in sharing the costs. Community support through local nongovernmental organizations, both in terms of small amounts of money and perhaps more importantly in terms of personal involvement of the individual citizens, provided a much more meaningful avenue of "education" regarding the aims and philosophy of community mental health programs than could be accomplished through lectures and the use of pamphlets.

Support for the program, including official endorsements, was also obtained from several state organizations, including the Mental Health Association, the Parent-Teachers Association, the Conference of Social Welfare, the Psychological Association, the Medical Society, and many others. These helped obtain state-level legislative and administrative support and local participation from their county units. The project psychiatrist was active in liaison with the state medical society and with its local units and continually interpreted the program and its resources to medical practitioners throughout the state. This was particularly important in a program staffed by nonmedical mental health consultants. Similarly, representatives in the project of the disciplines of social work, psychology, and nursing maintained liaison with their respective associations, so that the more traditional members of their professions could be kept informed (and reassured) that the innovations in community mental health practice that were occurring in several parts of the state were professionally sound.

℁ ACCOMPLISHMENTS ℁

The New Mexico mental health consultation project stimulated the development of the following new resources in local communities: (1) a day school for retarded children, (2) a mental health *checkup* project for second grade children, (3) a family casework agency, (4) a day center for emotionally disturbed children, (5) a training and consultation service to an orphanage, (6) training and consultation services to schoolteachers, law enforcement workers, and clergymen, (7) the selection and training of nonprofessional community project leaders and volunteers for work in a comprehensive local mental health program, (8) an alcoholism treatment and rehabilitation program for Navajo Indians, (9) formation of citizens' organizations for planning and supporting local mental health services, (10) formation of parents' organizations for retarded and emotionally disturbed children, (11) organization of *case panels* to assemble all relevant expertise around an individual or family mental health problem, for planning and coordinating a unified program of early detection and community management, using existing local resources.

These services were developed over the four-year project period, and virtually all of them, as well as many new ones, have continued in operation to this day. Almost all local services in the thirteen New Mexico communities included in the project districts were developed only after professional mental health consultants were made available to these communities as locally-based fellow citizens. Before the establishment of the project, a decade of experimentation with traveling teams and periodic "clinics" conducted by nonresident professionals had resulted in no sustained local mental health services.

Perhaps an even more important accomplishment of this approach than the specific facilities developed was the general adoption of the project's philosophy by state agencies, institutions, and organizations, and by local communities. For example, in three additional districts not included in the original project, there are now "community service coordinators." Another area has a "community mental health consultant," similar to the district consultants in the project. Several areas have "community alcoholism workers." One community has a "community services center," which coordinates the resources of all state and local services with all varieties of local problems. The 1965 State Legislature, for the first time in New Mexico history, made a specific appropriation for community mental health services. The superintendents and directors of all the state institutions and agencies concerned with health, welfare, education, corrections, and rehabilitation have gone on record as supporting the "community development" approach and locally based community coordinator and consultant positions, each serving more than one problem area and the interests of more than one agency. Most importantly, these local workers serve the interest of the community in improving its own capacity for coping with human problems.

Maximum Service—
Minimun Manpower

William P. Hurder
UNIVERSITY OF ILLINOIS

V

A top state health official said, in a letter commenting on a widely heralded guide for planning state mental health programs,

> I was very much interested in reading through the policies and tenets that are expounded as highly desirable. I was, of course, hopeful of finding something that would be applicable to "Southeast" and its problems. Unfortunately, most of the present shibboleths of mental health planning are based on community resources. Communities, as I understand them from the words of . . . others, mean groups of approximately 100,000 in one economic and geographical unit with reasonable transportation from home to facility.
>
> To "Southeast," with its wide expanse and limited population, no such community or geographical unit exists. (Our largest community has a total population of some 70,000 in a geographic unit that requires three and a half to four hours to traverse from edge to edge. The next largest community in the state has some 14,000; the next, some 12,000; all other communities, some 70 per cent of our population, are less than 1,000 and the majority . . . less than 500 people.)
>
> It is a bit difficult to think of community resources in, for

instance, one of our fairly populous villages with a population of 400 people. . . . There is no doctor; the visiting nurse comes by every couple of weeks or so; and perhaps every two to three months there is a visit from a physician in conjunction with the nurse's visit. . . .

These graphic words describe, in their most extreme form, two major barriers to community mental health services—a scattered and sparse population and a lack of professional manpower. Yet, these conditions, so widespread in "Southeast," exist on a lesser scale in isolated packets throughout the United States.

There is still another barrier to community mental health services which, although it may exist independent of these, almost invariably accompanies them. This is a sociocultural barrier. To see this barrier in sharpest relief, it is necessary to consider the sociocultural characteristics of the services we propose to provide.

The mental health movement has been characterized as humanitarian and middle-class in its values. It has been called a middle-class, urban phenomenon. The most valued mode of treatment for mental and emotional discomfort and disorder—psychotherapy—has been described as ". . . primarily congenial to middle-class life styles." Middle-class patients are preferred by most treatment agents and are seen as more treatable; psychotherapy is viewed as the treatment of choice, and more hopeful diagnoses are assigned to members of the middle class than those of the lower income group even when symptoms are similar.

By contrast, members of the lower income group are involved in mental health services largely as patients in public mental hospitals. Their entrance into treatment is usually involuntary, as most commitments to public facilities are involuntary. Treatment usually comes at a point when the illness is grossly disturbing to the family, neighbors, or both.

This cultural factor is important to the topic of this chapter because more often than not patients from isolated, rural, and sparsely populated areas that lack professional services are predominantly from the lower income level.

In the examples that we examine, it will be apparent that success in providing mental health services is partially contingent upon adapting the proffered services to these cultural realities.

℀ REPRESENTATIVE PROGRAMS ℀

Three programs are described; the first two in summary form, the third in considerable detail. All illustrate differing approaches to the problem of providing specialized help to areas that in some cases not only lack specialists, but may also suffer a shortage in the generic professions such as medicine and social work. This description will be followed by an analysis of their common elements, and an examination of principles derived from these three separate experiences.

The Florida Department of Public Health, working through its Bureau of Mental Health, has developed a type of professional staff member known as the mental health worker. These personnel have undergraduate training—in most instances a bachelor's degree—with major course work in nursing, social work, psychology, education, sociology, or religion. Ten years of experience has shown that persons who have worked successfully in the community as public health nurses, social workers, visiting teachers, or in a mental health clinic, are best prepared for this new type of work. Personality characteristics are very important—mature, stable individuals, with warm personalities and an ability to tolerate new and unstructured situations, are needed. It has been said that they must have a "pioneering spirit." In addition, to be effective, they must be able to work not only with all sorts of individuals in the community, but with a variety of groups.

The mental health worker must also be able to accept guidance and supervision from two sources. First, although his salary is paid out of the budget of the State Bureau of Mental Health, the worker is housed in the facilities of the local health department and has the same relationship to the local health officer as do other members of the staff of the local health department. But by initial agreement between the local health officer and the state department of health, the mental health worker also has an intimate relationship to senior professional personnel in both state and local mental health agencies. The mental health worker receives support and consultation from psychiatrists, psychologists, psychiatric social workers, and psychiatric nurses on the staff of the mental health clinic, which serves the area in which they work. The worker has a similar relationship to the senior staff of the Bureau of Mental Health. By the very nature of these administrative relationships, these individuals serve as an important link in the chain of communication between general health services at the local level and specialized mental health services at both local and state levels.

What do mental health workers do? Just what individual workers do and just how they do it varies from locale to locale. The major reasons for this variation are initial differences in the background of the workers and inevitable differences in the communities themselves. Even so, their duties and responsibilities can be divided into four areas.

The first area of emphasis is *mental health education*. These educational activities are carried on as part of the overall health education program. They may be accomplished by a mental health worker in a direct fashion; where there is a health educator on the staff of the health department, the mental health worker consults with this colleague and gives assistance in shaping the mental health component of the overall health education program.

Second, mental health workers provide *direct services to people in trouble*. A major service, for example, is helping with the after-care of patients released from the state mental hospitals. Such after-care is a responsibility of local health departments, and mental health workers play a key role either in counseling such ex-patients or in helping other health department staffs to do this through a consulting and teaching relationship to these less specialized staff members. The counseling case load responsibilities of the mental health worker include helping the families of patients newly committed to the state mental hospital to understand and adjust to this family crisis. Generally, limits are set on the extent of these counseling relationships so that the mental health worker rarely enters into an extended or intensive interpersonal relationship with a client or patient. Rather, they are expected to refer such individuals to more highly trained professional persons for more intensive counseling and psychotherapy.

The third area of major activity is *community oriented*. Because the responsibility of the local health department is so heavy in the area of community orientation and organization in matters of health, this phase of the mental health worker's total effort receives considerable emphasis. For example, the workers may be key figures in the development of local mental health associations. They may be prime movers in organizing local Alcoholics Anonymous societies. The organization of workshops for school personnel, clergymen, and law enforcement officers has proved to be one of their most substantial contributions to the mental health of the community they serve. And as community reorganization and acceptance of the need to develop more intensive programs in mental health increases, mental health workers often play a key part in the study and deliberation needed to develop such programs. They are especially alert to the need and the desirability of maximum utilization and coordination of those mental health resources already available through existing agencies and individuals at local, county, or state levels.

The fourth area, considered extremely important, is that of serving as an *advisor in mental health matters to other members of the staff* of the local mental health department. The opportunities for the incorporation of mental health principles into the various ongoing services of the health department are numerous. Such principles can be brought to bear in well-baby clinics, maternity clinics, and school health projects. The mental health worker's role in this may be that of a consultant to other staff members, a teacher in a formal program of in-service training, or an expediter in the development of such in-service training who draws upon the resources of the total community as well as the State Bureau of Mental Health to obtain the personnel and specialized knowledge essential to such educational programs.

At the core of much of the activity of the mental health worker is a concern for the coordination of a variety of resources that may well already be at the point of potential availability to the community. This coordinating function is so central to the work that the term *mental health coordinator* would probably be more descriptive than the designation *mental health worker.*

Personnel of the State Board of Health have recently offered a testimonial to the value of the mental health worker. Perhaps the best index of value is the fact that this program, begun some ten years ago, with one individual, and was clearly experimental, has now grown to to the point that over thirty are employed in local health departments throughout the state. Furthermore, it seems likely that their numbers will increase. Although their salaries are paid through state and federal funds administered by the State Bureau of Mental Health, the actual placement of mental health workers is done at the initiative and with the consensus of the local health office. Accordingly, the continuing growth in their numbers attests to the satisfaction of these local health officers as well as officials in the State Bureau.

Experience indicates that mental health workers with a background in public health nursing or social work find it easiest to integrate themselves into the local public health team; those from other disciplines are usually faced with a more difficult problem of entry. Some of the handicaps and hazards can be identified. For example, long-time staff members are sometimes threatened by the new colleague who has a relatively senior rating and has come in as the possessor of specialized knowledge. If, as occasionally happens, the mental health worker is rejected by veteran staff members, his efforts may be completely blocked. Clearly, the local health officer must bear major responsibility for anticipating and dealing with such inter-staff problems.

Faced with the problem of introducing psychiatric services and know-how into the isolated mountain area of eastern Kentucky, the State Department of Mental Health developed a novel and courageous method of attacking seemingly insoluble problems. A team composed of a well-trained psychiatrist and an equally well-trained psychiatric social worker travels to these isolated areas in order to render direct psychiatric services to patients in greatest need and to provide consultation to personnel such as public assistants or welfare staff to whom these patients look for continuing assistance.

Citizens in eastern Kentucky do have access to the state mental hospitals, hospitals originally developed and operated by labor organizations, and to a regional mental health center. Furthermore, psychiatrists from the state hospital that serves these mountain communities make regular trips to serve patients released from that hospital. However, in spite of these more traditional psychiatric services for those who have become sick enough to need hospitalization, there is a vast untouched area of need not only for intensive psychiatric care but for other aspects of mental health programming.

The psychiatrist and the social worker visit isolated communities once each month, if possible. On a typical excursion they will spend three days traveling from county to county and covering, in this way, as many as six counties. Two major activities fill each day. The first is the holding of a "clinic," usually in the office of the county health department. In these clinics, direct psychiatric services are given to patients and their families who may have come from as far as seventy-five miles to see the "nerve doctor." The other major formalized activity consists of rather intensive conferences with personnel of the public assistance agency that serves those counties and with the staff of the health department. Here, although the focus of the conference is a review of the progress of many of the patients seen by the psychiatric team earlier in the day, the major purpose is to provide education, consultation, stimulation, and support to local staff members.

The psychiatric services offered to patients and their families are unorthodox. In a typical "clinic," the team sees nine or ten old patients—those who have been seen before—and perhaps a dozen new patients. Most patients are accompanied by their relatives, whom the psychiatrist refers to as the "collaterals," so that in all thirty or forty people may have entered into a rather intensive relationship with the doctor and the social worker during a three-hour clinic. In an initial departure from the usual practice, the patients and their relatives enter the clinic room in groups. Often the psychiatrist seats himself at the head of a table, around which patients and their relatives are also seated; if there is an overflow, the others take up chairs around the room. We are talking here not about just one patient and his relatives, but rather about as many patients and their relatives as can be gotten into the room. Usually, old patients are seen first, separately from the group of new patients. The psychiatrist first goes around the group in a systematic way, saying a few words to each of the patients he knows, asking how they have been and how they are. In this way, he is able to determine whether there is anyone so disturbed that he should be seen immediately, or someone who should be seen separately and needs extra attention. As these preliminaries are going on, the psychiatric social worker also talks with patients, observes them, and organizes the case folders on each patient so that they are available to the psychiatrist in the order that he needs them. It is also her responsibility to see that the proper patients get into the clinic room, and if it is judged necessary that a patient be seen alone, she arranges for that. She is helped in this by the personnel of the health department.

A very similar procedure is used with new patients, except that the social worker interviews these patients before they see the psychiatrist. Also, because they are new patients, it is often necessary to see them alone.

The psychiatric services actually rendered to these patients and their families in this unusual setting take at least three forms. First, the psychiatrist talks with each briefly, assessing his present status, and in these few moments gives verbal support, and indicates his understanding of and empathy with the suffering or the problems described by the patient and the family. Because both the psychiatrist and the social worker are native to this mountainous area—in part they were selected for this reason—they are unusually capable of communicating with the members of the group.

Second, the psychiatrist makes liberal use of psychotropic medication—tranquilizers, anti-depressants, or energizers. They may be given to the patient or, in the case of a man, to both him and his wife if the indications are that she has become unusually distressed by his behavior. It is not unusual for the psychiatrist to prescribe sleeping pills for key family members who have been losing sleep because of the patient's behavior. Responsibility for seeing that the patient takes his medicine is placed upon both the patient and members of the family, with the apparent result, in many cases, that the family members have a sense of sharing in the treatment of the patient.

The third kind of "therapy" that evolves from this unusual setting can only be inferred. The indications are that the very process of providing this highly specialized service by the "nerve doctor" in the presence of so many patients and their families has therapeutic benefit. It appears that the patient and his family become members for a time of a community of sufferers. They share their suffering, and perhaps their guilt or other reactions to the illness, and they see evidence of improvement in others. The patient (or his family, if he cannot do so) tells the doctor about his complaints in front of the others. Whatever his reaction to this process of public description of his discomfort, a most important consideration may be that everybody, including the doctor, seems to accept the fact that he is sick. Finally, he has every reason to believe that, although the individual patient and his family speak directly with the doctor for only a few minutes, each enters into a vicarious interaction with him by virtue of their presence when he talks with each of the other patients.

The term *nerve doctor* is one that seems to explain his special interest and skill to the patients and their families. Accordingly, the psychiatrist and the social worker use this term freely. Also, the liberal use of medication reinforces his image as a real doctor. Further reinforcing this image is the fact that the doctor sees many epileptic patients, and is able to help them overcome their seizures through the use of proper medication. These successes in treating a form of physical illness get known in the communities and serve to make his image as a doctor even sharper.

It is in the process of consulting with personnel of the welfare department and the health office that the team gets at the fundamental problem of increasing the skill and competence in the mental health area of personnel already available to these mountain areas. The mechanics are quite simple. In a regularly scheduled conference, the psychiatric team reviews each case seen from the county or counties served by the local staff. In these patient by patient reviews, emphasis is placed upon seeking and giving not only factual information about patients, but the local staff members' judgment and interpretations of specific cases. It does need to be emphasized, however, that at no point in the proceedings, either with patients or families or in these conferences, does the psychiatrist or the social worker enter into any depth analysis of the patient's condition. With the patient, the discussion is limited almost entirely to the symptom level, and there is no probing into the individual motivations, nor is there any condemnation or setting of expectations.

The psychiatric team's objectives in these case conferences are modest. Basically, they are trying to develop more sensitivity and understanding of emotional and mental problems on the part of the local staff of welfare or health agencies. In addition, they have the objective of getting and giving useful information with regard to particular patients. There is a definite press on the part of the psychiatric team toward getting local workers to give more attention to patients with mental and emotional problems and toward getting them to assume more and more responsibility for both judgment and action with respect to patients' mental difficulties.

These case conferences do not exhaust all of the consultative services rendered by the team. For example, they give assistance to local health officers who are concerned with program planning in such areas as the development of specialized mental health services as an integral part of the health department or in the form of specialized mental health clinics.

In Louisiana, services for the mentally ill and the mentally retarded are administered by the State Department of Hospitals. In an effort to provide coordinated services throughout the state, hospital and community services have been partially decentralized by the creation of three relatively autonomous districts. The districts were created so as to equalize to the greatest possible extent the factors of population numbers and the geographical area each serves. The director of each district, a psychiatrist, is responsible for the development of a broad range of services within his area, and with the determination of monetary, manpower and other needs, which in turn are transmitted to the State Director of Mental Health Services in the Department of Hospitals. As experience grew with this decentralization of services, it became apparent that in spite of the availability of community services provided by three state hospitals, nine community mental health centers, and more than a dozen mental health clinics, special action was needed to bring services into a number of communities. In an effort to extend service into these communities, a new type of community service was initiated. The circumstances surrounding this innovation are described next. Because anonymity permits more detailed description and analysis, all principals and places have been disguised.

Allstar Parish has nearly 40,000 residents. (The economy is largely agricultural.) The county seat, Lodestar, with a population of 4,000, is the largest community in the county. Next in size are towns of 3,500 and 3,000. About 10,000 of the counties' citizens live in an isolated swamp area and use boats for much of their transportation.

The parish is about thirty miles from a metropolitan center of over 100,000 people where there is a state mental hospital and a community mental health center operating in close conjunction with the hospital. The office of the District Director is also located here.

A census of the helping professions and services reveals twelve physicians, three welfare workers, and a Veterans Administration officer whose office is in Lodestar.

The major hospital facility is in Lodestar. It is a thirty-bed private clinic operated by five physicians who serve Lodestar and the surrounding countryside.

By tradition and habit, most people in Allstar Parish take their troubles and problems to the courthouse. Here they prevail upon the sheriff, district attorney, or the county judge, all elected officials, to help them solve a range of problems as broad as life itself.

For several years before the project got started, professional staff members from the regional mental health center and the hospital had been giving talks on mental health and related matters before various civic and professional groups in Allstar Parish. As these went on, it became more and more apparent that there was a need to provide more substantial services closer to the citizens of the parish. It was equally obvious that the leaders of the community would support such service.

Although the citizens of the parish were only thirty miles from the broad array of services offered at the district center, what was lacking was some effective means of linking them to these services. Equally important, it became apparent that the community already had the nucleus of services adequate to help with milder problems and in the early stages of most disabilities. It was in recognition of this need that the concept of the "community worker" was developed. This individual was to be the agent whereby the existing specialized services could be better placed at the disposal of Allstar Parish. Through this person, the resources of the community were to be pulled together and strengthened.

As a first step in starting this new service, the District Director of Mental Health Services initiated discussions of the proposition with the political and professional leaders in the parish. These included the sheriff, the judge, the district attorney, representatives of the welfare department, and practicing physicians throughout the parish. In addition the matter was presented to members of the police jury—a governing body—somewhat comparable to the county commissioners in other states. The result was a decision to go ahead.

A major factor in the decision to undertake such an experiment in service was the availability of a well-trained, widely experienced psychiatric social worker, who was well known and accepted in Allstar Parish. She had worked successfully with the mentally ill and the mentally retarded in both community and institutional settings and was then on the staff of the area mental health center. We will call her Mrs. Jones.

One of the earliest decisions was to base the operation in the parish courthouse. With the concurrence of the police jury, the sheriff made an office available in the courthouse. (The police jury also agreed to pay for an unlisted telephone for the office. The phone number was unlisted because it was desired that, at least in the beginning, clients would be seen only by referral from the local physicians, the judge, the sheriff and district attorney, and personnel of the welfare and other agencies in the parish.)

Plans were made to open the office one day a week. Monday was chosen, since experience showed that many mental health problems arose over the weekend.

The first action taken by Mrs. Jones was to visit each of the five physicians in practice in Lodestar to discuss plans for the new service. It was an early ground rule that she would not see any patients under their care unless they were referred by the physician. She also made personal calls to the local Veterans Service Officer, the coroner, the judge, the district attorney, and the sheriff to review plans for her activities and those of the "clinic."

Mrs. Jones began her therapeutic activities by selecting from referrals those patients who showed promise of a successful prognosis. This was done quite deliberately in recognition that her competence to manage "sick" people would be subject to close and curious attention by the professional and political leaders with whom she was working.

These patients were chronic schizophrenics who were stabilized on appropriate medication. Experience showed that if these patients were given concrete advice concerning the use of their medication and about everyday matters such as paying their bills, they could make highly visible and even dramatic adjustments to community life.

As the program developed, the demand grew. In about two months, Mrs. Jones was receiving five or six calls from local physicians every Monday morning. Soon thereafter several of the physicians suggested that their patients be free to go directly to her without their prior approval, but it was decided not to do this because it would put her role as an adjunct to local services in jeopardy. Also, there was the concern that the social worker might be construed to be "practicing medicine."

It soon became apparent that one of the unique services that Mrs. Jones was able to provide to those referred by the local physicians was to help them find the more specialized mental health resources available to them in the state. These included the private psychiatrists and mental hospitals as well as the public services.

In a few months the "community worker" found a number of requests for consultation from welfare workers awaiting her each Monday morning. These did not come, however, until a crucial experience involving an especially competent and conscientious welfare worker and a client had taken place. The client was receiving public assistance because he had been diagnosed as suffering catalepsy. The welfare worker had never seen any evidence of illness in this client and was convinced that he was a malingerer who had put something over on the authorities. She came to Mrs. Jones for help in revealing this client as a malingerer. Several fruitless discussions followed; then the critical event took place.

The welfare worker was interviewing this client when he went into a cataleptic seizure. The worker was terrified. But, more important, she no longer doubted the gravity of the patient's handicap. At the next appointment, she discussed her experience with Mrs. Jones and from this point entered into a much more accepting and helpful relationship to her client. With guidance and consultation from Mrs. Jones, she took steps to get him needed medical attention, helped see that he was adjusted to his medication and helped him learn to avoid situations that triggered off the cataleptic seizures. Inasmuch as she was an informal leader in her own agency, her change in attitude, toward other clients as well as this one, had a beneficial influence on others with whom she worked.

An initial problem for Mrs. Jones was the early development of unrealistic expectations for her services. The judge and the district attorney began to refer sociopaths to her for care or other disposition. It was immediately apparent that these individuals were not at all uncomfortable, and in no way motivated to undertake any type of treatment or self-improvement activities. This led to a long series of discussions with the judge and the district attorney concerning the realistic limits of service she provided as well as of those at her disposal in the mental health center. In time, such referrals ceased, and her relationship with these officials developed on a much sounder and more realistic basis.

The judge and the district attorney began to call upon her for advice and assistance early in the course of cases brought before them. The question put to her was usually whether the individual should go to prison or to the maximum security division of the state mental hospital system. By drawing on the professional resources of the mental health center, she was able to obtain the best possible advice for them —and to get it early in the proceedings. A specific instance involving action by the court illustrates another facet of the "community worker's" impact on the community. A 50-year-old male, diagnosed as a simple schizophrenic during repeated stays in the state mental hospital, came to the attention of the court as a public nuisance. He lived alone in the swamp, having lost his family some years ago, and would periodically come into town and go from house to house and through the business district begging money for food and alcohol.

The case was brought to Mrs. Jones' attention and she found that he had a small pension, which he received every few months. He would spend the entire allotment in a few days—much as a child would—and be penniless until the next check came.

She recommended that the court appoint a curator to care for this man's money, and that the funds be given to him on a weekly basis prorated over the several months' period between checks. The judge appointed such a curator and the individual in question is now seen once a week when he comes to town to get his check. The only alternative course of action would have been a lifetime commitment to the state mental hospital.

In time the Veterans Service Officer began to use Mrs. Jones' services. One of the most helpful relations they have is that Mrs. Jones helps to provide or obtain after-care services for veterans released from VA mental hospitals. This kind of attention made the return to the community smoother for a number of veterans, and their relapse rate reduced. In a similar way, Mrs. Jones is called upon to help assess the need to hospitalize veterans who are suffering mental disturbances.

By the end of the first year, the requests for help threatened to swamp the new service. Schoolteachers and public health nurses were telephoning and asking advice informally. The sheriff's deputies began to consult her more and more. The attorneys of Lodestar and surrounding villages were sending their paranoid clients to Mrs. Jones. It was at this point that she began to develop her role and sharpen her image as a consultant. The first step was to push the responsibility of the management of many cases back on the individual referring the case. Mrs. Jones began to work with carefully chosen welfare workers, public health nurses, and schoolteachers, in relation to specific cases, rather than continuing to accept the referrals. She emphasized the strengths of their position and encouraged them to make decisions on the basis of their knowledge of the problem at hand. At the same time she made it clear that she, and the resources at her command, were at ready-alert to intervene if needed.

In the second year of the experiment, the community began to call upon the "community worker" to perform a number of educational tasks. She was asked to give talks on personality development to homemaker classes offered by the extension division of the state college that served Allstar Parish. She was recommended for this by several local physicians who gave lectures on other aspects of development.

Civic clubs began to ask her to speak on mental health, and one club adopted a continuing project in the mental health field and asked her to serve as major advisor to the project. She found herself discussing careers in the mental health field with high school students who were referred individually by school officials.

An interesting change in court proceedings grew out of informal discussions with the clerk of courts. It had been established procedure to use the phraseology "In the matter of the insanity of ———" when alcoholics were committed for treatment of their alcoholism. When it was pointed out that this was not only an error, but added an additional stigma for the individual, the clerk of court changed this to read, "In the matter of the commitment of ———."

One of the most difficult problems was controlling intake. Even though publicity was studiously avoided and the telephone number remained unlisted, citizens began to come to the courthouse to see her on their own initiative. In the first year, five such self-referrals were previously hospitalized patients who came in the belief that they needed to be hospitalized again. They were all correct in their belief, and their readmission on a voluntary basis was expedited by the community worker.

Initially, the vast majority of persons referred to the service were socially and economically dependent or marginally dependent —at best, their situations were precarious. After two years of operation, individuals from the higher economic classes began to appear at the office asking for guidance and assistance with emotional problems. This trend has continued.

After a little more than a year of operation, the director of mental health services for the district made the decision that the venture was a success and should be extended to other communities of his district. Mrs. Jones was brought into the district office and assigned responsibility for selecting and preparing others to provide such service in other parishes. The necessity to replace Mrs. Jones forced the question: How much of the success of the venture was dependent upon her unique competencies and personality? Her position in Allstar Parish was assumed by another psychiatric social worker, Mrs. Smith.

Mrs. Smith, who has been in the job about a year, is evidently enjoying the same degree of success as did Mrs. Jones, indicating that the technique itself was the critical factor.

During the third year of the program, I visited Allstar Parish to talk with local officials and others to get their reactions and their estimates of value of the service. The comments of the sheriff, the district attorney, the judge, and a medical practitioner were most revealing.

The three elected officials were enthusiastic about the program. All agreed it was of value to the citizens of Allstar Parish. All thought it would be even more effective if the community worker could be in Lodestar three days a week instead of one. Each volunteered that having easy access to Mrs. Jones or Mrs. Smith had improved the quality of their own services. They cited the value of early consultation with a mental health expert when people in trouble, or causing trouble, came to their attention. The ease with which the community worker could draw upon the resources of the district offices was cited as a factor in her effectiveness. All of them emphasized the advantages of being able to obtain an intensive psychiatric examination or to get a patient admitted to the regional mental hospital with minimum delay.

These officials felt that a major strength of the service was that, by its very flexibility, it was possible to act at the point of crisis. In fact, so convinced were they of this factor of intervention in crisis that it was advanced as a major argument for having the worker available three or more days a week.

In the course of conversation it became apparent that there was no single or fixed name used to identify this program. It might be called "the out-patient clinic," "Mrs. Smith's office," the office in the courthouse, or just simply, "the office." Particularly striking was the lack of the identifying phrase, *mental health*. The explanation given by these officials was that they just didn't think of it as a "mental health service." They described it as a service for people with certain kinds of problems. In fact, the judge said that when he referred a person to Mrs. Smith, he usually said, "I'm going to send you to a person who specializes in the kinds of problems you have."

One explanation for this anonymity of the service was that if it were called "mental health or psychiatric," it would either have had little meaning to the citizens involved, or more likely, would have elicited rejection of it. The opinion was offered that much of its usefulness was due to the fact that it blended so well with the established way of solving personal problems in Allstar Parish. The guess was hazarded that had the state or the parish opened up a separate mental health clinic or center it would have been avoided by many local citizens.

The local physician, a member of the only medical clinic and hospital in Lodestar, was equally pleased with the services rendered by the community worker. He said that a major advantage was the assistance he and his colleagues got in the administrative aspects of referring very sick patients to the state hospital. He cited the instance of a twenty-year-old male admitted to the local hospital in a totally incoherent and extremely agitated state on a Saturday afternoon. The youth was sedated and kept at bed rest until Monday morning. Then Mrs. Smith, who was notified immediately, took over, and, working with the relatives and the coroner, arranged for his immediate admission to the state hospital. At the same time she assumed responsibility for helping the relatives adjust to hospitalization and began planning for his after-care when he was released from the hospital.

The physician said that as a result of this service by Mrs. Smith, he and his colleagues were much less reluctant to provide emergency psychiatric care in their small hospital. He noted especially the tremendous value to them—the physicians—of having an experienced person to take charge of both the administrative and clinical-social aspects of admission and release from the hospital. He pointed out that the physicians themselves were barely able to meet the demands for somatic medical care of Lodestar and environs. He said furthermore that, speaking for himself, he felt that these social workers were much better prepared by training and experience to handle the psychiatric and social aspects of such cases than he.

Perhaps the best summary of local attitudes to this unusual "mental health service" was provided by Mrs. Jones, who said, in correspondence with me, "I guess, however, that the main thing is that psychiatry was pulled from an esoteric, frightening position to a rather comforting, homegrown way of help."

PROGRAMS COMPARED

Examining the commonalities among the approaches and contrasting their differences highlight problems in such undertakings and offers some insights into problems surrounding the development of a variety of programs in the mental health area.

Each approach is an attempt to make the most of minimum local resources. Each represents a blend of clinical activities with consultative, interpretive, educational, and supportive activities. Each illustrates to varying degrees recognition of the need to adapt the services rendered to the expectations, and the frame of reference of both the decision-makers and the citizens of the community.

In each instance, experience has shown the importance of the specialist's being able to meet the test of "treating a sick person." The mental health worker must be able to accept a modicum of responsibility for working directly with people in trouble. The psychiatrist working in the mountain areas must be able to perform as a doctor. The social worker or nurse spearheading services in Allstar Parish must be able to step into clinical responsibility without flinching. In fact, it has been found to be so important that the incumbent prove himself as a "therapist" that new community workers are advised to select, early in the program, cases in which success is likely for the purpose of demonstrating their competence.

Consultation plays a major part in each of these programs. The goal is to help local personnel gain competence and confidence to assume increasing responsibility for patients and clients. Consultation is accompanied by informal or formal educational activities by the specialist designed to develop the knowledge and skill of local personnel. This is best developed in the Florida program where development of in-service training programs gets considerable emphasis. However, though much less formal, the educational efforts of the workers in the Kentucky and Louisiana sections are no less significant. The ultimate objective in all instances is to bring local staff to a point of competence to manage appropriate cases themselves, recognize those that exceed their capabilities, and either seek expert consultation or make referrals to more appropriate sources.

Each program is characterized by an awareness of the need to adapt the services rendered to the attitudes and expectancies of the local community. This is less urgent in Florida because the mental health worker operates from a base that has already been accepted and assimilated into the attitudinal structure of the community. Working as an integral part of the health department, the mental health worker benefits from that department's established relationship with the community. Because the mental health worker has an explicit relationship to the mental health clinic serving that area, community attitudes are to a degree already shaped to accept the concept of a mental health specialist. By contrast, in Kentucky, as illustrated by the use of the term "nerve doctor," the prevailing concept on the part of the patients is that they are getting medical services rendered by a medical doctor. Terms such as mental health, mental illness, and psychiatry would be poor currency in forming rapport with these patients and communities. The situation in Louisiana illustrates the adaptation of the sponsors of services to the expectancies of local communities in a most vivid way. In Lodestar, the service simply has no local name. The specialist is designated in a variety of ways, all of which center around the common denominator, "a person who can help with problems like yours."

Certain contrasts among these community mental health programs are striking. Each has a different administrative base. The mental health worker is embedded in a well-defined, highly visible community agency—the local health department. The Kentucky team has no fixed base of operations other than that these are representatives of the state who have come into the mountains to help the people. The fact that physical meetings between the team and the patients may shift from the health department to the welfare department and even to other settings probably makes it difficult to identify this service with any particular agency. The administrative base of the operation in Louisiana is even more flexible and amorphous. It is as if the services were simply implanted in the setting that the local citizens have come to view as the one to which you go for help. Although community workers have a direct line to the regional division of the state mental health agency, this relationship is minimized at the local level.

These programs differ in the emphasis placed upon the development of local resources. In Florida, the effort at development of local manpower is to a great extent channeled into work with non-mental-health personnel inside the health department. By contrast, in Kentucky and in Louisiana, emphasis is much broader and attempts to bolster local manpower resources extend into virtually all governmental agencies.

A striking difference among these programs is the availability of more highly specialized resources for the management of complex and difficult cases. At one extreme is the traveling team in Kentucky, where factors of geographic isolation necessitate the assumption of considerable clinical responsibility on the part of the psychiatrist and the psychiatric social worker, and where the lack of local personnel and the difficulty of travel to the resources of the hospital pose serious problems. At the other extreme of accessibility to more specialized resources we find the services developed in Louisiana. By design, the community worker has at his disposal the resources of the regional mental health center and the mental hospital serving that area. Thus, on very short notice these personnel can arrange for a visit to see a psychiatrist, or for day care or hospitalization if indicated. The Florida circumstance is midway between Kentucky and Louisiana. The mental health worker can call upon the resources of the mental health clinic that serves the area and the state mental hospital. However, because the mental hospitals are in a separate state agency, and since the necessity of immediate recourse to more specialized help is not given the emphasis that it is in Louisiana, they are mobilized with greater difficulty.

Obviously these programs differ in their "visibility" as mental health services. In Florida, the designation *mental health worker* or *mental health coordinator* leaves little to the imagination with regard to the major business of the specialist. The name *nerve doctor* evidently leaves little unsaid about the work of the psychiatrist in the mountains of Kentucky. In Allstar Parish we find near-anonymity with respect to mental health. Neither the worker, the office, nor the function has a fixed name in local circles, much less the designation, *mental health.*

An Urban Community Mental Health Center

Sheppard G. Kellam and Sheldon K. Schiff

WOODLAWN MENTAL HEALTH CENTER[1] AND
THE UNIVERSITY OF CHICAGO

VI

Since the Middle Ages, if not earlier in history, the treatment of the mental patient and the development of mental health programs have been prominently related to social, political, and ideological factors, as well as to scientific ones.[2] It is not surprising, then, that the

[1] We are indebted to Dr. Edward H. Futterman for his important contribution to the development of the Center. He shared with us the trials and problems of the formative period as our collaborator.

We are grateful for the support of the Mayor of Chicago, Richard J. Daley, and of Dr. Samuel L. Andelman, Commissioner, City of Chicago Board of Health. We are also grateful to Dr. Harold Visotsky, Director, State of Illinois Department of Mental Health; and Dr. Melvin Sabshin, Head of the Department of Psychiatry, University of Illinois College of Medicine, with whom we discussed many of the problems described in this report.

This facility could not function without the support and active participation of the people of Woodlawn. The Advisory Board of the Center has been fundamental to the work of the Center. The relationship of the authors to the Board has provided them a deep sense of personal, as well as professional satisfaction.

[2] Reidy, J. P., *Zone Mental Health Centers: The Illinois Concept*, Springfield, Ill.: Charles C Thomas, 1964.

historical determinants of the community mental health legislation[3] passed by the Eighty-eighth and Eighty-ninth congresses are rooted as much in the general evolution of American society as in strict scientific empiricism. The contribution of the recent scientific advances, primarily in psychopharmacology and hospital care, to the origins of the new centers is no doubt important, but is, as yet, difficult to discern. An impressive weight of opinion of both an increasingly sophisticated lay citizenry and a proportion of the mental health professional community has helped create these centers. The weight of this opinion has done more than create a new health institution. It has brought about a rapid transition in the conception of mental health services and a changing view of the nature of the relationship between the mental health professional and the community he serves.

The history of the Woodlawn Mental Health Center is not independent from these broad social and scientific processes, even though its functions and goals are relatively specific. While the authors are not historians, it may be useful for the purposes of this volume to describe several aspects of this mental health center's history and, in the light of that history, explore the rationale of its current form and function.

The Woodlawn Mental Health Center is a service facility and field laboratory in social and community psychiatry, located in an urban Negro community of 82,000 people on the south side of Chicago. Woodlawn is a geographically defined community whose characteristics and history, like most of the seventy-six community areas of Chicago, have been described in a multitude of sociological studies. These studies stemmed mostly from the basic conception of the ecological theory of cities developed in Chicago from 1915–1925.[4] Woodlawn has traditionally been described as a transitional community. It has served many ethnic groups as the area through which populations have passed on their way from inner-city to middle-class status. In Chicago there are, at present, fifteen more or less completely Negro communities. Woodlawn generally ranks in the middle five of these communities along such indices as income, condition of housing, em-

[3] Community Mental Health Centers Act of 1963, Title II, Public Law 88–164, *Federal Register,* May 6, 1964.

[4] Martindale, D., "Prefatory Remarks," in *The City* by Max Weber (translated and edited by D. Martindale and G. Neuwirth), New York: Collier Books, 1962; and Park, R. E., E. W. Burgess, and R. D. McKenzie (Eds.), *The City,* Chicago: University of Chicago Press, 1925.

ployment, and prevalence of disease. On the other hand, considering all seventy-six communities in Chicago, the neighborhood ranks among the ten worst along these same indices. It is specified as Community 42 in Faris and Dunham's classic study of psychiatric hospitalization and urban areas, published in 1939.[5] It remains Community 42 in the 1960 Local Community Fact Book.[6]

The Center has committed itself, from its beginning, to working with the community to assess its mental health needs, assess resources available to meet its mental health needs, establish, in collaboration with community leaders, priorities of mental health needs, and help to establish mental health programs that take into account the size and kind of mental health need in the total community. The research carried out by the Center is integrally related to these service commitments. Assessment of mental health need entails a conceptualization of how to identify people in need of attention, by either mental health professionals or others in the social structure of the community. A conceptualization of psychopathology must thus be defined along traditional psychiatric lines and social functional lines. Thus, studies of social functioning and psychiatric symptoms are a major part of the research carried on at the Center, as well as studies of the results of assessing need. Assessing need is viewed as a longitudinal process, just as intervention programs have been traditionally viewed as longitudinal processes. Periodic assessments of need, then, measure the impact of intervention.

The work of the Center is carried out collaboratively with a community Advisory Board, made up of approximately twenty to twenty-five people from the neighborhood, who represent as wide a variety of political and social values as possible. Most of these citizens come from various organizations and represent the variety of values and aspirations in the neighborhood. The Advisory Board represents a commitment by the various community organizations—political, religious, and social—to the programs of the Center. The Board also represents the commitment of the Center to respect the community's

[5] Faris, R. E. L., and H. W. Dunham, *Mental Disorders in Urban Areas,* Chicago: University of Chicago Press, 1939.

[6] Kitigawa, E., and K. E. Taueber (Eds.), *Local Community Fact Book, Chicago Metropolitan Area—1960,* Chicago Community Inventory, University of Chicago, Philip M. Hauser, Director, 1963; see also U. S. Bureau of the Census, *U. S. Censuses of Population and Housing: 1960 Census Tracts,* Final Report PHC(1)–26, U. S. Government Printing Office, Washington, D.C., 1962.

right to be taken into account. The basic position of the Center is that its community-wide technical functions are completely dependent upon the broad sanction originating from and maintained by the community.

Early in October of 1962, the authors and a third psychiatrist,[7] who had trained with them at The Yale Department of Psychiatry, reviewed their experiences over the past several years and decided to design and build a public health-oriented psychiatric treatment context for a circumscribed community. A major goal would be to allow longitudinal studies of the relationship between the social processes of the community and the advent of psychiatric illness. Our conceptualization was built on the principle that such a scientific interest could only be undertaken from a vantage point of basic psychiatric service commitment to a community. In our judgment, it seemed clear that such a service commitment could not be satisfied by attempting to duplicate traditional psychiatric treatment services. The commitment to a total population required longitudinal methods of assessing mental health need in the community and the development of ways of intervening on a broad scale. (All three psychiatrists had a variety of clinical and research experiences during and after residency training.)

At the time of our decision, President Kennedy had not yet given his address on mental health and retardation to Congress.[8] Uneasy about what might seem "romantic" or impractical about this idea, we began to talk to people at the National Institute of Mental Health about our decision and its feasibility. These early conversations were crucial in supporting our decision, and provided the initial base of practical advice and assistance we needed. In many lengthy conversations, Leonard J. Duhl[9] and, later, Bertram S. Brown,[10] and many others informed us of the then current thinking regarding the proposed community mental health center legislation. Duhl directed us to Alan D. Miller,[11] who, at that time, directed the regional offices of NIMH.

[7] Edward H. Futterman.

[8] Kennedy, J. F., *Message from the President of the United States Related to Mental Illness and Mental Retardation*, February 5, 1963.

[9] Formerly, Psychiatrist, Professional Services Branch, NIMH; at the time of this writing, Senior Consultant to the Secretary, Department of Housing and Urban Development.

[10] Formerly, Assistant to the Director, NIMH; currently, Associate Director, NIMH.

[11] Formerly, Special Assistant for Field Operations, NIMH; currently, Commissioner of the New York State Department of Mental Hygiene.

Dr. Miller responded enthusiastically to our idea, and immediately committed himself and his staff to assisting us in the project. The first task was to assess which communities might be interested or could afford such a program.

The enthusiasm and support given to us by Alan D. Miller and his staff were essential to our early efforts. Dr. Miller's interest was partly related to the Public Health Service's concern over how communities might respond to the implications of the mental health center legislation then being prepared. He was interested in evaluating how the various communities we contacted might accept the idea of a community mental health center and what problems it posed for them.

✘ SEARCH FOR A COMMUNITY ✘

Initially, out of approximately thirty-six states that seemed to offer possibilities for the support of the project, we narrowed our focus to twelve states that offered the best possibilities. We then contacted and visited each of these twelve states, beginning late in October of 1962. In each case, we sought to meet with the state, city, and local public health and mental health officials, as well as their local community organizations. We also visited nearby universities to get some idea of how available their resources would be to support our efforts. As these contacts were made, we became aware of several main kinds of administrative bases on which to build such a community mental health center. This evolving understanding came in part from the Public Health Service and in part from the state and local officials and citizens in the communities we were visiting.

Early in our search, we received a number of offers from rural, county health officers to develop a mental health center for their county, with the understanding that we would first obtain a federal grant for its support. In some cases, although not all, the offer from the public health official was supported by an invitation from the local mental health organization, representing the community. In some instances this kind of suggestion as to financing seemed to come largely out of the limited amount of funds available locally to support the development of a center. In other cases, it clearly indicated the community's ambivalent interest in participating in the development of such a center, and highlighted the tentative and time-limited quality of that community's commitment.

Where the community was clearly interested in being involved and in supporting a center, this kind of invitation, although related to the paucity of local funds, was often also a function of the problem that these officials faced in the lack of definition as to their relative roles in mental health responsibilities. For example, in several states the state department of mental health paid the bills for hospitalized patients, while the public health office reluctantly paid the bill for psychiatric medications for after-care. In this case, acquiring funds for the support and development of the center highlighted this confusion of responsibility, since financing of the center involved the provision of funds for comprehensive mental health care. As a result of these issues, it became very clear to us that it was important to require the local community to provide the basic funding for the center's operation. This would help resolve the ambivalence as to whether the people wanted a center and the confusion as to mental health responsibility.

Another model for relating to the community was that of approaching the community from the base of a state hospital. In some states, we found officials interested in regionalizing the state hospitals so that each unit, ward, or service was related to a geographically-defined community area. Some suggested that we take over one of these units. We would then work out of this hospital base toward the community, using the ward in a variety of ways so that families could come in and participate; community groups, ministers, and social agencies could also be involved in a way that would make that unit less isolated and unrelated to the community.

However, this model had a number of serious drawbacks. One of the most important was that it did not freely permit the mental health center to develop program priorities with the community. Once based in a hospital with a psychiatric ward, it would be hard not to have that population become the first priority problem population, whether or not the community felt that this population represented its major and most distressing mental health problem. Another problem was that such a base might restrict the flexibility to think in terms of prevention and early treatment. Also, the capacity to spell out a community mental health center model with a commitment to the total population might be limited, leaving us restricted to the traditional acutely disturbed population. Our experiences with this kind of invitation made us more convinced that our base of operation should be in the community as part of its health service structure.

About midway in our search, we became very aware that we would need to be related in some way to a university in order to have available social science consultation and facilities for data processing, necessary adjuncts for our laboratory function. One possible base was a university department of psychiatry that would be interested in the development of such a community mental health center. We visited a number of university departments, some of which had strong interest in developing ties with their community. Many of them had members of their faculty on the boards of education or involved in various aspects of the local and state government political process. On closer look, it became clear that many of these ties, however, were bridges, and did not often represent a real synthesis with the community. This caused us to think more seriously about the kinds of involvement we would require to give us the appropriate community mandate to operate. Town and gown problems, in many cases, had made many communities suspicious of the universities' true interest in their welfare. In retrospect, the idea of coming from a solitary, university base may well have represented our own reservation about developing close collaborative ties with a community.

By early spring of 1963, we found that our experiences with state, county, and local officials, as well as community organizations and universities, had helped us define more precisely the criteria by which to make a choice of a community. From the beginning, we felt it essential that the community be geographically bounded, identifiable both to its citizens and to the larger governmental context in which it existed as a distinct community. We also felt that there should be local, specific sanction from the citizens of the community for us to develop our idea of a community mental health center. Another criterion was that the center should be funded for its basic operations through the local county, city, or state apparatus. We intended that grant funds would be sought to support the research functions. Finally, although less critical, was the criterion that there be a university community near the area of our work.

𝕏 DECISION TO COME TO WOODLAWN 𝕏

We were initially invited to consider an urban neighborhood in Chicago by Harold Visotsky, at that time the Chief of the Mental Health Division of the City of Chicago Board of Health, and by Melvin

Sabshin, Head of the University of Illinois Department of Psychiatry. Under Dr. Visotsky's leadership, the Mental Health Division of the Chicago Board of Health, over the preceding several years, had begun developing community clinics that were crisis-oriented and committed to dealing with a large population of patients. These clinics were budgeted from $100,000 to $150,000 a year, with approximately half of that money coming from the State of Illinois Department of Mental Health. We had learned from the Public Health Service that the zone plan for regionalizing mental health services of the State Department of Mental Health[12] had been very important in the preparation of the federal community mental health legislation.

Some years before, Dr. Francis Gerty, Director of the State of Illinois Department of Mental Health, had regionalized the State of Illinois into zones, providing a decentralized administrative authority responsible for the assessment of need and provision of mental health services. At the time of our first visit to Chicago, Dr. Gerty was nearing retirement; and Dr. Visotsky was planning to leave his post as Chief of the Mental Health Division of the City of Chicago Board of Health to assume Dr. Gerty's position. Dr. Samuel L. Andelman, Commissioner of the City of Chicago Board of Health, supported the idea of the center and of our need to have sufficient autonomy to collaborate with the community, as well as to carry out the rest of our goals as a service facility and field laboratory. This seemed to offer us an unusually strong base of state and city support for the center's basic operations, a base within the public health and political structure of the community.

Though this base might cause some groups within a community to be suspicious of our motives, it allowed the best base for developing agency sanction for programs in the schools, welfare, police, as well as in many other governmental contexts. Our determination was that this sanction was essential and might not be possible if the base were not within the city's political structure. While community suspicion might be a problem, we felt it would be easier to work this through on a personal basis rather than attempt to work outside the political structure of the city.

Dr. Sabshin's interest was important to us. He offered us the

---

[12] Rosen, G., "The Mentally Ill and the Community in Western and Central Europe During the Middle Ages and the Renaissance," *History of Medicine and Allied Sciences, 19*:388, 1964.

use of the Department of Psychiatry's resources and, as Chairman of the Mental Health Advisory Board for the Mental Health Division of the City of Chicago Board of Health, he could provide a broad academic and community sanction for the development of the center. The possibility of forming a collaborative base with the City of Chicago, the State of Illinois Department of Mental Health, and the University of Illinois was clearly the best opportunity available to us. This base covered most, if not all, of the criteria we had come to consider important in our deliberations. The only questions that remained were which community in Chicago would be interested in having such a center, and for which would there be funds available?

Woodlawn appeared as a possible community in a dramatic fashion. The Mental Health Division of the City of Chicago Board of Health, then still under the leadership of Dr. Visotsky, had many of its staff working on the problem of developing support for a mental health clinic in Woodlawn some time prior to our visit to Chicago. Mrs. Faye Price, Community Organizer for the Division, had become a member of the Woodlawn Services Council, the inter-service-agency forum. Many community leaders supported such a facility, although more militant community groups had reservations about psychiatry as a cure for prejudice and poverty. Mrs. Almita Robinson, head of an agency then known as the South Side Community Committee, had been much involved in organizing support for a mental health clinic. The heads of many other agencies, most of whom were members of the Woodlawn Services Council, had already begun developing community interest in a mental health clinic.

However, the year of 1962–63 was an economy year for the city, and the funds for this mental health facility had been deleted by the City Council. As negotiations with Dr. Visotsky, Dr. Andelman, and Dr. Sabshin proceeded, the agencies and community citizens had been active in seeking out the mayor and obtaining from him the promise that the funds would be returned to the budget for this facility. At this point, we began to approach those community leaders who were identified for us by Dr. Visotsky and his staff. We met with many of them to discuss our conception of a community mental health center and to seek their support for such a program in Woodlawn. We informed them that their sanction and support were absolutely necessary for us to consider coming to Chicago.

The first group in Woodlawn to which we were directed was

the Woodlawn Services Council.[13] When we discussed our idea of the center with them, they voiced concern about the absence of traditional service. When we pursued this question, many of the agency executives could agree that any attempt to provide such services would render the center unavailable to them and the community by overwhelming its capacities. Some agency directors candidly stated that each agency alone could produce a serious waiting-list problem in one month's time. Generally, the agencies agreed, some more reluctantly than others, to wait and see what we would produce. However, they were prepared to support our coming.

At the inter-agency meetings, we noted few representatives from the various community organizations. It was apparent that we would have to discuss our idea with the community leaders directly in other contexts. The Mental Health Division, the agency executives of the community, and others informed us which groups and people they thought we should see and whose support we should obtain. We had particular concern about what support we could expect from the community organizations, including one important citizens' group, The Woodlawn Organization (TWO), a confederation of approximately 100 block clubs and churches in the neighborhood.

After reading an article written by one of the first staff members of The Woodlawn Organization,[14] we saw that this organization regarded the social agencies as palliations from "downtown," a form of "welfare colonialism," providing "Band-aids for the social wounded." The dramatic history of this group has been described by a number of authors who have detailed its embattled position and struggle for power within the city political fabric.[15] On the other hand, there were

[13] There is an extensive literature describing the role of the mental health professional as a consultant in agency contexts. The specific problems of sanction development and maintenance have been most broadly developed by G. Caplan in "Types of Mental Health Consultation," *American Journal of Orthopsychiatry, 33*:470–481, 1963; and in *Principles of Preventive Psychiatry,* New York: Basic Books, 1964.

[14] von Hoffman, N., "Reorganization in the Casbah," *Social Process,* April 1962.

[15] Blakeley, U. B., and C. T. Leber, Jr., "The Great Debate in Chicago," *Presbyterian Life,* June 1961; Cofield, E., "The Battle of Woodlawn," *Chicago Defender,* November 19–December 3, 1962; Farman, C., "Negro Slum," *The New Statesman, 67*(1715): January 24, 1964; Jacobs, Jane, "Chicago's Woodlawn *Renewal* by Whom?" *Architectural Forum,* May 1962; Silberman, C. E.,

other confederations that did not agree with these views. We interviewed the leaders of all of the major groups we were aware of, and enlisted their sanction to come to Woodlawn. We discussed with them our interest in collaborating with the community in a way that was different.

We discussed the uses the community might make of a neighborhood mental health center. They stated very directly that if we were interested in strengthening the community by programs of prevention, they would strongly welcome our coming. By prevention, they meant collaborating with teachers, police, ministers, and other key people in the community, as well as working directly with people before they became ill or maladapted. However, if our intention was to treat only those already ill, they were less interested. There were two primary issues in their position: first, their essential interest in building a strong future for the community, and second, their question as to whether we would respect the community's aspirations.

Following these meetings, we felt sufficiently secure that the organizations and community leaders were willing to collaborate with us in developing the center. We felt confident that whatever uncertainties remained would be resolved, once we arrived. It was only at this point that we decided, late in the spring of 1962, to move to Chicago and begin to develop a community mental health center with the community of Woodlawn.

We had now made a commitment to the community of Woodlawn, for a minimum period of five years, to collaborate with the community to accomplish the following goals: (1) to assess the mental health needs of this urban, neighborhood community; (2) to assess the resources available to meet these needs; (3) to establish with the community a system of priorities that would indicate the sequence of problems to attack; (4) to develop, with the community's support and participation, mental health programs directed at the top priority problems.

A major obstacle in the community's sanction of the center was our interest in investing a substantial amount of the center's resources into programs of assessment and longitudinal measurement of the mental health needs of specific subpopulations. These measurements would

"Up from Apathy—the Woodlawn Experiment," *Commentary*, 37(5): 51–58, May 1964.

provide necessary information about the quantity and kinds of mental illness and social maladaptation, information about precursors, and measures of the impact of whatever mental health programs we were to design. These operations came dangerously close to being confused by the community's citizens with the major question of trust expressed by practically every person who had roots in Woodlawn, a question expressed very directly as a fear that our basic intentions were to use the neighborhood and its citizens as "guinea pigs" for exploitative research interests that would provide Woodlawn little in the way of benefit and much, perhaps, in the way of indignity. The position of many of the agencies in Woodlawn was that this basic need for assessment of need and evaluation represented further evidence of the minimal service they might expect from the center.

The development of sanction in the Woodlawn community was possible only in a context of continuing and rapidly evolving national, state, city governmental, and professional sanction, which allowed us to make new relationships with the local community. These new relationships were likely to place strain on the outside social and political structure because of their newness and because of possible conflicts of interests and ideologies. It was necessary, therefore, to work through these possibilities with our outside sources of sanction and to obtain their permission to move ahead with Woodlawn.

The sanction that preceded us when we visited other local communities prior to Woodlawn had been developed primarily through the Public Health Service and its network of regional offices. This sanction included permission to use the personal recommendations of Dr. Alan Miller and others, as well as the broad recommendation of the Public Health Service, in approaching each of the community areas, the state, city, county, and the university bases. It allowed us an introduction to the people in these locations and helped validate our seriousness and professional integrity.

The national support of the U.S. Public Health Service, represented by the sanction of those specific people in leadership positions, was important to our obtaining local sanction in the state of Illinois and the city of Chicago. In turn, this local sanction was crucially enhanced by the support of the Director of the State of Illinois Department of Mental Health in the form of providing approximately half of the basic funding of the center's financial needs. The basic support of the governmental structure of the city of Chicago was especially critical. The Commissioner of Health committed the Board to pay the remainder of the basic cost of the center for a minimum of five years, including the salaries of the Co-Directors. The support of our work by the Department of Psychiatry at the University of Illinois provided important professional sanction nationally and locally and helped allay the natural fears of the lay community as well. This support was in the form of unqualified academic faculty appointments for the Co-Directors, and financial aid for emergency situations.

None of these basic sanctions had been tested under the fire of adverse criticism or tension at the level of the Woodlawn community. The degree to which the city would support the center as it began to work with community organizations, some of which felt antagonistic toward the city's political structure, was uncertain at the outset. We had not worked through with the leaders of the city government the question of our own loyalty to them as directors of a city agency as we proceeded to begin the process of engaging with the community of Woodlawn. This issue was less important to the University of Illinois Department of Psychiatry, and to the State of Illinois Department of Mental Health, since these institutions were less embattled with the neighborhood of Woodlawn.

While this introductory phase was proceeding, Dr. Kellam continued to maintain and develop national sanction from the base at the National Institutes of Health, in Bethesda. The development of continuing ties in the Public Health Service, whose critical early importance we have already described, was essential, as was the development of new relationships with those consultants who would be important to the planning of adequate programs of assessment and evaluation.[16] Experts' help was needed in the area of the formation of community mental health registries, consultation in demography, sociology, mathematical statistics, and, most fundamental, the development of a basic resource offered by the National Opinion Research Center.

With the help of Dr. Melvin Kohn, in Bethesda, this author had an opportunity to meet with Dr. Peter Rossi, the Director, and Mr. Richard Jaffe, the Assistant Director, of the National Opinion

---

[16] Without the help of Dr. Anita Bahn, Dr. Melvin Kohn, and many others at the National Institute of Mental Health, the process of the formation of the center would have been far more difficult and, most probably, less successful.

Research Center, and present our interests to them. The N.O.R.C., with Dr. Kohn's recommendation, promptly offered to make their resources available to us, including consultation and facilities for data processing. This fundamental resource has been crucial in the development of the Woodlawn Center's work. The National Opinion Research Center has characteristically spoken of us as their "favorite charity." To be granted such an amount of help with no immediate financial capacity to repay the debt has been a very impressive experience to us. At no time has this organization decreased its commitment to us and to the problems with which we are concerned.

With the development of these broader resources, Dr. Schiff initiated a parallel intense activity of early entry, after his arrival in Chicago in July of 1963. He began the second stage of engaging with Woodlawn, its groups, local neighborhood leaders, and its agencies; this time as a new agency, rather than a prospective one. He was joined by a second psychiatrist in September, and the third in October. Since it was primarily with the agencies that the Mental Health Division had negotiated in the several months prior to our considering coming to Woodlawn, it was with the agencies that he initially sought to develop further an understanding about our purposes and the nature of our commitment. On the other hand, we could not ignore the necessity of simultaneously expanding and deepening our involvement with the variety of community organizations and individual leaders in the neighborhood whom we pursued with increasing intensity. The major functions of these early contacts with the neighborhood agencies was not only to explain our goals but also to learn something about their functions and the services they supplied. We also sought to learn their views of the nature of the various community organizations, what they were like at present and historically, and who their key representatives were.

Along with this development of relationships with the agencies, we initiated intense efforts to continue the development of relationships with several of the key leaders in the community organizations. Meetings were held during this period with as many of the agency heads as possible as well as with many of the ministers of the larger churches in the community, block clubs, PTA's, women's groups, and physicians. The maintenance and development of further sanction among the local community organizations and agencies was accompanied, during these early months, by efforts at similar sanction operations at the city and state levels. These took the form of learning, in more detail, about the processes of the city government, current and past, particularly in relationship to Woodlawn.

It became increasingly clear through these early meetings with agency heads on one hand and community leaders on the other that there was a vast difference between these two groups. The agencies clearly were part of a professional community, broadly social welfare in type. These agencies, whether private or public, were, like the center, funded mostly from outside the community of Woodlawn. Their leadership base was most frequently situated outside of Woodlawn, whether their central office was part of a broader city political structure or part of the political structure of the private charities. Not only was there a basic difference in the economic and political structure of the agencies and the community organizations, but there was also a basic awareness on the part of each of these groups of the distinction between themselves and the other. Thus, the community organizations spoke of the agencies as part of the outside power establishment; the agencies, while they varied considerably in their description of the community organizations, in general clearly identified them as distinct from the agency world.

As far as we are concerned, it is impossible to relate mental health services to the total population of a community unless one defines the community within some basic, implicit sociological framework. Briefly stated, this framework consists of the essential idea that the community is a population of people living near each other, with common services, in a loose social-political organization. The assumption is that the center can reach the total population by itself becoming part of the social-political structure of the community and placing its operations of assessing need and intervention into strategically chosen parts of the rest of the structure. These structural locations for assessment and intervention should be characterized by the fact that large populations of people pass through them at certain points in their life. Schools, churches, political organizations would be examples of elements of the social structure.

Some of these groups are quite distant from others in regard to such aspects as the seat of decision-making. The schools are governed internally, independently from the local community, until one reaches the Board of Education level, where community and professional-educational decision-making is negotiated. The Board of Health base allows us close access to the Board of Education base, but not necessarily to the local community groups. It became clear that we needed a community advisory board to the center in order to reach these latter groups for overall community sanction, and specific sanction to collaborate with any one of them. This board was intended to allow a single major arena for collaborative planning and sanctioning between the more loosely knit community groups and the center.

The realization, then, that the agencies represented a different part of the neighborhood's social structure than the community citizens' organizations was a critically important stage in the development of the center. The differences between these groups, in part, stemmed from the fact that the needs, aspirations, and personal identification of the members of community organizations and the agencies' staffs were widely disparate. Those in the community organizations referred to the need for representation and dignity in the broader middle-class social context of the urban city.[17] The agency professionals, on the other hand, needed professional recognition, respect and gratitude from the community. Both were aware of a distinct distance between the community and its social welfare agencies. The degree of this distance varied, depending on the specific agency. For the most part, the schools as a social agency were most sharply seen as a part of the outside white middle-class community, without sanction to operate in the community of Woodlawn.[18] The differences in power between "downtown" and Woodlawn were a source of continuing controversy and bitterness.

In addition to this basic distinction between agencies and community organizations, there was soon evident among the community organizations a variety of groups whose aspirations and identifications were quite distinct, one from another. Often, these separate social organizations were competitive and antagonistic, since they represented different viewpoints by different people in different parts of the social structure within the community.

Given these divergent groups and the complexity of their interrelationships, the development of our relationship to the community

---

[17] Blakeley and Leber, *op. cit.*; Cofield, *op. cit.*; Farman, *op. cit.*; Jacobs, *op. cit.*; Silberman, *op. cit.*; von Hoffman, *op. cit.*

[18] Flynn, B., "The Battle of Ben Willis: A Chicago Dilemma," *Renewal*, 3–6, March 1965; Hauser, P. M., "Crisis in Chicago's Public Schools," *The University of Chicago Magazine*, 12–17, December 1964; Star, J., "Segregation Crisis: Chicago's Troubled Schools," *Look*, 59–61, May 5, 1965.

proceeded slowly, but intensively. We gave a good deal of thought and care to the planning of our first contacts, in order to respect the social status of those members within each social welfare agency or social organization. On the other hand, the development of the sanction at the city, state, and national level proceeded as rapidly as we could manage. We felt that it was vitally important, as this process of engagement with the community continued, to explain ourselves to political and professional organizations outside of the community if we were to avoid threatening our relationship to the broader community as we involved ourselves more deeply in the neighborhood of Woodlawn.

✗ CHOICE OF SITE ✗

By the fall of 1963, all of the Co-Directors were in Woodlawn, working full time and concentrating very heavily on the problem of learning what the community of Woodlawn was like. We spent considerable time during this period debating the question of how soon we should obtain a site for the center, and where this site should be located. In contacts with the agencies up to this time, demand was placed on the Co-Directors to provide services as rapidly as possible to care for the major psychiatric problems that each of the agencies was coping with at the time. To this group, seeing the center materialize and seeing the psychiatrists spending more of their time doing familiar, but rare psychiatric treatment, seemed to be an important aspiration of almost all of the neighborhood agencies.

The pressure to begin direct services was far more manifest among the agencies than it was in the community organizations, where the real question was why the three Co-Directors were white and how they would relate to the community. This community concern and suspicion regarding its relationship to mental health programs has been reported in other communities.[19] As the site question reached its peak, in the winter of 1963, there was increasing tension from the community organizations over the questions: Who were we? Why had we come to Woodlawn? One of the first public signs of this tension was the appearance of a small article in one of the Negro newspapers,

---

[19] Aberle, D. F., "Introducing Preventive Psychiatry into a Community," *Human Organization*, Fall 1950; Cumming, E., and J. Cumming, *Closed Ranks,* Cambridge, Mass.: Commonwealth Fund, Harvard University Press, 1957.

describing us as three foreign doctors who had come to Woodlawn and seemed to be ignoring the community in our deliberation over a site location for the center.[20]

Over these months, we had reviewed very carefully the several sites available in the community for the center, almost all of which had been already identified before our coming. All but two had been eliminated for gross inadequacies. Of the last two, one was owned by a respected businessman in the community, a member of several very important community organizations, and a citizen of the community from his birth. The other site was owned by a corporation administered by a group of men with offices in the Loop. Needless to say, these men were white. Given this choice, the Co-Directors were quite reluctant to choose the latter site, even though, by every "professional" criterion, it would better serve our purpose. It was in the right geographic location and available to transportation; it had an elevator (which would alleviate the problem of the elderly); the interior space could be extended and modified; and equally important, most of the physicians in the community were located in the building, which had been a medical building used by all groups within the Woodlawn community by historical as well as current tradition. Thus, the Co-Directors were reluctant to choose the site owned by the Negro businessman. But we were aware that this decision might cause a serious crisis. Accordingly, we met with many community leaders during this very hectic period, including Dr. A. L. Reynolds, President, Associated Clubs; Mr. William Ward, President, West Woodlawn Council of Block Clubs; and Reverend Arthur Brazier, President of TWO. We conferred with these leaders over the question of our dilemma and were told to make a "professional" decision. The degree of our naiveté over the process of engaging with the community may be illustrated by the fact that we assumed that this was a direct statement of the community's willingness for us to proceed according to our objective evaluation; and, in fact, we supported the city's signing a rental contract with the "absentee white landlord." We have termed the ensuing several weeks our "site crisis."

When the knowledge that we were not going to take the site owned by the Negro businessman had spread through the community,

[20] *Chicago Courier*, October 12, 1963.

there was an immediate and explosive reaction. The neighborhood newspapers carried banner headlines:

DISPUTE RAGES OVER SITE OF MENTAL HEALTH CENTER

HEAVY CRITICISM ON HEALTH CENTER SITE FOR S. SIDE

MENTAL CENTER SITE STIRS HOT DISPUTE

S.S. MEDIC CENTER SNUBBED IN DEAL[21]

As this major crisis in our relationship to the community was developing, the inter-agency forum, the Woodlawn Services Council, discussed the question of our site, and came to the conclusion that we had made a wise choice. One of the neighborhood newspapers carried a headline to that effect, preceding the headlines shown above.[22] The news that the social welfare agencies in the neighborhood had supported our choice added highly flammable fuel to the community's reaction to our "not taking them into account." A rapid succession of telephone calls followed, with stern invitations to appear at a wide variety of community organization meetings. At all of these meetings, community citizens accused us, in the most severe terms, of being representatives of a political system that ignored them and was unconcerned with their dignity. Even the least militant of the community organizations took part in this severe reprimand.

However, there was a quality to these meetings of wishing to engage with us and to test our availability for such engagement in the context of this severe fight. It was as though the fight had offered a major occasion for the community to express its wish to be taken into account and acknowledged as the major source of sanction for the center. The intensity and frequency of these meetings, as well as the intensity of the informal contacts with citizens of the community, increased to a point of extreme crisis when we heard that TWO was planning to picket the Board of Health and the mayor's office.

Our reaction to all of these invitations and to the whole series of severe attacks was to respond to each invitation promptly; all three of us were available for confrontation at any time. Our introduction at these meetings would frequently entail a polite presentation of how we had come to the community, followed by a description of how

---

[21] *Ibid.; Chicago Courier,* December 7, 1963; *Woodlawn Booster,* December 4, 1963.

[22] *Woodlawn Booster,* December 8, 1963.

we were depriving the community of the dignity of allowing them to
help us make a choice about the site of this "so-called community
mental health center." It was also made clear that we were depriving
the community of an opportunity for economic gain by offering the
rental to the white power establishment. We belatedly recognized that
the "professional" grounds on which our choice was made were not
entirely, nor even in large part, "professional." Though there were
some "professional" issues, we should have worked out a way of relating to the community so that both the community and we were
satisfied in the areas of dignity and collaboration, prior to the choice
of the site.

As the crisis with the community deepened, we had the second
of two critical meetings with Saul Alinsky at the home of one of the
aldermen for the community, Mr. Leon Despres. The first meeting
occurred shortly after all three of us were in Woodlawn, late in October. At this second meeting, we were told in no uncertain terms that,
though we might be experts in the area of engaging with individual
patients, our expertise ended sharply in the area of engaging with the
community. We had not, in Mr. Alinsky's view, sufficiently pursued
various community organizations by insisting that they help us form an
advisory board. That advisory board clearly must have representatives
of as many of the dissident opinions, values, and aspirations as we
could find in Woodlawn. Such a group, Mr. Alinsky felt, would have
helped us work through the question of the site of the center. He emphasized that this very crisis presented a prime opportunity for us to
utilize these "crisis confrontations" to return to the community organizations and insist that they help us in the planning and development
of the center's functions.

Following this meeting, we pursued the various leaders of the
organizations more strongly, urgently asking for meetings with their
steering or executive committees. At a meeting of the steering committee of TWO, the local Negro businessman was present, along with
ourselves, for an open discussion of our site choice. The facts were presented and, again, there were open and intense accusations made, to
which we responded with an open statement of our regret at not having pursued them sufficiently on our need for an advisory board. Still
hanging in the balance, at this point, was the threat of picketing at
City Hall and an invitation from the Board of Health to appear there
to answer formally all accusations. At the last minute, the picketing

was canceled and, instead, a "watchdog" committee was appointed by TWO to make sure that our future plans took the aspirations of the community into account.

Having learned from our experiences, we requested an immediate meeting with this committee to talk over the next stages in the center's development. The committee members seemed somewhat surprised, but obliged by offering to meet with us on Saturday afternoon. There was the clear expectation that we would renege or send a representative. We agreed immediately and stated that all three of us would be there. At the meeting, we talked over the mistakes of the "site crisis" and the problems of establishing priorities for the center's beginning operations. At the end of the first meeting, we insisted on another appointment. The committee looked at each other, looked at us, smiled, and said Saturday afternoon, to which we agreed warmly. After several meetings, the members of the committee raised the question of meeting at some other more convenient time, since they felt we had sufficiently demonstrated our availability. In all of these meetings, the conversations concerned the question of the center's need for a broadly representative community advisory board.

In the meantime, the "watchdog" committee reported to TWO, and we began to have a circle of people who, though not friendly, had an increased interest in collaborating and participating in the discussions. We continued our extensive visits to all of the community organizations, being particularly interested in visiting and being involved in similar ways with those groups in the neighborhood which did not particularly approve of the militancy of TWO. After several weeks, the "watchdog" committee supplied us a preliminary list of people in the community who, they felt, should be on the advisory board. The list included many of those in the neighborhood who were not members of TWO and who represented quite antagonistic viewpoints in the areas of politics and civil rights. Though all of these groups had a strong interest in civil rights, the methods by which they dealt with this issue were often divergent. We approached these leaders, most of whom we had conferred with earlier about whether they wanted us to come to Woodlawn, and asked for their help in the formation of the advisory board of the center.

The first meeting of the Advisory Board of the Woodlawn Mental Health Center occurred shortly thereafter at its newly opened offices. One of the immediate questions raised by the Board was the question of the furnishings of the center, and the question of whether the sign on the front door and the letterhead would state clearly that this was the "Woodlawn Mental Health Center," and not a "Board of Health, City of Chicago" facility, without mention of the neighborhood. The furnishings, in the view of the community leaders, and particularly our Advisory Board, should be a clear-cut statement of commitment by the city to Woodlawn. These issues required a decision by the mayor's office, which was readily forthcoming, and which represented to us an extremely important sanction on the part of the political structure of the city for our engaging in the way we had with the community organizations in Woodlawn. This sanctioning process by the mayor's office has been an ongoing aspect of our work in the neighborhood, even though, at times, it has seemed to run counter to the ways that other city agencies and private social welfare agencies related to the community.

The next stage in the Advisory Board's functions with the center staff consisted of the very important question of establishing priorities for programming and the Advisory Board's participation in the planning of the first mental health program.

Our commitment to the Advisory Board is to discuss with them all of the major decision-making necessary in the center's operations. We define the technical aspects of the problem in need of solution, while the Advisory Board informs us of the community's attitudes and aspirations relevant to the problem. Repeatedly, throughout the history of the center's presence in the community of Woodlawn, there have been episodes similar to that of choosing the site for the center. Each one of these crises appeared to occur immediately following a new stage of increasing reality of the Woodlawn Mental Health Center and ourselves. The site crisis, for example, occurred immediately after the choice of the site appeared to become a reality. We have responded to an accusation of not taking the community into account on each occasion by immediately insisting on a multitude of community meetings, and by inviting the most dissident and vocal citizens to become members of the center's Advisory Board. At these meetings, whether outside the center or at the Advisory Board itself, we have fostered the expression of the accusations of not taking the community into account and have enlisted the aid of those concerned about the program. Many new members of the Board have been added in this way, while other citizens in the community have contributed heavily in the development of various programs.

The Advisory Board thus functions to provide basic community sanction for the Mental Health Center's programs and has increasingly played a central role in planning the use of nonprofessional community resources. The Board informs the community of the programs and defines them as community programs. Unless the Advisory Board and the staff of the center agree on the solution to a given problem, the problem is considered unresolved. Thus far, this relationship has worked extremely well. An example of this process was the decision as to which subpopulation within the community should be given first priority for assessing need and providing service programs.

The technical staff of the center gathered epidemiological information concerning the size and kinds of acutely disturbed people in the community, the numbers and kinds of teenagers involved in delinquent acts, and other such general information. On the other hand, the Advisory Board felt that the major subpopulation of the community of primary concern to most people was that of the young school children making the change from home to classroom. They pointed out that about half of the children in the community do not graduate from high school. This meant, to them, that a program directed at helping young children make a good start in school was of primary concern, as illustrated by the focusing of their civil rights efforts on school and education.[23] There was no technical reason for ignoring this generally felt community concern. We agreed to develop a major first program of assessing the mental health needs of the 2,000 children who enter first grade each year, and of developing a program of intervention, in order to maximize the adaptation and mental health of the children of the neighborhood.[24]

Other programs that the community and the center have developed collaboratively now include: a program for consultation between the welfare agencies and the community organizations; a program for the acutely disturbed patients in the community, necessitating

[23] Flynn, *op. cit.;* Hauser, *op. cit.;* Star, *op. cit.*

[24] Dr. Curtis C. Melnick, Superintendent of District 14, Chicago Public Schools, has provided fundamental support and assistance to the Center's work in the Woodlawn public schools. His continuing collaboration in the program has been a crucial factor in its development.

the development of new concepts of ward team and hospital-community interrelatedness. This program illustrates the degree to which the mental health programs being developed represent an integration of the mental health agency with its community. The Advisory Board and the center staff have evolved a model, in collaboration with Dr. Bernard Rubin of the State of Illinois Department of Mental Health, in which the members of the ward team are citizens of the community. They are now being designated by the local community organizations, and each will function in his own three- or four-block area as the community mental health worker who is contacted at times of crisis. It is planned that these community mental health workers will spend half-time in the neighborhood, and half-time on the community's hospital unit.

OBSERVATIONS

We have been describing the origin and evolution of a particular kind of community mental health center. The basic assumption on which this model rests is that if the center is a part of the social structure of a community, mental health services can be developed to reach the total population. Is it true? To what extent does this model allow for that portion of the population not immediately involved in schools, churches, social agencies, political groups, and so on, to receive mental health services? Some parts of the social structure contain total subpopulations of the community. The schools, for example, contain all of the children in the community over a specific span of their lives. Therefore, by placing assessment and intervention programs in the social structure of the classroom, it is possible to reach all of this subpopulation of the community. For purposes of prevention and early treatment, such a social context provides an ideal setting in which to identify and intervene. On the other hand, what of the childless families? Is there an alternative context in which to reach people who are not involved in such a major social context as the classroom? We are not sure of the answer to this problem, but our speculation is that from the vantage point of a mental health center that is part of the social structure of the community, alternative ways of contacting those people not involved in the social structure can be determined more easily than in other kinds of mental health facilities. Nevertheless, the thesis remains to be demonstrated.

One of the most crucial questions is the problem of how to test the real efficiency of these various models. One research design might include the deliberate creation of standardized models and the standardized characterization of communities into several categories, then randomly distributing the standardized models in each category of community. Such a program of research into the efficiency of community mental health centers of various kinds would be expensive and difficult, and would have to be administered from a state or national level.[25] Prevalence rates of adaptation, maladaptation, and mental illness could be determined along specifically chosen dimensions and data collected longitudinally from each community. Ultimately, such a public health research project may be as important as the question of the relationship between cigarettes and cancer. A brief review of the morbidity for mental illness would quickly substantiate this point.

The cost involved in the development and maintenance of sanction should not be ignored in this model of administering mental health services. In many ways, the great cost of the hospital-based psychiatric services is not radically reduced in the kind of mental health center we have been describing. While the financial cost may be much less, the cost in manpower and developing and maintaining relationships to agencies, community, and the broader social-political structure outside of the neighborhood is an enormous effort. Since many of the agencies do not have interrelated decision-making structures, nor relationships to the community in this regard, such a center must provide for a multitude of informal as well as formal meetings. If another model could achieve the same degree of impact while not expending as much effort in sanctions, it might prove, in the long run, more efficient by conserving mental health resources for program development. On the other hand, the traditional isolation of psychiatric services, while saving the manpower necessary to develop strong ties to the social structure of the community, did not, certainly, come close to reaching the mental health needs of the total population. At this point, it would appear that the most promising community health center models available entail the expenditure of this manpower.

A more efficient model for the future might well involve a realignment of agencies and community organization interrelationships

[25] Such a categorization of communities should include rural as well as urban areas and, therefore, requires the administrating agency to be on a state or national level.

so that the mental health function is more closely coordinated with such agencies as schools, police, and so on, and the social functions of the community organizations. Such a synthesis might save community mental health resources by eliminating the need for constant bridge-making among the various aspects of the social-political structure not now related to each other in a natural way. It will be extremely important that the development of such a new model not merely bring together various agencies but also include community organization functions. Thus, the total synthesis around the community handling the problems of enhancing the child's full development, for example, should include the activities carried out by churches, civil rights organizations, block clubs, as well as schools and mental health facilities.

A Psychiatric Program in a Rural Mental Health Plan

Frank Hladky

TULSA PSYCHIATRIC FOUNDATION

VII

From July 1954 until the end of 1962, I was associated with the Rip Van Winkle Clinic in Columbia County, New York. Although the bulk of my time was spent working clinically with patients, I was the psychiatrist-in-charge of the mental health section, was directly responsible for its direction, and greatly interested in the community aspects of psychiatry. The experiences are told in retrospect, as no records were kept in any organized, usable way. I will try to describe my experience chronologically, for the most part, and as objectively as possible. The thoughts and reflections set down here are my own—even the "facts" may be true only in my eyes.

Columbia County is a picturesque rural area, bounded on the west by the Hudson River and on the east by the Berkshire Mountains and the Massachusetts state line. It is beautiful country with many streams, thick woods, and grand views of the Catskill Mountains; an old area settled by the Dutch who followed Henry Hudson. It is an area rich in history, and the people seem very much aware of their historical roots. There are still remnants of an aristocratic feeling among the descendants of the early Dutch landowners. These people

maintain high status in the community in spite of the fact they have
in many instances over the years lost their wealth and even in other
instances their social position. The population is stable; it has not
grown in the last sixty years, primarily because young people fre-
qently leave and don't come back. The county has the usual subcul-
tures and in the county seat, Hudson, a town of some 12,000 people,
there are Negro, Jewish, Italian, and Irish minorities, which to varying degrees function as groups. There has been little or no financial
growth in the community for years; some residents say new industry
is actually discouraged by people in positions of power because they
want the community unchanged. It is an area of beautiful old homes,
interesting and often highly educated people, some of whom became
dear and lasting friends. It is the area made known to the world by
Washington Irving: Katrinka Van Tassel's house still stands, there is
a "Pumpkin Hollow," one of the public schools is "Ichabod Crane,"
the bridge over the Hudson is the "Rip Van Winkle" bridge; the
Clinic, too, was named after that legendary figure. It is an area of
contrasts, of great wealth and poverty, artists and bushwhackers, of
many who look backward rather than forward, and this, with the
provincialism, gave one the feeling that the United States was going
on while this area was being left behind.

The Rip Van Winkle Clinic was founded in 1946 by Dr. Cald-
well Esselstyn, who was born and brought up in Columbia County
and returned just before World War II with plans to build a medical
group practice. He was unable to put his plans into operation until
the war was over. The Clinic, based on its associated Foundation, was
a group of specialists attempting to bring to a rural area specialty
medicine available to all, economically and geographically. The main
Clinic offices were in Hudson, but there were three branch offices in
smaller communities throughout the county; since that time three
more branch offices have been added, to make a total of six. The
group of well-trained, idealistic professionals was community oriented,
and at times embarked on programs to carry out what was thought
best in community health, but, unfortunately, had neither official nor
general community support. Because of the public health orientation,
because of the group practice itself and belief in such things as medical
insurance on a per capita basis rather than a fee for service basis, there
was marked conflict between the group and most of the other physicians in the area. This conflict, most marked during the establishment

of the group, was somewhat less in 1954 when I joined the group, although it was still intense.

The Clinic had previously had one psychiatrist on a part-time basis, who had to leave because of ill health, and later another psychiatrist on a full-time basis, who also had to resign because of illness. The latter psychiatrist still resided in the community and attempted to be helpful to me, but died about the time I became enough acquainted with the community, its peculiarities and problems, to be able to ask intelligent questions. The only other psychiatrist in the county was on the staff of the New York State Training School for girls, in Hudson, but he left shortly after our mental health section began to develop.

I first visited the Clinic when I was still in the process of being discharged from the service after having completed an overseas tour, and was immediately impressed by the warmth of the individuals in the group, their ready acceptance of me and my wife, and the spirit of pioneering and idealism that pervaded the group. In the beginning I had no knowledge of either the community or community psychiatry, but I did have a conviction that psychiatry should be made available to people of all socioeconomic levels: I believed that one had to get out of the office and reach out toward others to do work of preventive nature; I was convinced that a full range of services should be available in the community and wanted to see what could be developed.

DEVELOPMENT OF A PROGRAM

Our mental health section had the support of the Commonwealth and Milbank Foundations and additional federal funds distributed by the state. When I arrived, fees for psychotherapy had been established on a sliding scale, with the fees varying between fifty cents and $7.50, depending on income, number of people in the family, medical bills, etc. As a part of a medical group practice, the mental health section did not want to be a financial burden on the group as a whole; also it was our philosophy that patients who were able should pay realistic fees; and finally, if we had no other income except from the foundations and state-federal monies our work would be as limited as were these funds. Thus, fees were raised several times, although the individual's ability to pay remained the basic criterion. Fees finally ranged from nothing to what was considered a realistic fee for those in the upper income groups—for example, twenty dollars a session for psychotherapy. (The minimum fee was two dollars, because it was felt that a fifty-cent fee was degrading and if a patient could not pay two dollars there should be no fee.) The fee in no way determined the type of treatment the individual received, but many staff meetings were spent discussing the philosophy of the sliding scale and how to determine a just fee. With the income from fees (from both individuals and institutions), foundation support and the grant-in-aid, there was thus the financial possibility of developing a real community mental health program. A green light was given to go ahead and develop a program and add staff as indicated and I began with optimism and enthusiasm.

In considering the overall situation at that time, we decided to work in three general areas. The first area was building up the clinical outpatient services for both adults and children, and, because there were no provisions in the county for hospitalization of psychiatric patients, working toward permission to treat psychiatric patients in the local general hospital. A small liberal arts college just outside the county line was requesting psychiatric services for their students and a private school for delinquent boys in the county was also requesting psychiatric consultation; our second interest was to provide clinical services in institutions when requested as a way of providing income, establishing relationships with other institutions, and beginning to function in the community. Lastly, we planned to make efforts to work in the community in areas not only where there were no psychiatric services but also where psychiatric services had not been requested. These areas included the schools, the public health department, the courts, and the department of welfare. The aim was to demonstrate to these agencies and institutions how psychiatric and psychological services might be of use to them and then to try to fulfill their clinical and consultative needs.

In order to make possible realization of the aims that had been set forth, a sizeable staff would be necessary, and recruitment of personnel was begun. One of the first persons who wanted to live in the country and work with us was a psychologist of fine background and experience who was the chief psychologist at one of the well-known eastern medical schools. His arrival on the scene was a great asset in planning and development and also in the recruitment of other personnel. We worked long and hard building staff and were quite successful. Within the course of the next several years our staff grew until, at its peak, there were three full-time psychiatrists, two psychiatric social workers, a psychologist who specialized in working with organic cases and "minimally brain damaged children," a child therapist who did dynamic psychotherapy with children, a psychologist who worked primarily in the schools and did therapy in the Clinic, two psychologists who worked part-time to provide psychological testing services to adults, and an efficient and adequate secretarial staff. We also had the services of a well-trained, likeable health educator; later the chief psychologist developed a research team and their presence at staff meetings made discussions more fruitful and our work more stimulating. About half of the staff had had personal psychoanalyses and the general theoretical orientation was an analytical one. This was not unanimous, however, and many points of view were brought up in staff discussions. Regardless of theoretical orientation, it was agreed that the needs of the patient be clearly evaluated and that treatment be appropriate to the particular patient rather than that the patient should fit into any preconceived type of therapeutic approach—whether that be psychoanalytic psychotherapy or electric shock. It is realistic to say that a well-trained, capable staff was assembled whose members were idealistic and enthusiastic about their work, and that good staff relationships generally prevailed.

Much effort was made in the clinic to maintain an academic atmosphere. Toward this end all professional staff members were encouraged to establish working relationships with medical schools. For two years the chief psychologist and I taught at one medical school one day every other week; for several years another psychiatrist held clinical conferences at another medical school. For a time we felt that this was a valuable experience, but we were not closely enough related to the schools, in terms of distance or in any other way, for us to feel part of the school. Thus, after a period motivation began to wane, interest lagged, and then contact ceased because the professional relationship was only a one-way street.

There were many patients waiting to be seen by a psychiatrist when our work began and most were chronic, very sick individuals, difficult to help. Our first referrals by agencies and other physicians were also the most difficult, chronic patients; in addition, they were from the lowest socioeconomic level, so that we collected only little in the way of fees on our sliding scale. However, the demand for clinical services grew rapidly. Patients began to walk in and ask to see a psychiatrist or social worker and as word got around that some people were helped, more patients came in; they were often patients that were less severely disturbed, and in many instances we were able to help them. Thus the patient load increased, the results grew better, and gradually patients from the upper economic levels began to come in, until eventually there was a more balanced caseload.

As experienced professionals, trained in working with children, were added to the staff, more and more children were seen for evaluation and treatment. Our main problems in this area were twofold. We were not sufficiently effective in working with parents and, even when we were able to work through problems with a child and see positive results, we often found that our efforts went down the drain as the child returned to the home situation. The other problem was a sociocultural one; middle and upper class adults, although they were quite willing to come into the clinic, were less likely to bring in their children. Thus families whose children had emotional problems that might be more amenable to psychotherapeutic intervention came less often than those families who were in every sense deprived and needed many other kinds of help besides psychotherapy.

In the beginning, we had offices in the main clinic building—in the business district on Main Street. This had its advantages in that as patients came to this building there was no way for friends or acquaintances to tell whether they were going to the dentist, an internist, or psychiatrist; also, it furthered close working relationships between the members of the psychiatric team and other personnel in the Clinic. As the staff grew, office space in the building got tight, and finally an old residence was purchased in the residential section near the hospital to provide offices for our department and adequate meeting rooms for the whole staff. All personnel in the mental health section moved except one psychiatrist who felt it very important to maintain the close physical contact with the medical men in order to preserve his working relationships. This seemed to have been an accurate choice, because as time went on he had proportionately more referrals from the other professionals on the staff, and we in the other building had proportionately less. The move did not deter patients from coming—even though in the small community they were labeled as psychiatric patients from the time they parked their car and walked into the building. Some were anxious about it, afraid of what others would think, but nevertheless they came, and when patients faced this difficulty and worked it out, they seemed to be helped by having in this sense admitted they had emotional problems. The move helped the staff in that it established closer contact among them and made it possible for them to function more as a team than they had been able to when scattered among other specialists.

As staff psychiatrists came to the group they applied for and were given courtesy privileges in the local community hospital to see patients on a consultative basis; this was a beginning, but we wanted permission to hospitalize patients with primary psychiatric problems. The nursing staff and the administration of the hospital were apprehensive about this; they felt we would not be able to control "mental patients" and were attempting more than could be done. Only as it was demonstrated that postoperative surgical patients often had psychoses as severe as those of patients admitted primarily as psychiatric patients, that there were many other patients in the hospital who were seriously disturbed from time to time and were able to be handled, was it possible to swing some of the staff over to our way of thinking. As they became convinced that, if it were known that a patient was upset, he could be treated for his emotional condition from the first and difficulties anticipated, permission was granted to admit patients directly. At first, patients could be admitted only to certain partially stripped rooms with safety screens on the windows; and it was considered best to go along with this policy then. However, as the administration and nursing staff realized that these patients were no more difficult to handle than any others, permission was soon given to admit patients wherever there was a vacant bed; finally, the practice became to assign psychiatric patients to double rooms with other patients with all types of illnesses. Our patients seemed to do better in this setting, because of the lack of stigma, because the patient was treated like any other patient as far as possible, and because often the interaction between patients seemed to be beneficial to both.

Using these arrangements (and using private rooms only when patients were very disturbed), it was possible to take care of almost all psychiatric emergencies in the general hospital. Some extremely disturbed patients—for example, hypermanic agitated patients—were treated in a regular private room on a medical ward with a combination of intensive drug therapy and constant supervision of the patient by nurses, aides, relatives, and friends. Over the years, many people were committed on a regular or emergency basis to the state hospital and many others went to the state hospital for voluntary admission but it was our impression that the patients sent to the state hospital were those whose families were not able to afford private care, patients who had no families or means of support, or those whose families believed that the patient would not get well and thus wanted to get rid of the patient and the problem. In other words, we felt that admission to the state hospital often was related less to psychiatric condition than to socioeconomic conditions or serious family conflicts. The state hospital to which we referred patients often brought patients through a severe psychosis with good results. Some of these patients would return to our clinic voluntarily and we could work to consolidate the gains made in the hospital. However, many patients did not contact us again until they were in serious difficulty and some had to be hospitalized again. We tried to work this problem out with two different superintendents of the hospital and their staffs. Some gains were made in arranging for the interchange of records regarding patients and like matters, but we made no gains toward establishing real working relationships. These men knew the need for such close working relationships; yet, although we tried on several occasions, we were never successful in our efforts. One factor was their feeling of responsibility about their patients; thus, although they could offer little after-care service, they did not feel able to "give" the patient to someone else. The other operative factor, I think, was a suspicion that we were trying to gain in some monetary way by offering such service, since we were neither a state agency nor any kind of official community agency.

In spite of constant dissension in principle between the members of the group and most of the other physicians in the area, social amenities were observed and some of the physicians who did not refer patients to the medical group as a whole did refer patients to the psychiatric section, worked well with us, and maintained good relationships. This was a trend that was gradually increasing and might in the long run have significant meaning for the relationships between the medical group and the non-group physicians. In the relationships within the group—between physicians of other specialties and the psychiatric section—much more could have been done. A number of individual physicians were well oriented psychiatrically, very interested in what was going on in the mental health section, and referred most of the patients that came from the group. Other physicians in the group seemed not especially interested in the work of the psychiatric section, often seemed critical, and referred few, if any, patients. The whole professional staff met for dinner and professional meetings each Thursday night and for years also met for Friday luncheon. These meetings made possible personal acquaintance with all group members and provided an opportunity to discuss cases informally, as well as to give short case presentations or papers thought to be of general interest, or to participate in joint presentation of medical topics. This led to better communication and professional understanding between the other disciplines and the mental health section. Nevertheless, certain individuals were not reached, and we had little professional contact with them. At times we considered a campaign either to discuss these problems with the individuals concerned or to spend more time on the problem in the group as a whole, but at no time was any concerted effort made, and the situation remained basically unchanged.

A most important aspect of our clinical work was our membership in a medical group, which reinforces a medical orientation. For example, there was no waiting list, because we were expected to function like the internists, surgeons, and other physicians. Every patient would be seen at least briefly at the time he contacted the clinic if the patient or staff considered the situation an emergency, or in the next day or two if it was not an emergency. This policy not only helped in our therapeutic results because treatment often began at crisis times or at the time the patient had decided to ask for treatment and was therefore more amenable to it, but it also made the patient feel that he was considered as important as someone with an organic illness, and it seemed to help in the relationship between patient and therapist. Another practice that arose from our basic medical orientation was that someone was always on call for emergency situations and we made house calls when necessary (sometimes getting embroiled in quite difficult situations). Because we were able to help in crisis situations, we prevented hospitalization in many instances. In situations where hospitalization was necessary, the patients felt we were genuinely interested and the transition to the hospital was better for both the patient and the family. Furthermore, after discharge from the hospital the patient usually wanted to continue treatment with the person who showed enough concern to come out on an emergency call.

WORKING IN OTHER INSTITUTIONS

Pursuing the policy of providing needed psychiatric consultation and clinical service wherever possible, we gradually came in con-

tact with several institutions. At a small liberal arts college just out of
the county, where one of the former psychiatrists with the medical
group had previously served as psychiatric consultant, I spent one day
a week over the period of eight years, seeing individual students in
brief psychotherapy. Most students were self-referred and usually there
were more students than available time, so they often had to be seen
every other week instead of every week. Again, in this setting, patients
were at times seen in emergency or crisis situations, and in these instances it was my impression that one or two interviews afforded the
student the opportunity to stabilize by being helped to understand at
least some of the issues involved, state them in a definitive manner,
and take a course of action based on his own decision.

Because there were some students who were disciplinary problems or so ill they had to be removed from the school, there were a
few meetings with the Dean in the first year or so that I visited the
college regularly, although I had very little contact with any of the
teaching faculty or the administrative officers. Over the years I began
to know some of them better, and eventually, although there was a
change in Deans, I was asked to set aside a regular time each day I
visited the college to talk with the Dean. Some time was spent in clinical problems, although it was accepted that I would not be expected
to divulge information that was private. I kept no records on the students so that they would not have a psychiatric record on file. Only
on those rare occasions when a student had to be sent home or hospitalized because of mental illness would a written note be filed with the
registrar along lines of a medical excuse for dismissal. Gradually, however, more and more of the time was spent in discussing the general
problems that the Dean felt the students had at college; problems of
discipline, social regulations, morale, academic attitudes, and the like.
These discussions helped me understand the students better from a
clinical standpoint, because I was more aware of their general problems and the problems of the college. Further, I began to get more
interested in the problems of the institution to identify more closely
with the college.

This same process was repeated at a private school for delinquent boys in our county, though at times different psychiatrists gave
psychiatric consultation to this institution. Close personal contact with
the Director produced an atmosphere of involvement and a more intense interest in the organization than would have been generated if

we provided only clinical services. The Director was able to share his concern about his institution and his problems with the staff in open discussion with the psychiatrist. This kind of relationship is the most helpful type, in a consultative role to another institution because it not only enriches the clinical experience, but makes for a closer working and personal relationship between the consultant and the institution personnel.

In another experience, the failure to form such relationships led to a failure of function. The health educator and the psychiatric social worker had lectured to the student nurses in the local community hospital on psychology, sociology, and social work. Both staff members had been in the community a long time and were well accepted by the students and certainly by the full-time teaching staff of the school of nursing. As more professional people were added to our staff, we believed more lectures and teaching of a higher academic quality could be provided by having a Ph.D. psychologist lecture on psychology and later, when the research team was functioning, having a sociologist lecture on sociology. After a time conflicts arose between the staff people who had assumed these teaching roles and the administrators in the school of nursing about small and (to the social scientists) very insignificant things. Regardless of the details of the conflicts, the point is that neither of the professionals who lectured became personally acquainted or formed good working relationships with the administrative or teaching staff in the school of nursing. They never identified with the program, and relationships with the full-time nursing staff deteriorated completely. This experience strengthened my conviction that fruitful teaching or consulting relationships are possible only when the outside teacher or consultant finds some way of identifying with the personnel of the institution for which he is supplying these services—and that identification is possible only when genuine personal and professional relationships are established.

WORKING IN THE PUBLIC SCHOOLS

As a nucleus of staff was formed—psychiatrist, psychiatric social worker, and psychologist—one of the first things believed necessary from the standpoint of community psychiatry was to begin a psychiatric program in the schools. We assumed that this should begin on a team basis, so that we would have available the psychiatrist's clinical interview, the social worker's history and impression of the family gained from a personal visit to the home, and the psychologist's battery of tests and clinical impressions. Two school administrators, one from the county seat and another from a rural area, were persuaded to try the program. They were charged only a token fee for the services as a demonstration. Students were referred by the teachers or school nurses through the administrative system in the schools. Each student referred was seen in the school by the psychiatrist and examined by the psychologist; a home visit to the parents was made by the psychiatric social worker. After all the data were accumulated, a staff meeting was held in the school on each case. The child's current teacher, the teacher from his preceding year, the teacher he would move to in the following year, and any ancillary teachers (gym, music, and so on) who had known the child, were asked to attend, as were the administrators, the school nurse, and the guidance counselor. Although there was a good deal of curiosity, there was little real interest. The psychiatrist in this program felt it might be fruitful to have regular meetings with some of the teachers to explain what type of children might need to be referred and the benefits that might result from this type of casefinding and consultation about youngsters with emotional problems. Although there was good attendance at these meetings, they were of dubious value because there was strong opposition from some teachers who thought they were being "psychoanalyzed." Others, who did not object, quickly became involved in a "therapeutic relationship" in the group and wanted to be "psychoanalyzed." Therefore the attempt to educate the teachers was given up. Instead, time and energy were focused on the case conferences, and more consideration was given to hearing the teacher talk about her impressions of the youngster, endeavoring to draw her out and to get her involved in the process. Gradually the fear that many of the teachers and some of the administrators seemed to feel diminish. Although this focusing on the teacher's thoughts and feelings often left little time for our findings and recommendations, we felt that giving the teacher a chance to ventilate her own feelings to verbalize ideas that might be beneficial, and to feel more secure in her relationship with the child because of the support she had received in relationship with the professional team, might in the end be more important and helpful to the youngster.

Nevertheless, the fear of the teachers and administrators about the possibility that the psychiatrist might intend to investigate their emotional problems led to a certain amount of unconscious sabotage; this showed itself as occasional inability to have conferences when scheduled, forgetting to notify us when a child was not in school, and so on. Even so, as we focused on the teacher and were able to get her more involved in the process, our results improved; yet the fear of the psychiatrist and inability to understand him, and perhaps his inability to understand the school people, continued to some extent throughout the program. Some parents resented the home visit by the psychiatric social worker as an unwarranted intrusion. Since the social worker revisited the home after the conference to report the findings to the parents in order both to prevent any misunderstanding and to gain confidence and cooperation, we always wondered how much resentment from the parents was real. One aspect of this resistance may have been the resentment of the school nurses who felt that the psychiatric social worker was getting into their territory. Some of the nurses had been with the schools for long periods of time, knew the families well, and felt accepted everywhere. We tried to work closely with them and particularly to draw on their own expertise, but in some instances even these efforts were resented. The nurse might feel that the social history was unnecessary as she already knew everything about the families and children and perhaps felt that her competence was being questioned (actually the nurses were often very familiar with difficult situations and were of great help to us). Later a psychologist who was especially interested in working in the schools, had studied educational psychology, and had special training in education joined the staff. The school programs then went better. Later we realized that the psychologist had begun the process of identification with the institution, and the school officials related more personally to her while becoming less identified with the psychiatrist and the psychiatric social worker, who in turn became less identified with the school. Before the situation was clearly understood, one school asked to have the services of the psychologist increased and the services of the psychiatrist and the social worker only when requested on a consultative basis. The other school dropped the program completely.

After several years of working with the schools, many of the schools in the county had become associated with the program. The psychologist who had been working for the mental health section was eventually hired full-time by the school that she was most interested in; then other schools in the county also began to hire psychologists. What began as a team approach to school consultation with a broad clinical base, ended up with the conventional system entrenched; but we could feel that we had succeeded to the degree that the schools had been oriented toward the need for understanding the emotional problems of children and sufficiently convinced of the need that they hire full-time psychologists for their own staffs.

At the height of our school program (which lasted several years), we offered another service. The schools had classes for mentally deficient children, and our psychologists were sometimes called upon to do placement testing for these youngsters. As a result of this testing and also of our clinical work with children, the psychologists discovered the "minimally brain-damaged children"; children who were not mentally deficient but who have great difficulties in school because of poor concentration, hyperactivity, and perceptual problems that interfere with learning. Such children rapidly become behavior problems and a disturbance to the class as a whole. With the help of the State Department of Education, the local schools and one of the local men's service organizations, a summer school was held for a few of these youngsters. They were seen in very small groups (of two or three) and through retraining were helped to develop higher frustration tolerance, better concentration, and development of better perceptual skills. Since this summer program proved itself, some of the schools employed the psychologist expert in this field to work in the schools part-time during the regular academic year.

Even in the case of the schools that never were served directly by our team, the number of their referrals to the clinic for evaluation and treatment continued to increase and our working relationships became better. I can't explain this deviation from "the rule of identification" except that perhaps they were less threatened, since we were not going into the school, and thus were able to identify with us more easily—although we were less able to identify with them.

WORK WITH OTHER AGENCIES

The county had a health department, which was headed, when I joined the group, by a part-time physician, but some two years later was headed by a full-time public health officer. There were five or six full-time and some part-time public health nurses who were very dedicated individuals, identified with the patients they worked with, wanted to help them in every way possible, referred many for evaluation and treatment, and came in to discuss others. These nurses would come to conferences on their own time in spite of the fact they were very poorly paid; more underpaid than the school nurses or the teachers. We attributed this difference to the basic clinical orientation of the public health nurses, their deeper understanding of emotional problems, and their public health approach. The psychiatrists of the group were appointed deputy officers by the public health officer in order that they could assist him in handling emergencies and committing emergency cases. We were asked to talk to the public health nurses on a few occasions, but never did become closely identified with the administrative officials in the Public Health Department, that is, the Public Health Board. They were able to accept our clinical work, but never allowed us to form a working relationship with them so that they might have become more involved in the problems in the field of community mental health and we might have been able to be of more help to the Health Department in our endeavors. It might be that if we had expended more effort in forming working relationships with the public health officer and some of the people on the board, the outcome would have been more fruitful. On the other hand, the situation here again was that of distrust of the medical group per se, and since the mental health section was part of the medical group, there might have been no more success here, and further attempts might have actually made the situation more difficult instead of better.

Our major failures lay in our attempts to work with the Welfare Department, the courts, and the Mental Health Association. We were aware that the Welfare Department had many patients on its caseload who were emotionally disturbed or even quite ill mentally, but who were never referred to the mental health section. After some years, we decided to make a determined effort to work with the Welfare Department in order to see these people, get them into some kind of treatment, and offer services in the community before the situation deteriorated to the point where they had to be hospitalized. Some meetings were held with the Commissioner of Welfare, who seemed most concerned with the amount of unexpended funds he could return to the state at the end of each year. He did agree orally to send us such patients as his workers considered to be in need of psychiatric services, but in very few instances were patients referred. One of the social workers in our group had established a good relationship with one caseworker in the Welfare Department, who was the single source of these few referrals. This caseworker would also come in to discuss other patients; however, only a few patients were referred in this manner, although some of these would come to us of their own volition. We learned that some of the individuals we *could* have seen were indeed finally committed to the state hospital, having never been seen by a psychiatrist. We had offered to see all the Welfare Department referrals without fee because this was considered part of our community program and we had the financial support to make such service possible. But this was not sufficient inducement. Here, again, our initial error was in failing to make strong personal contact with the administrator of the program; our more serious error was in not making contact with the social workers who dealt with the individual cases. Were it not for these errors in judgment and tactics, we might have established a working role with the Welfare Department more like the one we had established with the Public Health Department; at least, they might have accepted the clinical work, although work on any administrative or community planning level would probably have been rejected because of the considered threat to the administrator.

In the courts we faced a similar situation, although over the years we were able to be of use as consultants on quite a few cases, especially in the Juvenile Court. We seemed to have been able to establish good working relationships with both the judge and the chief probation officer, but in the end these proved not good enough. When we needed their cooperation and support for the referral of cases that might have benefited from our services—and finally, needed their support for the very survival of the program—we found we had not succeeded in building either the personal or the professional relationships we had hoped for. In the first several years of working with the courts, we saw cases on an individual basis, and those who could not pay a fee were seen without charge. But when our financial support decreased, we hoped the juvenile court would be able to pay for the actual costs of the services provided. Actually, such an understanding was made; however, it was in its operation that difficulties became apparent. Agreements had been made to take care of their cases up to a certain monetary limit, yet few referrals were forthcoming. Here, again, we failed to spend enough time, consideration, and energy in the establishment of good personal and working relationships with the individuals involved. We were not sufficiently aware of their point of view, and this is essential for this type of community work.

About midway in this period, a worker from the New York State Mental Health Association came to the county. She contacted various people who were active in community affairs and stimulated interest in a local Mental Health Association. She was effective enough —and there was sufficient interest—that in a relatively short time a local association was, in fact, organized. The psychiatric social worker from the mental health section and I were asked to join the board of directors, a well-meaning lay group which was, unfortunately, quite naive about psychiatry and "mental health." New York State's progressive community mental health act provides for matching state funds to local communities for psychiatric community clinics, psychiatric patients in general hospitals, and so on, but the local community had first to set up a mental health board and provide the initial funding. We in the mental health section of our clinic were hopeful that a board could be set up in our county and monies raised, either to support the work we were doing or to establish another clinic for the community, in which case we would be relieved of a large clinical case load and could direct our efforts toward new areas. I hoped that the Mental Health Association would spearhead the drive for the formation of a mental health board and, indeed, that was one of the stated aims.

In the first year or two of the association little was accomplished, but interest remained high, the annual suppers were well attended, and some positive action seemed probable. I played a minimal role in the association, feeling that this group of responsible community-minded individuals should make the decisions about what they wanted for their community; that it was not my place, either as a psychiatrist or as the most interested individual in the county, to influence them toward what I conceived to be desirable goals. But in the next two years, two local physicians—both opposed to our clinic— became active in the organization. One was elected president. Although he gave lip service to psychiatry and mental health concepts, he took no action either to support the mental health section of our clinic or to organize any other; the second physician, who was appointed chairman of the professional advisory committee, has since spoken out openly and directly against mental health programs as part of an international conspiracy. The refrain is familiar to all of us in the mental health field. The painful conclusion forced upon me was that I had lost a battle by default. I stayed out of what seemed to me to be an essentially political arena—and I had not conceived my role as political—but because I did not attempt to provide leadership or direction, which would have required a kind of community activity that is indeed in part political, the anti-mental health forces took the initiative and carried the day. Except that it is not just a day —such events wipe out opportunities that arise but seldom and turn back the wheels of progress in terms of years.

Shortly after this the health educator left our group. Although he was not primarily a *mental* health educator, he had been active with our group and he, more than anyone else, was active in the community. He knew many people on a first name basis; he knew the relationships between people in the community and participated in many community functions. But his importance was not recognized until after he left. As a matter of fact, some of us felt he was often "goofing off" and wasting time because he often was neither seeing patients nor delivering lectures, but just chatting with people in the community. In retrospect, we can see that this activity had a vital function, and after the function was abandoned our community relationships began to worsen and our work in the community began to disintegrate. Shortly our school program began to falter—as described earlier—and when the Director of the Clinic, wanting to understand the situation, tried to ascertain where the blame lay, relationships among the mental health team became strained. These problems were faced, discussed, and dealt with in staff meeting and with the individuals concerned, but from this point on our morale was not the same, both because the health educator had left and because, although we felt something was wrong, we could not define it. With the decline of morale, both our community efforts and our esprit de corps suffered. Soon after this point, our foundation funds were reduced on the grounds that the pump-priming had been sufficient to demand that the community begin financially to support the ongoing work. In fact, this was fairly true of a good deal of our clinical work. Our fees had increased over the years and we were now assured that there would at least be some continuing psychiatric service even with little outside support. However, as we lost ground in the community programs and the community still showed no evidence (except in the schools) that they were interested in contributing to the financial support of a community mental health program, together with the lowered morale, some of the staff began to leave for other positions, contributing to a further lowering of morale. We were no longer building and expanding and pessimism grew. This point was the beginning of the end of our attempts to develop meaningful community psychiatric programs, and had to do with my eventual reasons for leaving the area. The clinical work continued; and some of the community aspects of the work *were* for a time successful, but we never succeeded in establishing a genuine *community* mental health program. Our failure to enlist community support, especially from the key individuals in the power structure who could have provided support when we needed it at crucial times, was our critical failure.

After the presentation of a difficult clinical problem or the report that followed every patient's death, Dr. Esselstyn, the founder of the Rip Van Winkle Clinic, usually remarked, "What can be learned from this case?" It provoked thought, made one think in terms of what could be gained from a negative result, and frequently turned an unhappy or disappointing clinical experience into a positive learning experience.

A mental health program, if it is to get financial support from the community or expand into new areas in community agencies must first obtain active community backing and support in the nonfinancial sense. Services can be provided to a community without community support and individuals will make use of the service. However, if such wide-based support is lacking, the community will not opt for consultation or service to its agencies and certainly not take over the financial responsibility for such service.

Throughout my tenure as Director of the Mental Health Section, I took the position that only the professional aspects of psychiatric problems were my responsibility, that I should not have to sell the worth of our services to the community. Although I still feel this way to some extent personally, if I again wanted to build a community program in the same sense, I would devote much more time to the community effort and would try to think of institutions or agencies and the people in them as if they were clinical cases. In other words, I would take myself out of a primarily subjective attitude toward the individuals and the institutions involved and think about their problems as I would in trying to analyze a patient's problems. I would recognize rejection of programs as defensive reactions and try to understand and circumvent the anxieties aroused in agencies by the intrusion of psychiatric personnel. I am convinced that we would have been much more successful in our community efforts if such an approach had been made persistently; if we had not looked for early success but waited for propitious moments to gain entry into the community structure. The psychiatrist who is interested only in his private practice can take off his clinical hat and be an individual after he leaves the office. The community psychiatrist must constantly view situations from an objective clinical viewpoint, whether the situations involve personal relationships with people from other agencies or relationships between agencies, and handle them in clinical—that is, in objective and purposeful instead of subjective and reactive—ways.

POSTSCRIPT

Since this account was written, the Rip Van Winkle Clinic has closed its doors. It failed because it was not able to do the work it had set out to do and remain financially solvent. I believe that some of the remarks concerning success or failure in the community would apply to the medical clinic as a whole.

It is interesting to note that after the closing of the Clinic the Mental Health Association did become active and made possible a small community mental health clinic, staffed by a full-time psychiatric social worker and psychologist, and a part-time psychiatrist who had been on our clinic staff.

A Project
That Failed

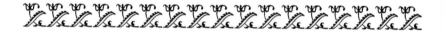

Daniel DeSole

VETERANS ADMINISTRATION HOSPITAL, ALBANY, NEW YORK

Philip Singer

UNITED NATIONS, NEW YORK

Edward Swietnicki

KNICKERBOCKER NEWS, ALBANY, NEW YORK

VIII

For several years in "Northeast"[1] there had been a good deal of desultory talk about the need for better local mental health facilities. Of the seven counties in the upper area of the state, Northeast County had the highest per capita income but was also first in child neglect, child delinquency, and number of citizens resident in state mental hospitals. The city of Northeast ranked third in admissions to the state mental hospitals, and was fourth in persons receiving public welfare assistance. The city also boasted one of the lower tax rates in the state. Some of the medical leaders and concerned lay citizens had felt concern over the fact that local citizens and family members had to travel fifty to seventy-five miles to reach the nearest available mental health services. They felt that Northeast, having other hospitals and medical facilities, should also have better mental health treatment facilities. There was no sense of urgency, however, in trying to put these vaguely-felt civic needs into real plans of action.

"Dr. Marshall," an organically oriented psychiatrist, had be-

[1] For reasons that will become obvious to the reader, it was deemed expedient to render the locale and the actors in this story anonymous, although both place and persons are real.

come convinced that one of the best ways to keep patients coping and productive in the community was through a day hospital. Dr. Marshall exemplified the traditional, authoritarian physician and had long advocated electroshock as the treatment of choice on purely pragmatic grounds, and was one of the first psychiatrists to adopt the use of tranquilizers. His efforts were bent on keeping persons active in the community.

In the possibilities of a day hospital, Dr. Marshall saw the institutionalization of his pragmatic approach of keeping mentally ill patients in the community and doing so at minimal cost.

In his proposed budget for this hospital, Dr. Marshall provided a full-time psychiatrist-director of the day hospital at a salary 25 per cent less than salaries in adjacent counties.

In trying to realize his dream of a day hospital, Dr. Marshall entertained another basic assumption that revealed a lack of understanding of the nature of the city within which these services would operate. He assumed that the day care center could be divorced from community political involvement through the technique used by private agencies, that of the directorship of a community leader. He evinced awareness of the relationship between the private and public sectors only by his inclusion of matching state funds in his budget. Reflecting the general assumptions of most professionals, Dr. Marshall preferred to work by raising private funds, which would then be matched by state funds, with the approval of the county Board of Supervisors, but without the county putting in any of its own tax monies.

After nearly 100 years of fiscally conservative political control it was not surprising that most citizens felt as Dr. Marshall probably did: that there was no point in trying to get county participation in needed public facilities because the county never had contributed much and probably wasn't going to now.

Dr. Marshall, in choosing Dr. Resident to be director-designate of the proposed day hospital, selected a man who felt a great sense of personal obligation to him. Dr. Resident's admiration for Dr. Marshall as a man, a physician, and a clinician was such that some other residents in the program described him as a sycophant.

In spite of his strong positive relationship to Dr. Marshall, Dr. Resident was very much aware of financial realities. He told Dr. Marshall at their first meeting that funds were a crucial concern and that he would help raise the money. Dr. Marshall agreed and told him to go ahead as fund-raiser and make the day hospital a reality.

Meanwhile, in Washington, D.C., another, more far-reaching event, which was to affect all those involved in the drama for a day hospital psychiatric facility, was being played out.

In October of that year President Lyndon B. Johnson announced details of a nationwide $947.5 million "War on Poverty." In Northeast, the mayor announced that the city would become a part of this program.

Enthusiastically committed to the day hospital plans of Dr. Marshall, Dr. Resident began the task of marshalling support for the project in the fall and winter of 1964. He turned to Dr. Anthropologist, who had had wide experience in formulating grant requests and outlining projects for government support. Dr. Anthropologist was already involved as an advisory board member of the Interfaith House, which was making the transition from a neighborhood recreation house to a community action organization among the poor. He felt that it would be extremely impractical to try to launch a day hospital without involving the local power structure. He felt that without wider political support the day hospital could only be just another Community Chest agency, never really reaching out to those people who needed services the most—the poor. Dr. Anthropologist noted that Dr. Resident's own study of utilization of the Medical Center Hospital Psychiatric Outpatient Clinic had revealed de facto segregation. At the time of the study in 1963–64, there were no Negroes in individual psychotherapy or group therapy, and in the General Psychiatry Clinic, which uses organic modes of treatment, there were seventeen Negroes out of a total caseload of 167. This was particularly significant since of the approximately 10,000 Negroes who lived in the city, 95 per cent lived in the inner city poverty areas, virtually within the shade of the Medical Center.

Dr. Anthropologist suggested that county political support and tax monies might very well be forthcoming if the political structure could be reached. As a board member of the Interfaith House, he knew that its director was in close personal contact with the mayor and the health and welfare leaders. Indeed, he prided himself on the fact that, because of these close contacts, his agency was receiving city funds for work in slum neighborhoods. His agency was, however, interested in some psychiatric services. It was suggested that the two groups might help each other, and on that logic the day hospital plan included reference to the Interfaith House as part of its agenda.

Because Interfaith House was a part of the Community Chest, its funds were reviewed by the overall board responsible for Community Chest funding. At a later meeting, it developed that the Interfaith House program was actually in some disfavor and the broader board of the Community Chest did not at all approve of this newly proposed liaison.

The various vested interests began at this stage to fall somewhat into place. The agency was under pressure from the community to undertake some other activities, which would eventually become a part of the Community Chest, and of course constitute a further drain on its resources. The specific objection to the day hospital–agency liaison was based upon the view that Community Chest was already supporting other psychiatric activities, and on the concern it felt over the possibility of having to support some aspects of the day hospital plan. It was feared that if the day hospital became established with this connection, and without specific public tax monies, it would eventually come under the Community Chest.

About five months had gone by since Dr. Marshall had asked Dr. Resident to assume leadership in establishing the day hospital through raising of private funds. Within that time certain things had become clear: (1) There was no hope of getting the money through private groups and individual donations. (2) The Community Chest was reluctant to support efforts to get such money because it was reluctant to saddle itself with future support. (3) Most responsible and public-minded citizens felt that the day hospital should be supported by the tax funds of the county.

In his weekly meetings with Dr. Marshall, Dr. Resident made it clear that he felt that a dead end had been reached in trying to fund the day hospital by private means. He felt that to obtain support for the program, the county had to be involved. Dr. Marshall's reaction was that there was nothing in the history of the county to indicate that such an appeal would succeed. Faced with these realities and burdened by his many medical obligations, Dr. Marshall began to withdraw from the project. However, Dr. Resident had become increasingly involved with the emotional problems of the poor. More and more he saw the day hospital as playing an important role for the people in Northeast who needed psychiatric services most but received them least.

Beginning in October 1964, Dr. Resident and another psychiatrist, Dr. Psychiatrist, had been holding weekly meetings in inner-city churches and settlement houses to find out why the poor and the Negroes were not utilizing the psychiatric services technically available to them.

During this period in early 1965, when all movement toward the establishment of the Day Hospital was at a standstill, Dr. Marshall began to shift ground and actively seek public support for the establishment of a state mental hospital.

Dr. Marshall wrote a letter, which appeared in the newspaper February 6, 1965, appealing to the citizenry to revise outdated attitudes toward the mentally ill and support a hospital within the community.

During the five months of great community activity by Dr. Resident, the senior staff of the local Department of Psychiatry began to show some opposition to him. Possibly, his activities aroused a fear that involvement by the department in the community would threaten the private practices that most of the staff members carried on from the department. Certainly, it is conceivable that some department members might feel that Dr. Resident would upset the balance of power within the department, and that the establishment of new facilities would bring in new full-time men, and thus create a different base for Dr. Resident, which might eclipse the operation of the psychiatric outpatient clinic.

However, all meaningful efforts toward the establishment of the day hospital had effectively ceased. Suddenly, early in 1965, new hope appeared. The newspapers had announced that the governor had appointed Mr. George Little as state coordinator of the "War on Poverty" program.

Drs. Resident and Anthropologist discussed the significance of the anti-poverty program and the appointment of Mr. Little and concluded that the federal program offered a way out of the impasse of the county's resistance to any program that required local tax monies. Dr. Resident reported to Dr. Marshall and asked whether he would approve efforts to fund the day hospital through a single-purpose grant from the medical college. Dr. Marshall was in reality neutral, but this neutrality was enough to encourage Drs. Resident and Anthropologist to move ahead. Mr. Little was telephoned and readily agreed to a meeting to discuss the day hospital and related projects.

Mr. Little proved to be unusually knowledgeable about the political structure of the area and the special difficulties that anyone would encounter in trying to achieve something outside of the largesse of the traditional political machine. He informed them that there was a special provision in the "War on Poverty" legislation that made possible direct grants from the Federal government to universities and medical colleges for the purpose of funding "demonstration projects," and that he would support their efforts to establish such a project in all ways, from technical advice to personal appearances. He urged Dr. Resident and Dr. Anthropologist to prepare a demonstration project proposal and send it to Washington.

Dr. Resident enthusiastically reported to Dr. Marshall on his conversations with Mr. Little and his feeling that he would lend support to a day hospital funded by the Office of Economic Opportunity. Dr. Resident was impressed by Dr. Marshall's positive reaction. Dr. Anthropologist, however, cautioned that although enthusiasm was fine, Dr. Marshall would have to support the project at least with some cash for travel and secretarial work. At this point Drs. Resident and Anthropologist began hearing that some of the department members were scoffing at their "grandiosity"—a reference to the fact that the proposed OEO-funded budget for the day care center would be more than $300,000.

And indeed a shift *was* meanwhile taking place in the thinking of Drs. Resident and Anthropologist about the very concept of a day hospital. They had changed the budget figure from the original figure of about $70,000 to the current $300,000—and apparently had changed their attitudes and goals as well.

In sharp contrast to Dr. Marshall's first proposal for a day care center, the new proposal drawn up by Drs. Resident and Anthropologist, with the approval of Dr. Marshall, specifically mentioned the poor. The project application stressed that their aims included keeping low income persons who need mental health care functioning optimally in the community.

Between the meeting with Mr. Little and submitting the draft of a program sponsored by the medical college, Dr. Resident was very active. With Dr. Psychiatrist, he continued his meetings with the clergy in the poverty areas and addressed church and fraternal groups. With Dr. Anthropologist, he met with the poor in informal groups in the neighborhood houses and drafted rosters of potential indigenous nonprofessional personnel. They had taken a leaf from New York's Albert Einstein Neighborhood Service Center Project, which Mr. Little had praised highly, and were trying to incorporate the concept into a broadly based community psychiatry program. No longer were they talking about a day hospital center exclusively.

As a result of their meetings with sympathetic private agencies and groups already working in the poverty areas, Drs. Resident and Anthropologist proposed setting up community-based centers in each of the two poverty areas in the City. Both were to be closely tied to the day hospital located at the Medical Center, as originally conceived.

Meanwhile, in city hall, the political machine was reacting to the "War on Poverty" and the enthusiasm of well-meaning, middle-class citizens through a series of delaying public relations tactics. As of July 1966, Northeast had the distinction of being the only city among the nation's one hundred largest without some sort of community action agency in the anti-poverty program.

The county and city leadership responded to the "War on Poverty" law by appointing a three-member anti-poverty commission made up of the county welfare commissioner, the mayor of a nearby city, and a superintendent of the public school system. The commission in turn appointed a twenty-one-member advisory committee made up largely of Democratic Party leaders and the members of the power structure establishment, among them George Bird, Director of the Coordinating Board for Community Services and the Reverend Thomas J. O'Connor of Catholic Charities. This advisory commission was criticized by several groups for not having enough representation from among the poor. In March 1965, the Federal Office of Economic Opportunity announced that it was holding up development funds to this county because of objections that had been raised to the commission's makeup.

The political naiveté of Drs. Resident, Anthropologist, and Marshall can be gauged by the fact that they really felt that they could get around the political machine by going directly to Washington for funds. An advisory committee for the Medical Center Community Psychiatry Project was formed in March, headed by the Dean of the medical college and Dr. Marshall.

Meanwhile, Drs. Resident and Anthropologist completed the proposal for a Northeast Medical College Community Psychiatry Program. They wrote an accompanying letter that stressed several features of their program. It included reference to a variety of referral and emergency relief centers, to the coordination of all existing service programs, including churches, and to the staffing by both professionals and nonprofessionals. They stressed that this was not just another middle-class agency but one that had a firm base in various community centers and was in tune with the needs of the poor.

On the same date, a copy of the proposal with a now $400,000 budget was sent to the Office of Economic Opportunity in Washington.

Drs. Resident and Anthropologist were riding on the crest of achievement and Mr. Little's encouragement. Dr. Anthropologist was recommended for promotion to Associate Professor. Dr. Resident, proud of the proposal, freely gave copies of it to anyone who indicated an interest. Among those was a psychiatrist from the county mental health board and a part of the power structure in Northeast. As a psychiatrist, he is known for his efficiency in sending welfare patients as rapidly as possible to the state mental hospital and he administers a great deal of electroshock.

He went to Dr. Resident and told him that he thought the project should be phased in with the city and county agencies. Dr. Resident and Dr. Anthropologist responded with enthusiasm and commented between themselves that in a democracy, one should work with the power structure. Dr. Resident felt that regardless of how long a machine was in power, they were the "elected representatives of the people."

Shortly after this conversation, this psychiatrist invited Dr. Resident to come to his office where he was having drinks for Dr. Albert Stone, Director of the Division of Social and Community Psychiatry of a renowned college of medicine, and Dr. Robert Taylor, from the state division of mental health services.

Over drinks and before Drs. Stone and Taylor arrived, he told Dr. Resident that this program was "great" but that it had been criticized by Father Eggleston, who was representing Bishop Thomas Reilly's own anti-poverty commission for the Roman Catholic diocese. Eggleston felt the proposed project lacked a broad enough base in community support. This criticism surprised Dr. Resident since he had never heard of Father Eggleston and had never had any contact with him. However, he had been in contact with other Catholic agencies and indeed had solicited the support of the Catholic Church.

Dr. County Psychiatrist concluded by saying that Father Eggleston should not be offended because he was a "powerful man."

That week, Dr. Anthropologist received an invitation from the Council of Churches (Protestant) to speak at the spring meeting of the Council. Mr. Little and the deputy superintendent of a public school district and three members of the commission of the county were also invited to speak.

When Dr. Anthropologist spoke, for the first time a distinguished audience was to hear open criticism of the failure of the local political machine in doing something about its poor and the problems of local Negroes. His speech was widely reported in the local press and received favorable editorial comment. Mr. Little told the same audience that the city administration had bypassed the state in its so-called application for poverty funds.

About a month had passed since the program proposal had been submitted to OEO in Washington. Local pressures of various sorts were mounting. At this point, with the advice of a state senator, a meeting was arranged in Washington for Drs. Resident and Anthropologist. At this meeting, it was reported that the Community Mental Health Act had just been passed and that this was the appropriate route for funding for the day hospital idea. This was to the city's advantage, it was suggested, since this meant the possibility of two significant programs; one through the Community Mental Health Act and one through the OEO. The meeting stressed the desirability of a strong use of nonprofessionals in the poverty based program, and urged that Drs. Resident and Anthropologist undertake to involve more agencies now within the community. Drs. Resident and Anthropologist responded positively to these suggestions, since they felt they already had good relations with the necessary groups, both in agencies and among the poor.

It was said that the next step would be a site visit by an OEO consultant to help in drafting the new program. They were told that they would hear from Washington by phone during the next week.

Drs. Resident and Anthropologist informed the Senator's office and Mr. Little of the results of the meeting. Immediately they went to work implementing the OEO's recommendations. They prepared a memorandum to the agencies that reflected their optimism and their own desire to broaden the project. They assumed that they could involve significant private agencies in the city without first clearing with the power structure that controlled them through their boards of directors and the Community Chest. Until then, their organizing activities had been met with almost total cooperation. In their enthusiasm for the new outlook, Drs. Resident and Anthropologist decided to act as editorial consultants for a new paper for the poor.

Dr. Marshall arranged a meeting of local persons and various representatives of the state mental health department, to discuss these developments. Before the meetings, Drs. Resident and Anthropologist phoned the OEO. Their thought was that if there appeared to be OEO support for the anti-poverty program, they would work in that direction; but if not, they would devote their energies to the day hospital aspect of the double plan. At the same time, local officials were interested in knowing about OEO support as well, on the grounds that if it was forthcoming, some city or county support could be managed. OEO was at that time unable to commit itself to support. As a result, at the meeting Dr. Resident reported that there was a continuing OEO interest and concern that the project clarify its relationship with other community action programs.

Officials of the State Mental Health Department reacted with enthusiasm to both the anti-poverty health project and the Community Psychiatry program. Dr. County Psychiatrist said he would take the Community Psychiatry protocol to the Mayor and would report to him concerning the health project as well. There was general optimism. All present felt that the County could not hold out against additional mental health services given the favorable financial support seemingly in sight.

The results of this meeting were communicated by letter to OEO in Washington, to Mr. Little and the Senator. The following week Dr. Marshall left for his vacation, full of optimism and enthusiasm for what had been accomplished. For, indeed, a most unique event had taken place. Representatives of the State, the County, and the psychiatric department of the Medical College had met and apparently agreed on goals and methods for implementation—and Washington was interested.

The continuing link with the poor during this time remained the therapeutic meetings begun in September 1964 by Dr. Resident and a second psychiatrist. These meetings with a group of poverty area clergy, mainly Negro, had been prompted by Dr. Resident's discovery of de facto segregation in the psychiatric outpatient clinics. The only psychiatrist in the department to respond sympathetically to this fact was the psychiatrist in charge of the Group Psychotherapy program at the medical college and a psychiatric supervisor for residents.

Together, they spoke of this problem to the Director of the Child Guidance Center. They turned to her because the Child Guidance Center had a reputation for being more than simply an agency for middle-class clients. The director had a reputation as an outspoken fighter for the needs of the people.

Out of these initial contacts a regular weekly morning meeting developed. The first two meetings, held at the medical college, were attended by about twelve Negro and white clergymen.

These first two meetings focused on the attempt to determine the attitudes of the poor to mental illness and its treatment. All the Negro storefront ministers, white ministers in churches located in the poverty area, and some Catholic priests maintained that the poor needed and wanted psychiatric help. Most vociferous on this score were the Negro ministers. The major obstacle to the Negroes utilizing the psychiatric services appeared to be the difficulty in getting transportation to the clinics; the working-day hours of the clinics; and the feeling among Negroes that they were receiving second-class care from fourth-year medical students instead of "real doctors."

Dr. Resident and the psychiatrist proposed that the meetings be continued on a regular basis throughout the year and that they be held in the poverty area itself, at the ministers' various churches. The group met regularly. There were times when only one or two of the ministers and Drs. Resident and Psychiatrist were present.

In January 1965, when the organizing efforts of Drs. Resident and Anthropologist began to look as if they might pay off in relation to the War on Poverty program, Dr. Anthropologist spoke to the ministers about recruiting indigenous workers and themselves staffing various posts in the day hospital program. At that point there was a resurgence of interest.

This period of hope-filled planning continued through April. Early meetings elicited information about local conditions needed to prepare the community psychiatry program. After the program was submitted, the meetings continued with a shift in emphasis from information gathering and planning to discussions of program implementation. Stirrings of discontent began to be heard toward the end of April and May, as Drs. Resident and Anthropologist were unable to report any progress in Washington. Soon there were only three or four persons attending. Dr. Anthropologist then suggested that one way to try to achieve some cohesion and make their voices heard was to start a weekly, mimeographed newspaper. An assistant professor in the English Department at a local university who had been active in civil rights work with the university chaplain joined the others as editorial advisors.

Some of this group met with several of the ministers. One, the Reverend Cruz Gomez, had come from New York City to head a local church. He did odd jobs, ran a television repair service, was a former professional boxer and a veteran. A soft-spoken, quiet Negro, he regarded himself as a leader. Another came from Jamaica and was one of the early Freedom Bus Riders in 1962. He now acts effectively as a mediator between the power structure and his parishioners. A third came from Antigua in the Caribbean and now owns his own house in an average, middle-class, white bedroom suburb. A fourth was something of a man of mystery who always seemed to have money and connections.

In June, the first 1,000-copy, four-page issue of the Northeast *Crier* emerged from the basement of the Zion Church.

It reported facts about the poor derived from research done by Drs. Resident and Anthropologist in preparing the proposal for the community psychiatry project. The newspaper stated that there were 5,683 families with an income of under $3,000 a year. It pointed out that 91 per cent of the Negroes shared 53 per cent of all the poverty.

With the appearance of the first issue, Dr. Resident received a telephone call at the office from the county psychiatrist. At first he attempted to warn Dr. Resident that he was going to get into trouble because he was associating on the *Crier* with "criminals, prostitutes, and drug addicts." He said that the mayor was concerned about Dr. Resident's association with the *Crier,* and he felt that this kind of association could jeopardize negotiations for the Day Hospital. Dr. Resident responded by expressing the feeling that what he did as a private citizen was his own affair, and on the other hand, that by working closely with the poor, he could better know what was going on. The county psychiatrist then told Dr. Resident to write him a letter to the effect that he was really working on the *Crier* in order to gain information. Dr. County Psychiatrist emphasized that he could show the letter to the mayor, to which Dr. Resident replied: "If the mayor wishes such a letter, all he need do is write to me requesting such a letter."

This conversation was particularly significant because on the previous day Drs. Resident and Anthropologist had apparently finally succeeded in getting the mayor to give favorable consideration to the Day Hospital.

Drs. Resident and Anthropologist went to a meeting with the mayor and the county psychiatrist with a strategy in mind. It appeared to them that the first responsibility they had was to Dr. Marshall and the concept of the day hospital. Secondly, they felt, based on their many conversations with Mr. Little and their talks with the OEO, a larger, anti-poverty health project could bypass the political machine through the mechanism of medical college sponsorship, which would put it in the category of a "Demonstration Program" and qualify it for a direct grant to the college.

At the meeting, the county psychiatrist lauded Dr. Resident before the mayor as a physician possessing a great deal of "common sense." The day hospital concept was presented to the mayor, who apparently saw the advantages of such a program.

At the conclusion of the hour-long meeting, the mayor instructed the county psychiatrist to call an emergency meeting of the Mental Health Board, which would otherwise not meet until the next fall. He indicated to all present that he expected favorable action by the Board of Supervisors on an emergency recommendation by the Mental Health Board, to provide county tax funds for the day hospital.

Drs. Resident and Anthropologist left the meeting feeling jubilant. The mayor had not asked about their activities in the poverty areas with the *Crier*. He had apparently been convinced that the day hospital was a good idea and should be supported. As a result, Drs. Resident and Anthropologist felt that they had discharged their primary responsibility to Dr. Marshall, and they believed that they were now free to go ahead with the development of the Anti-Poverty Health Program.

At a second meeting with the mayor, the day hospital plans and financing were discussed. The mayor asked whether the projected new state mental hospital might not assume the functions of the day hospital. He seemed to accept Dr. Resident's assurances that it would not. On the morning of the day set for the special County Mental Health Board meeting the county psychiatrist postponed it two weeks.

Dr. Marshall was on vacation and Dr. Resident much preferred that he be directly involved. The postponed meeting was cancelled and no new date was set. When Dr. Marshall returned from vacation, the county psychiatrist saw him the day he returned. Before meeting with Dr. Resident, Dr. Marshall asked to see some copies of the *Crier*. Five issues had already appeared. When Drs. Marshall and Resident met, Dr. Marshall confronted him with the *Crier*. He asked whether Dr. Resident did not think that his association with the *Crier* was putting into jeopardy the chances of getting the mayor's support for the day hospital, and quoted the county psychiatrist as having reported the mayor's strong displeasure and the possible discontinuance of county support for the day hospital as a result of Dr. Resident's activities. Dr. Resident nonetheless insisted that, as a private citizen, he would act as he saw fit. He also pointed out that he and Dr. Anthropologist were two of the very few members of the medical college faculty living in the city, rather than in the suburbs, and consequently felt a responsibility to the community. Following that conversation, Dr. Resident wrote the mayor asserting that Dr. County Psychiatrist had informed Dr. Resident that the mayor now considered the day hospital project to be "technically and professionally incompetent"; that the Mayor disapproved of his involvement as an editorial consultant, on the grounds that it constitutes associating with "criminals, prostitutes, and drug addicts"; that Dr. County Psychiatrist regarded the day hospital as just a "research project"; and that the County Mental Health Board had met twice, but was "too busy" to consider the day hospital project.

Dr. Resident reminded the mayor that for a county expenditure of $17,000 in day hospital earmarked funds, the county would receive a facility that would provide not only day hospital services, but an evening, weekend, and after-care clinic, and $183,000 in federal and state matching funds, and that the proposal had been discussed with the key personnel in the State Mental Health Department, who had judged it to be a sound program worthy of support.

To this the mayor replied only that he "will look into this and be in touch with you again shortly."

The *Crier* continued to appear weekly, raising significant issues and detailing the life of the poor. According to Mr. Journalist, reporter for the *Daily News,* City Hall began to react about the fourth or fifth issue. From the mayor's office and the County Courthouse came word that the newspaper and the persons associated with it were "troublemakers."

Simultaneously, some officials at the medical college dropped the word to the metropolitan dailies that had been giving coverage to the *Crier* that Dr. Anthropologist was a former "newspaper bum," an opportunist, and was a "leftist" because he had written for the *New Republic*. As the summer wore on, the criticism focused on Dr. Anthropologist and *Crier* editor, the Reverend Cruz Gomez. A City Hall reporter spread word around newspaper circles that Cruz Gomez had served time in prison, and that the "District Attorney's office knows about it." Dr. Anthropologist indeed had written for *The New Republic,* had been a copy editor for the *Worcester Messenger* and Sunday editor for the Washington County *Evening Times*. The Reverend Cruz Gomez had indeed been convicted of assault and battery and served two months in prison until a higher court ruled that his conviction was not for a felony but a lesser offense. The machine had investigated his background.

Gossip emanating from the Medical College, the local Office of Economic Opportunity headquarters, and the Community Chest agencies charged that Dr. Anthropologist was "leading Dr. Resident around by the nose" and "manipulating" him. The insinuation of "manipulation" became the talk of the Department of Psychiatry. The chairman of the department, echoing the sentiments of other members of the department, told Dr. Resident that if it were not for Dr. Anthropologist's personality, he could be much more effective. They also appealed to Dr. Resident on the basis of the mystique of medicine and the split between M.D. and Ph.D., and asked that he sever this relationship.

The climax came in July when pressures on the other *Crier* consultants and its working staff produced resignations of two staff members and an editorial consultant. They were announced at a news conference.

As a result of the public resignations, the *Crier* was dispossessed from the church basement, but found a new home in a Methodist mission. Two of the society's key workers became contributing editor and staff editor.

In the minds of many persons of Irish-Catholic background, the *Crier* was now identified as a newspaper printed by and for Protestants, dealing directly with Protestant Negroes. Following the appearance of the first issue of the *Crier* from the Methodist headquarters, all Catholic interest and priestly involvement with the *Crier* ended. So did their efforts to establish the community psychiatry project.

The *Crier* suddenly found itself the "in" paper among professionals and intelligentsia. During the week of the resignations a score of new subscriptions came in from middle-class, white, university types.

The issues raised by the *Crier* dealt with City Hall inaction on the Community Action-War on Poverty front, failure to deal with slum housing and slumlords, failure to provide recreation facilities for the poor, lack of medical care facilities, an attack on the Community Chest-supported agencies for being too middle-class, and criticism of the County Welfare Department for its handling and distribution of surplus food to the poor. New subscriptions averaged about ten to fifteen per week.

At the Department of Psychiatry, and at the Medical College, the reaction was sharply different. One psychiatrist reacted to the *Crier* and its criticism of some of the agencies in the community headed by professionals in psychology by directly asking Drs. Resident and Anthropologist, "How can you do that to Dr. ———" and he named the director of an agency criticized by the *Crier*. On the other hand, many of the physicians in the College subscribed to the *Crier* and some lent moral support to Drs. Resident and Anthropologist.

One controversy was to make Drs. Resident and Anthropologist *personae non gratae* with the County Medical Society. In July 1965, the *Crier* ran a story about the unavailability of doctors in the poverty areas. The newspaper said, however, that poor people who had no doctors could call the Emergency Panel telephone number provided by the County Medical Society. In several succeeding issues the newspaper gave the number and names of the doctors on call.

The County Medical Society reacted by charging "abuses" of the emergency service and that as a result the listing in the public telephone book was going to be changed. Its executive secretary recommended that persons needing emergency service utilize the emergency service at one of the local hospitals. Under this arrangement, $5.00 is paid to the doctor and $5.00 to the hospital as a minimum visit charge.

Persons at the medical college would persistently ask Drs. Resi-

dent and Anthropologist whether they couldn't "control" the material
that went into the paper. Their response, that they did not set editorial
policy but only contributed technical assistance, was greeted with dis-
belief.

During these months, Drs. Resident and Anthropologist were
also completing the formal applications for the day hospital project
and the Medical College Anti-Poverty Health Project.

The day hospital proposal was completed in July and submitted to the county Mental Health Board, but not until September
did a meeting between the mayor, Drs. Marshall, Resident, and
County Psychiatrist take place. Drs. Marshall and Resident had agreed
before the meeting that their goal was to force the Mayor and Dr.
County Psychiatrist to make a definite decision as to whether the day
hospital proposal was to be presented to the Mental Health Board.
They believed that Dr. County Psychiatrist was blocking the proposal
and that, if the mayor knew the facts, he would break the deadlock.

During the meeting, Dr. Marshall stressed the need for such a
psychiatric facility in the county and the fact that the means were now
at hand to fill the need. After patiently listening to the tale of need,
interrupted by numerous telephone calls, the Mayor benignly asked
what he "could do" for Drs. Marshall and Resident. He was asked
to act on his earlier promise that he would have the county psychiatrist
call a meeting of the county Mental Health Board to consider the proposal and act on it in time for the Board of Supervisors to vote funds
for the establishment of the day hospital, which would permit the
county to receive the state and federal matching funds.

Blandly, the mayor denied that he had any authority to tell
the county psychiatrist what to do. He pointed out that the county
psychiatrist was a county employee and he, the mayor, only had charge
of the city. Dr. Resident pointed out that at the previous meeting he
had "directed" the county psychiatrist to call just such a meeting. The
mayor angrily replied, "I don't direct him to do anything." At this
point Dr. Marshall asked Dr. Resident to leave the office with him.
Apparently, the "walk-out" precipitated a hurried conference between
the mayor and the county psychiatrist, because as Drs. Marshall and
Resident were in the anterooms, the county psychiatrist rushed out
with the news that there would be a Mental Health Board Meeting
in three weeks. (At that meeting, the board was to say it was in gen-

eral agreement with the principles of a day hospital, but would like more information concerning location, staffing, patients, and so on. Dr. Resident promised that the details would be forthcoming.)

The reaction of the Department of Psychiatry to this meeting and the subsequent meeting with the board was one of surprise. Dr. Resident was also criticized at this point for having insufficient experience to become the director of the day hospital. It was suggested that Dr. Resident was being pushed too rapidly and was losing his interest in individual psychotherapy in favor of community psychiatry. In response to the volume of criticism along these lines, Dr. Resident made an arrangement in a hospital outside the county that would provide him with additional experience.

On his return to Northeast, Dr. Resident met with officials of the state to inform them of the progress of the day hospital proposal for the county and to get assurances that matching state funds would indeed be forthcoming. The reaction was one of pleased cooperation. The Commissioner of Mental Health said he had been concerned about the county's failure to provide adequate mental health services. He said that if the county would come through with funds the state would almost certainly match them. He gave Dr. Resident supporting documents and material to help him in giving additional information to the County Mental Health Board.

Dr. Resident then prepared another supporting document for the Mental Health Board, which he sent to the board early in January, anticipating a board meeting early that month.

When Dr. Marshall returned from out-of-town and was shown the letter to the Mental Health Board and the supporting documentation, his reaction was violent. He accused Dr. Resident of sending material that he had not reviewed. He would not accept Dr. Resident's explanation of urgency. His primary objections were to two possibly injudicious remarks in Dr. Resident's letter.

After the original meeting with OEO in Washington, Drs. Resident and Anthropologist initiated an intensive round of meetings with individuals and agencies. In the course of four days they met with and reinforced earlier contacts with some dozen agencies and groups of all sorts. Follow-up meetings for the next weeks were set.

All of these people and the organizations they represented were told that the medical college was in the process of drafting a proposal for a demonstration project to provide broadly based health services for the poor and their cooperation was enlisted. During this "touching-base" operation, most of the organizations contacted expressed their desire to be part of such a venture. There was one important rebuff, however; it came from Father Eggleston, Coordinator of the Bishop's Economic Opportunity Program for the Roman Catholic Diocese. In a letter that was brought to Dr. Resident's attention, and that Father Eggleston apparently sent to all the Catholic organizations contacted by Drs. Resident and Anthropologist, the priest informed the organizations that because of some strange irregularities it would seem best not to commit themselves to the program.

This latter rebuff, however, was modified by the fact that early that year, the Catholic Church appointed a new apostolic administrator who was interested in the poor. He went on a tour of the slums, joined a Negro protest march, and encouraged the local Catholics in supporting a community-based action group.

Between June 1965 and August 1966, Drs. Resident and Anthropologist worked intensively to draft a proposal for a Medical College Anti-Poverty Health Project. Shortly after the June meeting with an OEO official, they met with the Dean of the Medical College. They explained to him that the passage of the Community Mental Health legislation made the Northeast Medical College Community Psychiatric Program a venture which the Office of Economic Opportunity did not feel they could support. Drs. Resident and Anthropologist communicated to him the gist of OEO's message that the federal agency would probably look favorably upon an application from a medical college to provide broad-based medical services to the poor.

The Dean's reaction was enthusiastic. He saw several needs being met by such a program. His budget was in the red and the budget for 1966 had a built-in deficit. The poverty program was important because the 20.9 per cent overhead the college would receive amounted to about $126,000 for each year of operation. There would also be a transfer of salaries from the "hard money" of the college to the "soft money" of the grant, providing additional budget savings. Another attraction in the program was that it would do much to move the medical college into the national scene and presumably also help its image with the local residents. The Dean also felt that such a program was in the best tradition of medicine.

He felt that the existing framework of the Dean's Advisory Committee for the Community Psychiatry Project could be utilized for the Anti-Poverty project. He wished Drs. Resident and Anthropologist luck and indicated the full backing of the plan.

During this period of intense activity, Drs. Resident and Anthropologist thought they had managed to circumvent the political machine and the Roman Catholic church even though they had been rejected by the Church in the form of Father Eggleston's letter. Dr. Resident was told during this period that he should clear the program with the political machine and indeed try to get the program endorsed by the mayor. The Democratic machine was "decaying," and it was the right moment for men of good will and purpose to "bore from within," and not try to set up independently.

The machine made its opposition known through a midnight telephone call in late July from the county psychiatrist to Dr. Resident, in which he predicted that Dr. Resident was going to ruin his career by attempting to push through the anti-poverty program and that if he would only work with him and the mayor, something good might happen. He again brought up the *Crier* as an informant for the city administration. He concluded by saying that he had lived here all his professional life and realized that nothing could be done outside the machine, and that if Dr. Resident really wanted to do something he should "play ball."

Reinforcement of the "play ball" theme came when the State Health Department Medical Director informed Drs. Resident and Anthropologist that he could not cooperate in the anti-poverty program. The state had previously been very involved with the project in trying to work out a general practitioner training program within it. In a letter, the Director said that such involvement required "the full sanction of the Department." He added that "this is not forthcoming at the moment. . . ."

Informally, Drs. Resident and Anthropologist learned that the word had gone out at the State Health Department not to get involved with the local Anti-Poverty Health Project. Still another indication of lack of local support came from the county Department of Health, which denied there was a mental health problem in the county.

Despite all these intimations of defeat, Drs. Resident and Anthropologist thought they were going to succeed because the project would obtain a grant from OEO awarded directly to a private, non-profit medical institution. They believed that if there were going to be any obstacles they would come from Washington, not from within the medical college.

In August 1965, the Northeast Medical College Anti-Poverty Health Project proposal was completed in ten copies and laid before the Dean for his signature. During the week following, feedback began to mount. Within the Department of Psychiatry there were mutterings that Drs. Resident and Anthropologist were building an "empire" for themselves. Where once the word for the project was referred to as "grandiose," now, as word of the size, quality, and feasibility of the project filtered out of the Dean's office, members of the Department of Psychiatry bandied about the term "sociopathy."

One day, in the corridors of a medical research building, Dr. Anthropologist encountered the Medical Dean and asked him about the status of the project. The Dean told him that he had received word from a trustee that the project was not acceptable to the local political machine. The Dean indicated that he was in a quandary.

Dr. Resident also met with Dr. Marshall, who told him, as a member of the Dean's committee for the project, that it was his impression that Drs. Resident and Anthropologist were personally unacceptable to the machine because of their role on the *Crier* newspaper.

Drs. Resident and Anthropologist wrote Dr. Marshall indicating that they would be prepared to resign from the project, but they predicted that their offer to withdraw would have no effect. Nothing further happened. The Dean was reportedly agonizing over the size of the project and the loss of revenue to the college. Drs. Resident and Anthropologist suggested another Director to the Dean, but this man declined. He later told Resident and Anthropologist that the project was too big and too explosive and that there were too many independent doctors involved to permit effective administration.

With the poverty program proposal in limbo, Dr. Resident resumed his efforts on the day hospital and Dr. Anthropologist his teaching and departmental work. Occasionally, in the months that followed, someone who had been in the Dean's office would comment that the proposal still lay prominently on his desk. In ensuing months, Dr. Resident was informed that there were no funds in the budget for him the subsequent year, and Dr. Anthropologist that his contract would not be renewed.

A Mental Health Center
in a General Hospital

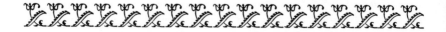

Seymour Perlin

THE JOHNS HOPKINS UNIVERSITY SCHOOL OF MEDICINE

Robert L. Kahn

THE UNIVERSITY OF CHICAGO

IX

*I*n January 1960, the authors and the nucleus of a clinical and administrative staff initiated planning for the opening of a Division of Psychiatry at the Montefiore Hospital in New York. The hospital allotted a six-month period in which to "think through" the goals and related methods appropriate to the establishment of a community mental health center program based in the psychiatric unit of a general hospital. Before the opening of the first treatment service, the outpatient unit, the team provided consultation to the rest of the hospital on a regular basis (April 1960). Shortly thereafter, a three-year study project was agreed upon, to run from October 1, 1960, to October 1, 1963.

The outpatient unit began functioning in July 1960; the inpatient unit, in October 1960; the separate day treatment unit, in October 1961. By October 1962 the full range of services of the Montefiore Community Health Center had been in operation for at least one year.

On October 1, 1963, the project officially ended and the formal follow-up period began.

185

Planning for all services was oriented to "good" patient care, the evaluation of service and administrative feedback based on such evaluation. It assumed that the physician and his patient would not be limited by any prior definition of a hospital boundary. Equal concern for the medically indigent and the medically affluent was a basic principle.

In considering possible treatment modalities, we wished as much as possible to be empathic and flexible within the community mental health center model. We reasoned that, just as the psychiatric therapist empathized with levels of need based on the health of his patient, so, we hope, the community mental health center might empathize with need by providing different modes of care in and out of the hospital.

At Montefiore, the establishment of a system of home care had already led to some redefinition of hospital boundaries. A number of physicians on the hospital attending staff conducted a group practice as a unit of the Health Insurance Plan of Greater New York. Prepaid insurance was available to approximately 25,000 subscribers, who constituted a functional and geographic group. They all lived within a postal zone area, but not all residents of that zone were eligible for the plan. That the community was concerned and interested was indicated in the fact that it leased land at nominal costs for the building of a community center, a neighborhood social and recreational resource, next to the hospital. Private patients from the area were admitted to the hospital by the attending staff. A variety of governmental reimbursements and private philanthropy made the admission of service patients possible. And for the indigent, there were also outpatient clinics of the type usually found in metropolitan hospitals.

✂ *PATIENT SELECTION* ✂

Avoiding the dichotomy of the "private" versus the "city" hospital[1] was indeed an especially happy feature for a meaningful relationship of care to an over-all "community." Defined in terms of the

---

[1] Ironically, the proposed affiliation with a municipal hospital, a community gesture in itself, was perceived as possibly leading to such a dichotomy. (One observer commented that the dichotomization of private and indigent facilities was the "reactionary" side effect of the expansion of medical care.)

spectrum of the patients it admitted, Montefiore was a community hospital. Service patients represented much more than a token percentage of hospital census. Administrative attitudes underlying such an approach were further underscored by the availability of accommodations according to clinical need.

But in selecting representatives of diverse income groups from the population-at-risk, we asked ourselves whether we were in fact defining "the community" for psychiatric service. If so, how many intakes and patients would we accept from each socioeconomic group? And would we randomize or would we select within such stratification? Was an open treatment clinic and inpatient unit for all patients served by the hospital, or for all comers in a geographic area, potentially myth or reality?

The hospital administration had decided not to fix the percentage of private versus service patients. Instead, percentages were reviewed annually to determine whether the percentage of nonprivate patients reflected the training needs and service goals of a hospital oriented to the community.

Our first task was to define the psychiatric community-to-be. Paradoxically, such planning was perceived by both psychiatrist and nonpsychiatrist as restrictive control, which interfered with a broad concept of patients and community. The team was caught between those community-minded people who perceived any definition of community as unfair, and those non-community-oriented persons who could accept any definition of community, provided it included those patients in whom they had a vested interest. Two special groups of objectors were the psychiatrists whose hospital practice consisted of diagnosis and referral, and the nonpsychiatric physicians who utilized these psychiatrists for the diagnosis and transfer (to a city or state hospital) of the "unmanageable," presumably psychotic patient.

In meeting with other outpatient clinic administrators, we were impressed anew by the usual reports that "open" or "community" clinics were being overwhelmed. But we noted that the clinics tended to be overwhelmed selectively: patient selection reflected "pressure points" in the hospital complex, traditionally relatives of trustees, referrals of hospital administrators, friends and relatives of secretaries of key personnel, and so on. At Montefiore Hospital, with approximately 3,000 personnel, all *direct* outpatient service could have been focused on the personnel and their families—roughly a population of 10,000 persons.[2]

Financing emerged as a major factor in influencing criteria for selection of patients for appropriate hospitalization and care. On the inpatient unit, private patients of the attending staff were admitted. For those with Blue Cross coverage (where authorized by the holder's policy) and various major medical contracts, full costs were often covered for a limited period of hospitalization, for example, three weeks, and then partial costs for a number of days. Although middle income patients were the beneficiaries of such contracts, hospitalization for extended periods was for the most part immediately available only for the very rich or "savings-poor" groups. However, the costs of treating special "teaching" cases were often met in part or in toto by hospital funds. In cooperation with the New York City Community Mental Health Board, we agreed to contract with the city (which in turn was reimbursed by the state within limits defined by per capita allotments) to provide a given number of inpatients treatment days. The city representatives would then work out a formula of repayment by the patient whenever possible. (Interestingly, the payment was less than cost.) Roughly 50 per cent of the "beds" were contracted for in this manner. Treatment of the inpatient under this contract was limited to ninety days per year, beginning with the first day of hospitalization; necessary extension periods, usually one month in duration, were often permitted. Thus, on the inpatient unit and, to a greater degree, on the day patient unit, the ninety-day period was an important factor in treatment programming; but perhaps equally important was the increasing emphasis on adequate and available outpatient treatment.

Later on, similar New York City Community Mental Health Board contracts for providing day and night hospitalization were formalized. But the lack of medical insurance contracts that would provide day or night hospitalization for middle income patients was certainly a factor in patient selection for these units.

The issue of medical responsibility for outpatient treatment

---

[2] An interesting perspective was gained from the personal pressure of Health Insurance Plan personnel who, although finding outpatient care too expensive for their own prepayment plan, saw the hospital as assuming such responsibility. Relevant data from insurance plans checking feasibility of limited outpatient (private) care were too recent for practical application to the situation. Services to union membership and to student mental hygiene clinics were the most frequently cited examples of medical responsibility for the psychiatric outpatient treatment of functional groups.

is a matter of priorities. This is true of both functional groups, and of geographic groups. Such priorities existed for both direct and indirect consultation and services. For example, a priority possibility was the assumption of responsibility for all present and former patients in the hospital wards and clinics. Since the average stay in this 662-bed hospital was a few weeks and the number of outpatients was, for the most part, limited only by hospital facilities, the potential pool of a presumably higher-than-average risk population was considerable.[3] Congruent districting of health services by both medical and psychiatric facilities would have obviated the *apparent* dilemma in choosing between direct community referrals to the psychiatric outpatient unit and referrals from the inpatient and outpatient units of the other medical specialties. To the degree that disparity of commitment occurred, supplementary resources were necessary.[4]

Other clinics took many ways out of the selection dilemma—the closed intake, the waiting list, selection of the "neediest" patient. Frequently, there was a tendency to reject the problem as administrative rather than clinical or to ignore it altogether. Usually selection seemed to hinge on the "suitable" case[5]—that is, the choice only of cases suitable for training purposes or amenability to psychiatric therapy. But even in treatment centers of such viewpoint, selective pressures from personnel and their families often created a dominant treatment group outside of such explicit selection criteria as IQ, education, and age.

Choosing the "sickest" or "most deserving" seemed an unwieldy dead end that would serve only to rationalize supply and demand. A large "floating" population of deserving psychiatric cases was certainly known to exist. The psychiatric staff had a sense of community responsibility. But again, how to choose!

---

[3] No discussion will be attempted here of psychiatric clinic patients, seen previously in another division of the hospital, whose needs could not be met because of insufficient contact with patient or family due to the distance of residence from the clinic.

[4] For municipal or state health facilities, commitment is assumed. But here, too, districting may vary according to specialty and according to working relationships of Departments of Health to Departments of Mental Hygiene or equivalents.

[5] We recognized early that our orientation had additional roots in the utilization for training of a heterogeneous and inclusive patient population. However, cases could be differentially assigned to resident and paid clinic staff, as required for teaching purposes.

⚓ *COMMUNITY SELECTION* ⚓

A reasonable community mental health center approach seemed to lie in the choice of the hospital-neighborhood, often overlooked as well as overshadowed by the medical center in its midst.[6] At the beginning, there was only limited recognition that such an approach would enhance teaching and research as well. However, such objectives were always very much a part of overall goals. It was quickly decided that *only* the outpatient clinic would restrict its services geographically. We were quite pessimistic about the ratio of needs to all resources—outpatient, day patient, and inpatient. Certainly, the outpatient clinic was seen as a sizeable undertaking for the medically indigent of the community.[7]

All other psychiatric units would be utilized for private and service, neighborhood and non-neighborhood patients.[8] However, neighborhood patients were to get priority when this was clinically indicated. For non-neighborhood inpatients and day patients requiring transitional care, treatment and follow-up would be provided by these units on an outpatient basis for a period of up to three months. It was agreed, too, that consultation and liaison would be provided without reference to geographic residency for all personnel and for the inpatients and outpatients of the other divisions of the hospital. The di-

---

[6] We were not ready to enter into a formal or informal "contract," but were feeling a sense of medical responsibility for this geographic community. We were ready to contract with segments, or institutions within the community whose purpose was providing consultation services, as well as with individuals referred from the area.

[7] Application was made to the New York City Community Mental Health Board for reimbursement; while the hospital received matching funds for personnel, capital costs for land and maintenance were borne entirely by the institution. Patient fees (scaled down to no-charge) were deducted equally from the matching funds.

As usual, the total amount was short of the eventual cost. A not atypical experience in such budgeting is the retrospective view that larger sums would have been matched initially, but that later increases in cost would not be matched, but instead borne entirely by the voluntary agency.

[8] The geographic restriction for one unit seemed always to imply, for many of the nonpsychiatric staff, restriction for the other units. The implicit restrictions, which were, in fact, more limiting, evoked much less reaction than the explicit.

visions included: anesthesiology, laboratory, medicine, neoplastic, neurology, neurosurgery, pediatrics, psychiatry, pulmonary, rehabilitation medicine, social medicine, and surgery. Supplementary specialty liaison outpatient clinics were envisaged as part of the treatment program.

Our relationship was with the individual patient or sometimes with the family as patient, or with the agency which assumed primary responsibilty for the patient. However, the feeling of medical responsibility for the neighborhood was emerging.

But we needed further information about this "neighborhood-community" as the "sense of contract" became more imminent—for example, geographic size and location, number of residents, and prevalence of known "patients" at some point of their interaction with hospitals or clinics. As noted, other units in the hospital had related to geographic entities. The Montefiore Health Insurance Plan Group had related its services to a postal zone; the Montefiore Home Care Program related its services primarily to a "within travel distance" criterion. Other units related services to what were primarily functional groups—for example, the Employees Health Service.

We undertook the analysis of descriptive data of our neighborhood. Because of the scarcity of funds and personnel we could not undertake a mental health survey.[9] Survey data from the U.S. Census Bureau were available for the Bronx County and for the subdivisions. The largest units, Health Districts, are composed of Health Areas, which are aggregations of contiguous census tracts.[10]

In recent years, both city and state agencies have compiled specialized mental health information based on these subdivisions. The New York State Department of Mental Hygiene provided annual Health Area statistics on admissions to state hospitals and terminations

[9] Only very few extrapolations could be made from surveys of other neighborhoods—differing in so many ways. Further, such surveys always seemed limited in differentiating symptom presence, impairment and treatment criteria. Response to *available* services would certainly vary markedly by "community" and this was usually not examined in the surveys known to us.

[10] Health Areas were convenient statistical units for tabulation of health and social data in addition to the demographic information obtained from census figures. The New York City Department of Health has recorded vital statistics for these population units since 1929, and computes on this basis such rates as venereal disease and infant mortality. Other city agencies provide additional social information by Health Area, such as data on juvenile delinquency and public assistance furnished by the New York City Youth Board.

from psychiatric clinics, with additional data such as age, sex and diagnosis of psychiatric patients available on request. The New York City Community Health Board has a program of obtaining Health Area statistics on inpatient treatment other than in state hospitals.

A hospital neighborhood defined by size, location and number of people and surveyed relevantly by a number of reporting agencies seemed an ideal choice for a Community Mental Health Center program; and thus Health Area 4.10, a geographic and statistical unit, was selected as "the community." A desirable feature of this selection was the potential for using an adjoining Health Area as a control or comparison area for certain efforts. Future planning, involving an affiliation with a city hospital, indicated the possibility of applying our program on the larger scale of the Health District.

The Montefiore Hospital is located in Health Area 4.10. This Health Area constitutes approximately one square mile, bounded on the north by a cemetery and a park, and on the east, west, and much of the south by major parkways. In the center of the area is a large recreation field and playground. Approximately 85 per cent of the people in the sixty-block area live in large apartment houses. It is thus mainly residential in character.

Three public and two parochial schools, twelve churches and synagogues, and one public library serve the area, which also has thirty-nine physicians' offices and two licensed proprietary nursing homes.

The 1960 census indicated a total Health Area population of 31,242,[11] almost four thousand fewer than reported in 1950. There had been an upward shift in age of the population in the last ten years, the proportion of persons sixty-five and over having doubled until they now constitute 15 per cent. The percentage of the widowed or divorced also rose. Twenty-two per cent were seventeen years of age or younger. The nonwhite population was less than 1 per cent. Twenty-seven per cent were foreign born; 39 per cent, native born of foreign-born parents; 34 per cent, native born of native-born parents. In de-

[11] The psychiatric literature increasingly refers to Community Mental Health Centers for 100,000 and outpatient clinics for 50,000. No attempt was made to consider the relationship of the size of the Health Area to larger issues of numbers and size of units planned for "total" coverage of the city. If the Health Area had contained 50,000 people, we probably would have assumed the same Health Area. A larger Health Area *might* have led us to restrict our assumed responsibility to several census tracts within a Health Area.

creasing frequency, the countries of origin of the foreign born *plus* first generation native-born children were: Russia (and Poland), 42 per cent; Austria and Germany, 16 per cent; Ireland, 11 per cent; Italy, 9 per cent; all others, 22 per cent. While there was a wide range in socioeconomic status in the population, there were relatively few at either extreme, and the distribution was somewhat disproportionate in an unward direction: In the 1960 census, the model family income was $5,000–5,999 per year, and in 1950, the median years of school completed was 10.6, compared with 8.9 for the Bronx and 9.6 for New York State as a whole.

℀ THE PROGRAM ℀

All Health Area referrals were systematically evaluated by a central intake team. Data from the clinical interview with patients and their families were routinely recorded and subsequently transcribed on IBM cards. Much of the personal and family information was organized according to census format.

The intake process and its recording began with the "message" to the receptionist, psychiatrist, or other personnel. The report of the clinical examination was dictated and recorded as such. Psychological testing was done systematically as part of the evaluation. All patients and their available relatives were also given a number of psychological evaluative procedures.[12]

For certain information, the "best" question was not always chosen or was not always asked in the "best" way. Rather, the focus of the procedure for both clinical and research goals was comparative information between the patient and the population from which he had been drawn. This also permitted comparisons to special groups within the population—for example, those who had been admitted to the state hospital from the Health Area, those who had been delinquent, and so on. Consequently, additional questions were presented in a form similar to those utilized by other agencies, such as the New York State Department of Mental Hygiene. The intake basic data form thus contains questions basic to two or more coding systems.

To focus on the choice of the appropriate mode of care in or out of the hospital, members of the intake team reviewed case recom-

---

[12] These procedures included a symptom check list, modifications of the F and CMI scales, Rorschach, WAIS or WISC, TAT and Figure Drawings.

mendations. At weekly intake meetings clinical judgments—such as the decision to hospitalize—were not held for the meeting, but the *decision* was reviewed. Emphasis on diagnosis quickly gave way to another type of presentation, which evaluated such factors as the timing of the patient's crisis, tolerance of the family and others for deviance, financing, mode of referral, the issue of admissions of persons in social crises, and alternative levels of care in and outside of the Division's facilities.

An interesting early experience was the weekend "social admission" of patients, especially the elderly. Although oriented to the clinical relevance of the "weekend crisis" for patients admitted to all levels of hospitalization, members of an intake conference seemed more willing than participants in the clinical conference to confront and think through the issue of staff coverage as a critical factor in weekend intake.

The need for traditional clinical conferences was as great as ever and was provided for by the various clinical units.[13] The very process of designating a "contact" as a patient and deciding the mode of hospitalization and care proved an important learning experience for both junior and senior staff. Decisions were intimately linked to the conceptualization and creation of the clinical resources. The staff acquired more "feel" for the community: who is and who is not emerging as a patient; who remains symptomatic in the community and does not function, and who has symptoms in the community but does continue to function. The staff became aware of the resources of the community and their use, the kinds of services that were lacking, and, beyond the lacks, the opportunity to create resources.

Ultimately the Division of Psychiatry consisted of an inpatient unit, a day and night hospital and an outpatient unit. Some cases were assigned to a home-care program. In addition, the Division provided psychiatric services to all other hospital divisions.

In July 1960, the outpatient unit was opened. A twenty-four-hour "open clinic" used for emergency and related brief therapy (un-

---

[13] There was a felt need for this separate conference, which focused material in terms of the decision-making process. As time went on, this conference could have been combined with the clinical conference were it not for the community research project. Nevertheless, such a focused conference may be periodically needed to review the decision-making process.

der ten visits) was staffed by intake and outpatient personnel. The outpatient unit included both adult and children's clinics.

Over the three years, special services were devised and abandoned: a separate psychopharmacology clinic was dropped in favor of consultation by specialized personnel; an "extended outpatient" unit, consisting of the usual outpatient service plus occupational therapy in the hospital, was a structured organization for a period. Often there was remarkable flexibility by all concerned in developing a level of care, but often also equal rigidity in abandoning a level of care. Utilization of a "new program" often resulted in staff opposition to Divisional review, which indicated other approaches might serve the same goals better or more economically.

The logistics of outpatient care often break down in the face of continued care or after-care of day patients or inpatients. In our experience, a useful tradition was for the ward staff to maintain responsibility for the discharged patient for a minimum of three months; thereafter, the outpatient unit was responsible for any necessary treatment. Exceptions were always made for clinical and teaching purposes. By shifting the tradition to three months after discharge, we were impressed by the number of doctor-patient "contracts" that were completed. If transfer had occurred at the time of exit from the ward, in our opinion, the "contract" would have had to begin over again. For example, for the patient who had received three months of inpatient care, goals for community residence might very well be achieved within the next three months; if transfer occurred at discharge, a six-month period was often essential for creating, working on, and completing the new doctor-patient "contract."

In October 1960, the inpatient unit was opened. This service could treat up to thirty male and female patients at any one time. Eight "beds" were reserved for night patients. Set up as a therapeutic community, its approximation to such a model varied considerably with each administrator. Patients and staff met daily to discuss problems of mutual significance. Separate staff meetings usually focused on the role of staff members in eliciting or responding to patient behavior. Each patient was assigned to a psychiatric resident or staff psychiatrist for individual psychotherapy. The frequency of sessions was determined by the individual treatment plan, but three sessions a week was the average. Flexibility of staff roles was encouraged where it seemed to enhance treatment. For instance, nurses often worked with patients in occupational therapy or recreation. All treatment was programmed to include the use of the general hospital community facilities.

A separate day unit, established in October 1961, had a capacity of twenty patients. This program, too, was based on therapeutic community concepts. On this unit, the patient's ability to continue living part time in the community and the lack of opportunity to withdraw into the inpatient role made it easier for him to engage in activities in the community.

Since each level of care had been added at intervals of approximately a year, some analysis of their separate impact on overall goals was possible. In October 1962, all services were "seasoned," and in October 1963, a study follow-up of the three-year operation began. The subsequent course of individuals seen in the Health Area intake process is under study.

In the original plan of clinical facilities, a transitional ward for medical and psychiatric patients was contemplated. In part, such a ward was seen as a means of enlarging the relatively limited inpatient census of the Division of Psychiatry. No such ward eventuated for the ulcer patient with depressive symptoms or the schizophrenic patient who had suffered a coronary infarct. However, a medical ward was revamped to include additional clinical-teaching facilities for psychiatrist and nonpsychiatrist for the evaluation of the psychological aspects of medical disease. Liaison to the other divisions consisted of direct extensions of clinical staff service plus semiautonomous and fully autonomous liaison units.

These dealt primarily with teaching and consultation on a diagnosis and referral basis, as indicated, rather than with problem-solving. The application of community psychiatry techniques was limited to more closely aligned specialties, such as physical medicine and rehabilitation, except in cases of ward "epidemics" of emotional disease, such as reactions to a sudden spurt in deaths on a neoplastic service, or the reactions of a group of patients completing a medical-research project to the loss of coverage of the cost of treatment.

In providing treatment on these units, we became impressed with the dichotomy between treatment and rehabilitation. We seemed to be mouthing the maxim, "Rehabilitation begins with treatment," but at the same time often prescribed *post-discharge* measures for rehabilitation. Our prior clinical experience seemed to indicate that the healthiest and the sickest are the likeliest to bridge the gap between the medical and nonmedical institution: the healthiest managed to travel the route on their own; the sickest were usually led by the hand. Although more research is needed to explore the percentage of drop-outs, we became aware that it was partly a problem of appropriate timing of rehabilitative intervention, even though nonmedical resources usually kept out of the medical institutions. The very real fears of role dilution, power to absorb, weakening of services—whatever their merits—run counter to possibility of providing those techniques of rehabilitation offered by nonmedical agencies early in the treatment. The argument usually boils down to the question of who is on top of the power pyramid and the absorption under medical leadership of nonmedical functions or vice versa. Under such circumstances, consultation is often used to maintain distance, the assumption being that any administrative involvement is, *ipso facto,* unnecessary because of the presence of consultation. Thus, consultation or "liaison" often excluded alteration of administrative structure. Obviously, alteration or even parallel administrative structure *is* more complicated for staff; the assumption cannot be that what is "good" or convenient for staff is necessarily good for patients. However, overlapping administrative structures may in fact reduce costs, lessen the number of conferences, and with practice even prove convenient for staff.

Growing emphasis at Montefiore on prevention and rehabilitation brought the recognition of the need for relating the clinical psychiatric resource to health, education, and welfare institutions in the community. Treatment per se is difficult to separate from prevention and rehabilitation. Thus, the hospital and the Community Mental Health Center evolved as a nodal point in a network of community agencies, such as schools, social, recreational, and family agencies. Within this context, the medical facility was developing both direct and indirect commitments.

While the hospital may focus on treatment, prevention and rehabilitation may be dealt with by other agencies, themselves differentiated into separate social, recreational, educational, or vocational services. Typically, the various kinds of community activities dealing with mental health and illness were fragmented among different types of agencies or institutions. Such fragmentation created problems in providing integrated assistance.

For its part, the medical setting provided diverse and flexible modes of treatment, including inpatient, outpatient, day and night hospital, self-care and home-care units. In addition to the type of care available in the hospital, however, our patient applicants required a multiplicity of services that were typically dealt with in separate non-medical settings.

Many difficulties arose in referral from one institution to another. There were long waiting lists or other administrative difficulties that led to the patient's dropping out or failing to receive the appropriate service at the appropriate time. Very often the patient's needs did not coincide with the services offered by the institution to which he was referred, but fell in between the criteria for rendering service of each institution. Even when needs were defined as mutually acceptable, eventually they often became unacceptable *by default* due to the time required to deal with scheduling procedures relating to priorities, vacancies, and intake processes. Institutions tended to be jealously protective in defining the type of service they offered as an assumed prerequisite for their optimum functioning. Sheltered workshop personnel felt they could not provide the best vocational experience for psychiatric patients in a day hospital atmosphere, while the staff of our day hospital felt somewhat uncomfortable in spending time on job training.

But, in the Community Mental Health Center, the community mental health team was committed to bring institutions and disciplines to bear on the patient and his needs. Let no one entering community psychiatry feel that this is done with ease. One possible reason is that there is no community mental health program blueprint that might delineate appropriate administrative models. Still, overall goals do permit guidelines for creating and examining administrative constructs for care-giving. In our opinion, the overlapping of medical and non-medical institutions is worthy of study.

Overlapping seemed to be an alternative to separating that may ease the relationships between institutions. It permits a focus on the patient-applicant and his needs rather than on the type of service. It can be achieved by sharing key staff and the cost of salaries by both medical and nonmedical institutions. The shared staff then can relate primarily to those patients whose needs required the simultaneous participation of both institutions and who were designated as joint clients of both.

Overlapping was achieved between the Community Mental Health Center at Montefiore Hospital and three nonmedical institutions, a neighborhood community center,[14] a local public school,[15] and a social agency concerned with children and their families.[16] In addition, an overlap program with a community rehabilitation agency was sought. A sheltered workshop, jointly sponsored by the Altro Workshops, Incorporated, and the hospital, and then continued under the aegis of the Divisions of Psychiatry, Rehabilitation, and Social Medicine, provided a paid vocational experience for psychiatric and rehabilitation patients in the hospital setting.

The joint program offered a greater variety of potentially therapeutic social and recreational activities than can be provided in either institution alone. Activities at the center have implications for "health" that are different from similar activities conducted at the hospital. The patient can experience a more meaningful set of peer interactions and reality situations than he can when therapy is conducted solely in a unit of a hospital or among peer relationships limited only to other patients. Early experience or re-experience in social and recreational roles is in accord with the concept that rehabilitation should begin when treatment is instituted.

To this end a number of groups were formed whose purpose was to serve as a bridge between the hospital and community culture. Among the variables manipulated to achieve integrated experiences were: the place where the group met—hospital or community center; leadership of the group—medical or center personnel; group composition—varying ratios of patient members to center members; group purposes—an experience designated as therapeutic or as social-recreational.

These variables of place, leadership, composition, and purpose created transition groups that varied in expected intensity of interpersonal relationships, toleration of deviance in behavior and degree of interaction between patients and center members. Many patients participated in the center's regular groups; about one-third of the outpatients did so.

To realize the rehabilitation potential of the community center, we had to overcome resistance from our psychiatric staff. They were reluctant to refer patients to center programs, and even more reluctant to assume psychiatric leadership of integrated activities at the center.

---

[14] Mosholu-Montefiore Community Center, Bronx, New York.
[15] Bureau of Child Guidance program at P.S. 94, Bronx, New York.
[16] Jewish Board of Guardians, New York, New York.

When the patients were off the floor, the nurses felt deserted—a fact noted and commented upon by patients and supervisors alike. Psychiatric residents, preoccupied with "formal" therapy, tended to regard social rehabilitation with disdain. The relationship between nursing, occupational therapy and social group work activities had to be closely scrutinized. The more usual practice of referring patients to a social recreational facility only after hospital discharge was critically reviewed by the social work staff. Eventually, staff members both supported and participated in the joint program. Both nurses and occupational therapists helped to lead activities in the hospital and in the center. Residents and staff psychiatrists recognized the value of the program and supported it.

The recreational activity groups for day hospital patients, although similar in many respects to the inpatient activity groups, retained certain characteristics of the less integrated community center groups in their emphasis on total group activity and structure. Because the typical day patient had maintained more of his social roles, his group experiences could generally begin at a point of greater integration.

The most significant day-to-day overlap between the Division of Psychiatry and the community center was provided by the joint staff member—a group social worker who received one-half his salary from each institution. This ensured his status as a staff member in both units. As the program developed, group work students were assigned to the joint program.

While the emphasis had been on the development of the community center as a transitional facility, the overlap program also enabled its use at another level of treatment. At intake, the patient-applicant was, on occasion, referred directly to appropriate peer-group activities in the community center as prescribed therapy, instead of more conventional treatment within the psychiatric facility. The joint group worker coordinated the integration of the patients. The group worker was also used as a mental health consultant for emotional problems of the nonpsychiatric center population. Often his work took the form of an indirect consultation with other group leaders. When appropriate, he arranged for psychiatric referral and evaluation at the hospital.

In extending the overlap basis of operations of the Montefiore Community Mental Health Center, the same arrangement was effected with a local public school. The center and the school jointly appointed a psychologist and shared her salary. The psychologist served half time in the school and half in the center. To qualify, she had to possess the qualifications and pass all the tests for each staff position.

Placing one psychologist in two institutions resulted in better information and communication, greater administrative and clinical flexibility, better timing, comprehensiveness, follow-up and prevention. The liaison psychologist had access to all records and conferences as well as information from personal discussions with other staff members. She could conform to the confidentiality requirements of both institutions, yet minimize the communication difficulties that ordinarily exist between cooperating agencies. As a trained person, understanding the modes of operation of both institutions, the psychologist provided a greater depth of information. Thus, this staff member gave the clinic staff detailed data on peer-group classroom relationships, and, conversely, helped teachers to understand a child's behavior by interpreting relevant clinical information. In each setting, she clarified ambiguous information from the other that might otherwise be misunderstood.

The flexibility of clinical approach afforded by the overlap was noteworthy. We could work with the child or the parent in the school or in the psychiatric clinic, or even with one in the school and the other in the clinic. This permitted making the clinical decision on the basis of the needs of the individual. For example, a child's problem in the school situation might best be dealt with by placing the mother in treatment. Instead of having to search around for an appropriate referral, the psychologist, a Montefiore staff member, arranged for intake at the clinic, knowing that treatment or treatment placement was assured. Similarly, the liaison afforded a maximum opportunity for comprehensiveness of service. This applied not only to the diverse psychiatric treatments offered, but to the other hospital resources, such as electroencephalograms, evaluation of speech problems, and so on.

As coordinator of evaluation and treatment, the psychologist was able to interpret the psychiatric clinic's findings and recommendations to the school personnel. As part of the school staff, the psychologist saw to it that the clinic's recommendations were carried out; as part of the clinic staff, the psychologist provided information on the continued course of the child in school.

In the early days of the program, the liaison psychologist experienced varying reactions from school staff, from those who saw her as relieving them of all responsibility for their problem children, to a small minority who had no dealings with her at all. In a relatively short time, the psychologist established excellent working relations with the school with maximum utilization of her skills and services. In our opinion, a significant factor contributing to this relationship was the psychologist's position as a regular staff member of the school system rather than a "volunteer" coming in from an outside agency. In addition to the administrative aspects of being a staff member, such as having access to records, the psychological consequences included a greater identification with the program on the part of other school personnel. Experience with this program also modified attitudes among the hospital staff, making them much more aware of the school resources available to them and possible ramifications of their work in the school setting.

Prevention may well have been the most important aspect of the overlap program. The psychologist was alerted to disturbed families with children in the school. Such observations permitted early intervention as needed. Often, the timing of the intervention seemed to be critical. Either the school or the clinic or both might be chosen as the setting. The overlapping position permitted earlier or later timing in the most appropriate combination of setting and resources and with adequate follow-up.

The Jewish Board of Guardians[17] and the Division of Psychiatry established a joint Children's Clinic in the outpatient unit of the Division of Psychiatry. Its personnel were simultaneously on the staffs of the two institutions, providing full professional and administrative integration. Since the two agencies shared the cost of the program, there was no split in the salary of a particular individual. The Jewish Board of Guardians provided the salary for staff psychiatrists, child psychiatry fellows in their fourth or fifth year of psychiatric training, a psychologist and senior supervisory and training staff. Montefiore paid for full-time social workers, additional part-time psychiatry and psychology and secretarial services, and provided the space and maintenance for clinic facilities.

---

[17] A social agency that has specialized in providing therapy for disturbed children for over half a century. While it has emphasized outpatient treatment, this agency has established four residential treatment centers, dealing with a variety of age groups and psychological disorders.

Overlap permitted a comprehensive therapeutic approach to the total family. There was no need to "coordinate" family care between several unrelated institutions. Hospitalization for a parent, therapy for a child and service for the home setting could all be provided by such a joint service. Overlap facilitated certain services between the two agencies. Thus Montefiore admitted children from the Jewish Board of Guardians residential treatment centers who required hospitalization. The Jewish Board of Guardians, in turn, provided to the Division of Psychiatry admission privileges to the residential treatment centers, and additional intensive outpatient therapy at its Bronx office. The overlap program of these two institutions thus enhanced the opportunity for integrating the medical and social agency approaches to mental disorders.

℀ PROGRAM ANALYSIS ℀

From the start research evaluation audited the program and fed back the result. The ongoing interaction between clinical and research operations provided the means by which care was reviewed, trends were noted, units were abandoned or created, and goals refocused.[18] We found it useful to place a pin noting each contact on the map of the Health Area. The pin's color represented the mode of contact or care. Symbols on the head of the pin represented age. There was *direct* registration of contacts on the map and index cards.

On a pilot basis, liaison registration permitted the crossfiling of interdivisional consultations (stamped by hospital metal identification tab) according to Health Area. The possibility that such patients would later appear in the intake process was of especial value for estimating future needs. Other research included comparisons and follow-up of intake and non-intake patients with diagnosis of ulcer, ulcer and depression, and depression.

In the three-year study period, October 1, 1960, to September 30, 1963, plus the period July 1, 1960, to September 30, 1960, 622 patient-applicants were seen in the intake evaluation process. There were 163 applicants in 1960–61, 222 in 1961–62, and 212 in 1962–63.

[18] The limited number of examples in this section are used solely to illustrate data analysis, feedback, and feedback results and are drawn from a much larger body of Health Area data.

It should be noted that the Community Mental Health Center program was available as a service of a voluntary general hospital, Montefiore, and was not officially districted in the city and state system. These figures, therefore, are not inclusive of patient-applicants to other facilities during the study period. To this number we can add the follow-up groups seen in the liaison service to the other divisions of the Montefiore Hospital, the Bronx Municipal Hospital, New York State hospitals, plus the Bureau of Child Guidance and the Mosholu-Montefiore Community Center and others. Thus, in the comparisons between intake and total populations, recognition should be made of the fact that this is not a registry analysis of every Health Area individual's every contact within a psychiatric resource, but reflects the registration and evaluation of every Health Area contact (and when it occurs, treatment) within the Montefiore Division of Psychiatry.

The selection of Health Area 4.10 as the community to be served permitted comparison of the center's patient-applicant population with that of the total Health Area. The comparison data enabled us to evaluate continuously the extent to which we were achieving one goal: to have a comprehensive program in which the patient-applicants reflected the population at risk. We had already noted the number of aged individuals as well as the decennial shift in the relative per cent of aged individuals in the Health Area. This relative increase was due, in part, to the younger residents' leaving the area as their incomes increased. Comparative figures showed that 20.6 per cent of our intake was in the fifty-five and over age group. This group constituted 30.8 per cent of the Health Area population. New York State Clinic termination figures showed that the elderly were clearly underrepresented in similar clinics in the New York City area.

Another comparison indicated a significant disproportion by sex in the intake population. Our intake was 36.6 per cent male, 63 per cent female, whereas sex distribution in the Health Area was 46.9 per cent male, 53.1 per cent female. Epidemiological studies do not reflect such a large sex-differentiated incidence of emotional disturbance. The data thus indicate the likelihood of obstacles to the use of the facilities by wage earners as compared to dependents. Such analyses research can lead to practical policy changes, such as opening an evening clinic.

Other analyses showed that the head of a primary family and

the married person tend to be under-represented, while the primary individual and the single or divorced tend to be over-represented.

Family income analysis indicated under-representation in the higher income brackets and over-representation in the lower income brackets. This discrepancy may be based on many factors, but is consistent with the findings of other investigators that there is likely to be a greater prevalence of mental illness in the lower economic groups. In any event, the data do emphasize that the clinic serves this population.

A total of 622 evaluations were carried out. The number rose sharply between the first and second years,[19] and leveled off in the third year. Over the three-and-a-quarter-year period, 60 per cent (371) of the patient-applicants were actually assigned to a treatment unit.

During the three-and-a-quarter-year period, 74 per cent of the Health Area treatment assignments were for the outpatient unit and open clinic, with the remainder to the day hospital and inpatient units. As originally conceived, the day hospital was to separate out a segment of the patients who had previously been hospitalized. We were impressed with the addition of new categories of day patients in the third year and the reassignment of previously accepted day hospital patients to the inpatient unit. Thus after a year of functioning, the day hospital was redefined as a preventive and reparative instrument and a treatment mode in its own right, rather than as simply an alternative to full-time hospitalization. Here, too, projects for individual case studies grew out of the larger clinical-research operation.

The data also indicated that flexibility of approach to differential care resulted not only in a range of services, but also in the provision of multiple services within one unit for 12 per cent of the patients assigned to treatment. They show that services were provided in more than one unit for 18 per cent of these patients, including those whose use of different units was interspersed with periods of residence in the community. An interesting description of features of illness held in common by this group could be achieved by graphing the sequence and duration of living in and out of the hospital. Seventy per cent received a single service in outpatient, open clinic, inpatient, or day hospital units.

[19] During the second half of the first year, presentations by the staff were made at a local PTA and other lay groups in the Health Area.

Monthly average of new contacts of Health Area patients on the rolls of the outpatient unit increased steadily. The termination rate was very stable in spite of a conscientious program of case review.

In the first year, Health Area admissions were hospitalized on the average twice as long as non-Health Area patients. Case review revealed no obvious clinical issues to which the extended care could be attributed. Such differences will reflect a wide number of variables —finances of middle income groups, utilization of private services, the tendency to admit to the service patients from a stable family unit, of which there were many in the Health Area. But in addition—and especially early in such community programs—the involvement of staff in the "Health Area patient" must be considered. Such involvement may begin with the "getting them *really* well" long-stay approach, but may shift to a "revolving door" attitude.

How and by whom care was utilized went beyond mere statistical descriptions. The original data became questions for and from the community. Would applicants utilize our services in inverse proportion to distance from the hospital? The marked differences in the intake by census tract and Health Area intake established data for such a study. But in certain areas a smaller intake might nevertheless contain a higher percentage of sicker cases (at least by the criterion of subsequent hospitalization). The variables of income, religion, and so on, did not necessarily explain such findings, and such findings would affect the choice of relationship—overlapping, affiliative, consultative—with a given community resource. Earlier or different intervention yielded clinical dividends in those cases whose group mores or characteristics might delay or render ineffective the intake, where emergency and open clinic areas were significant possibilities.

"Signals" from the community were received and responded to in a variety of ways. Health Area physicians' referrals were studied according to such interests as number of referrals, level of care required for patient referrals, "appropriateness" of timing of referral. Such items could provide important cues for education and intervention.

Resources for community consultation become more efficient if they respond to "danger signals." One religious sect supplied an impressive number of patient-applicants; this sect required prior consultation with a religious leader. A nursing home made no referrals. We later discovered that its elderly patients were transferred in significant numbers directly to a state hospital. With the help of the

New York City Community Mental Health Board consultation was provided, and transitional or temporary hospitalization was offered (with guarantee of reacceptance of patient). Thus a truly preventive psychiatric program was implemented.

Much as we wished to provide consultation to a variety of community health and welfare agencies and to religious leaders, ward precinct political leaders, and others, we had to establish priorities. It was important to learn the degree to which priorities were based on preplanning statistics, general hunches, and purely arbitrary decisions. Some of the most effective consultation was given to units or agents discovered or emphasized by analysis of our registration data.

Even data perceived as almost exclusively for research were not without clinical implications. As the density of room occupancy increases, the intake admissions increase. At an occupancy rate of one or more persons per room, the intake population is significantly greater than the relative percentage of such individuals in the total population. Again, economic factors and others become relevant. Another area for research compared the intake population with the total population according to the country of origin.

Many of the techniques of community psychiatry were applicable to the intramural and extramural, geographic and functional communities served by the Montefiore Community Health Center. Such a program attempts to evaluate all contacts and to assume responsibility for follow-through either in the unit itself or elsewhere.[20] The operational definition of geographic intake reflects the equilibrium between demands and resources. This equilibrium is best understood and maintained by evaluation of patient-applicants. In emergencies, such evaluation serves as a guide to care. Liaisons with affiliated institutions may bring to the fore larger "patient-units," such as a family with many problems. Prevention becomes more meaningful. A follow-through registry linked to state hospital admission induces an appropriate humility as to the effectiveness of treatment and rehabilitation.

For those individuals who come to us we must think of both differential hospitalization and care, or if you prefer, care as a level of hospitalization or care as treatment. That is, we must not only concern ourselves with the designation of a contact as patient, but also act

---

[20] The temporary hospitalization of a "too-young" patient on the inpatient unit before adequate placement could be achieved elsewhere is a case in point.

to provide help in order to *prevent* such designation where it does not apply. Such a procedure would occur in the case of an isolated elderly individual, for whom "referral" is often a euphemism and for whom the designation of patient status in an outpatient unit may only heighten his dependency needs. The intake worker should be in a position to refer such a contact to another mode of treatment—for example, a community center, in which the functioning presence of a mental health worker, such as our shared group social worker, participates in the "strategy" of care as treatment. The elderly widow can be introduced via this social worker, or can participate in groups that have access to consultation by the shared social worker. It is essential that this worker be able to call upon immediate and effective psychiatric consultation and treatment resources as a backstop. The registry and intake follow-up thus serve a function beyond research per se— that is, thoughtful and orderly care.

Insistence on providing hospital consultation to community agency and agent may bypass the possibility of providing better administrative arrangements, which make possible better operational functioning. Such approaches are not alternatives. One must not overlook the need to alter the health and welfare institutions' provision of care by overlap practices, linking physically by structure, administratively by boards and trustees, professionally by disciplines and functionally by services.

Much has been said of *creating* levels of care, but little attention has been given to their abandonment, perhaps because successful abandonment depends on adequate information. What seems to us most basic is an emphasis on the principles of differential hospitalization and care—principles that can be equally lost in a brick-and-mortar approach or in rigid designation of "appropriate" levels. It should be noted that at first the ward was utilized for transitional day treatment and, on occasion, direct day hospital admission. Later, a separate day hospital was created for direct admission; at the end of three years, the philosophical direction was for a part-time hospitalization ward, which retained clinical-administrative responsibility for the levels of care noted. Obviously, such decisions reflect size of area, population served, staffing patterns, and finance. Again, the emphasis is on flexibility based on reasonable evaluatory feedback. Thus, the same level of hospitalization could appear, close, and reappear according to clinical needs. A level of care designated "extended outpatient" was abandoned. And a home care service was not utilized as a unit of treatment because of the small geographic area served by the day hospital and the utilization by several disciplines of home visiting and treatment (usually emergency) as part of the available program.[21]

The criteria for selection of the appropriate type or amount of hospitalization are still experimental. If we call upon the experience of staff members for supervision or consultation in the intake process, we must recognize that very few have had contact with a day treatment service, the use of night beds or the use of a ward or accident room (overnight ward) for twenty-four-hour admissions.

Knowledge of or interest in community psychiatric techniques may be especially lacking in liaison personnel. The ignoring of indirect approaches to both the patient and the larger clinical situation, which includes the ward community, will reflect, however, not only the practice of the consulting psychiatrist but also the expectations and desires of the nonpsychiatric physician. Suitable staff orientation may have to include, therefore, the consultee as well as the consultant.

Liaison limited to evaluation, diagnosis and referral, with little attention to problem-solving, often has little in common with the theories and practices of the "mainstream" psychiatrist in a community mental health center, who must come to terms with the traffic pattern of psychiatric patients within, from, and to the hospital.

The logistics of care may make it inadvisable immediately to assign consultation to community agencies, such as schools, and agents, such as religious leaders. Such "routine" assignments must be balanced against the deployment of resources according to feedback information. Such liaisons should be seen as additive, not competitive. As long as priorities must exist for personnel and services, thought is necessary.

Attention to the logistics of care will in itself make for more effective prescribing of care in an affiliated agency, intervention in waiting lists, home care therapy and multiple services in single clinical units. For in a community commitment, staff seeks to alter the hospital as well as the patient. Issues of continuity, communication between disciplines, and creation of new treatment personnel must be confronted.

The result may be crises. Facing up to moral choices in the

---

[21] Psychiatrists were utilized, however, in the Home Care Program at Montefiore for physically ill patients who very often also suffered from severe emotional disturbances.

selection of patients, new and less valued types of care for a larger number of patients, the need for feedback research in a service-oriented situation, the integration of the clinical and the administrative may all be crisis-precipitating issues. The more geographically oriented and committed the community mental health center program, the more likely the occurrence of such crises. This is especially true where such commitment is voluntarily rather than legislatively defined. The "community-contributing" program without a geographic area or functional group commitment will have an easier time of it. But the excitement and sustained sense of practicing community psychiatry may, however, be related to the commitment involved.

Community Psychiatric
Service in Paris

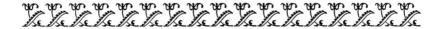

Serge Lebovici
ANCIEN MÉDECIN ASSISTANT DES HÔPITAUX DE PARIS

X

*I*n France, an act passed on March 15, 1960, governs the organization of what are called *district psychiatric activities*. Its aims are more modest than they may seem to be, namely, to ensure sufficient psychiatric facilities for every population group of 60,000 inhabitants. To-day, the act is still far from being generally implemented. Psychiatric care is still centered on the mental hospitals, which serve as its nuclei and operational bases.

In Paris, or at least in many of its wards (*arrondissements*), there have long been clinics for pediatric mental health, modeled on the organization for the prevention of tuberculosis, which has existed for many years.

The service to be described in this chapter is that of the thirteenth ward; so far, this has been an experimental service, which in its development is far ahead of the services operating in other wards of the capital.

The history of this community mental health service is a short one, dating back only to 1958, and it is difficult to give explicit reasons why the thirteenth ward was selected for its establishment. The fact is that one of the present directors of the mental health service of this ward had worked here for many years in a public first aid station for alcoholics. There was also a small mental health center serving the children of the thirteenth and of adjoining wards. Here we had the nucleus of the service that was to be established. Those who founded it had long recognized the necessity of organizing community services geographically adapted to the needs of circumscribed population groups.

The thirteenth ward, which will be described later, is one of the peripheral wards of Paris, with a population composed largely of craftsmen and artisans. Their spirit initiated many social movements in the course of the last century.

In the nineteenth century, the life of the thirteenth ward was centered on the river Bièvre, which traversed the district but which is now underground. Tanners had their workshops here. Honoré de Balzac frequently mentioned this ward in his novels and described its population as slightly on the wrong side of the law. What he described as "marriages of the thirteenth," for example, were illicit relationships, particularly between men of the nobility and the *Lorettes,* women of easy virtue. But this population organized itself into numerous local clubs for mutual aid and cultural and recreational activities. There are sports clubs, private charities, and cultural institutions (teaching music, dancing, and so on).

This fully developed pattern of active social organization seemed to be a felicitous foundation to those who decided to establish in this Paris ward a mental hygiene service for adults and children.

☙ *WARD AS SOCIAL MILIEU* ☙

The thirteenth ward is one of the twenty wards of Paris. It is situated in the southern part of the city, and its northern boundary is the Quartier Latin, or university district. The present population is 165,000, and this number is expected to increase to 175,000 in the next ten years.

The district is on the whole a poor one. Divided into four administrative quarters, like all Paris wards, the thirteenth accommodates a slightly more prosperous population in its two northern quarters, while the people of the two southern quarters are definitely at a lower socioeconomic level.

Living conditions are often mediocre, and sometimes bad. There are some exceedingly unhealthy boarding houses, and the annual census has in recent years shown that a large proportion of the apartments are still without running water. The critical limits of overcrowding are frequently reached.

At present, many of the unsanitary blocks are being demolished, and they will all in due course disappear. They are being replaced by large-scale suburban development projects, which are bringing to the thirteenth ward a younger population from a different socioeconomic level. Many of the new buildings offer not only apartments at moderate rents but flats, the inhabitants of which can become owners.

After World War I, many moderate rent quarters were built at the southern periphery of the ward. In these quarters, families who would be called asocial were allotted apartments in the post-World War I resettlement schemes. These families—now in the second and third generations—seem to be the foci from which adolescent gangs were recruited.

There are important industrial plants in the thirteenth ward, and they will probably be here for some time. Special mention should be made of an automobile plant (Panhard)—a medium-size works employing some 6,000 workers, whose families are only in part inhabitants of the district. There is also a factory manufacturing aircraft engines (SNECMA), and a sugar refinery. Throughout the ward, moreover, we find the remnants of small-scale crafts and precision industries, whose workers are still the proud representatives of a tradition of personalized manufacture. The tanneries have moved to the adjoining fifth ward.

The population represents a relatively low socioeconomic level. It is made up mainly of unskilled and skilled laborers and employees of public services. Supervising personnel and company officers are rare, as are businessmen and members of the professions.

The government has ordered the large works to move away in the next few years, and this will emphasize certain changes in the population already becoming apparent with the establishment of the large housing developments. There has already been an influx of younger families of better social, economic, and cultural background.

☙ WARD AS SOCIAL ENTITY ☙

Not too much importance should be attached to the bond between ward and inhabitants, because the division of Paris into wards
is chiefly an administrative matter. Every ward has its ward office
accommodating a government-appointed mayor. These establishments
are branch offices of a central service known as the "Préfecture de la
Seine." In the next few months this central service is itself to be divided into several subdivisions. Besides the mayor, there are politically
elected municipal councillors. The ward office includes branches of
the various central services of Paris (health services, social aid services,
child welfare and vocational guidance agencies, police services, and
so on). The National Education and Information services are not
directly subordinate to the Préfecture, but to a *département* (county)
directorate, the ward branches of which are represented by so-called
inspectors of National Education and Public Information (an inspector
for boys, one for girls, and one for preschool-age children).

The population itself lends a touch of reality to the boundaries
of the thirteenth ward; some of the aged inhabitants of this ward have
never been outside its limits. Also, some of its asocial adolescents consider the ward their own and hardly leave it to go to the city center
of Paris, although transportation facilities (particularly the underground métro) are excellent.

Yet the everyday life of the population is not oriented to the
four administrative quarters. In this respect, the actual social delimita-
tion can be discerned and various true foci have been studied. The
ward seems to be traversed by a north-south axis, the *Avenue d'Italie*
—a wide thoroughfare for high-speed traffic, which pedestrians find
relatively difficult to cross. In particular, the large department stores
along this avenue are the obvious commercial centers of attraction,
which make it unnecessary for the population to cross often to the
other side. Other centers of attraction, particularly for the sections of
the population with traditional religious ties, are the two or three
Catholic churches in the ward. Today, cinemas have no great attraction; some of them have disappeared because of insufficient business
and because the owners preferred to sell the sites to builders of housing
developments. In some of the main streets of the thirteenth, however,
there are still highly popular cinemas showing films rarely seen in the

more central Paris quarters, usually Westerns and violent detective films of American origin. These cinemas are frequented by more or less adjusted young adolescents. Families are more inclined to rely on television, which is now much in evidence in the living rooms of the thirteenth ward, unlike the rest of Paris and throughout France.

The thirteenth ward also has a relatively large number of immigrants from North Africa, particularly Algeria. Some of these have remained single and work in the factories, finding accommodation in the rather disreputable hotels of the southeast quarter. A relatively large number have married French women and settled down in the ward.

℀ HISTORY OF SERVICE ℀

A first aid station for alcoholics used to operate in the ward prior to 1958; it was established in a few small rooms that also accommodated a special clinic for the prevention of tuberculosis and constituted part of the public offices of the Préfecture de la Seine. There was also a private clinic, certain other consulting facilities, a maternity and infant care center (analogous to the Anglo-American Well Babies Clinics), and a small child psychiatry consulting center.

The starting point of the service was the establishment, in the center for alcoholics, of a general psychiatric outpatient clinic for adults.

The psychiatrist who became director of the mental health center for adults was at the time doing part-time work in the Paris city mental health department; consequently, he had the opportunity to interest the administrators of the mental health service in this project. He was also in a position to gain the attention of senior social security officials concerned with the local or general organization of this service.

This psychiatrist simultaneously promoted the foundation of a private mental health association in the thirteenth ward, to which a number of ward authorities or officials subscribed—in particular, one of the ward mayor's assistants, who was interested in problems of juvenile mental hygiene.

In view of the existence of the first-aid station for alcoholics, the National Committee against Alcoholism decided to grant the Mental Health Association a certain initial sum, and also decided to give the Association a cost-price lease on an important plot of land in a southern suburb of Paris, for a projected mental hospital for the adult patients of the thirteenth ward.

As is the rule in France, the existence of this (minimal) sum and the building ground made it possible for the central administration, the Ministry of Public Health, and the National Social Security Fund to finance, in 1958, the construction of a hospital of 165 beds, fifty of which were ready for use in 1963.

The Social Security officials were interested in the general plans submitted to them, namely, to cater to the mental health needs of a circumscribed group of the population, with emphasis on outpatient facilities so as to reduce the number of hospital admissions. The 165-bed mental hospital would allow only one bed per 1000 population—a proportion lower than that suggested by the experts of the WHO (two and one-half beds per 1000 population). The central idea was that the establishment of outpatient clinics and services would permit reduction in hospital admissions and would be more effective in terms of prevention and resocialization of mental patients.

This was the basis on which the mental health services of the thirteenth ward were organized. It was considered important to give them a special administrative structure and to make the Mental Health Association (a private association) the center of psychiatric activity, with authority to operate the institutions of this community service. For this purpose a special agreement exists between the two main sponsors, which are the Social Hygiene services for mental prevention of the Préfecture de la Seine (City of Paris) and the Social Security Service (Paris Regional Fund and the local fund for the thirteenth ward)—and, to a lesser extent, the Central Social Security Fund and the National Federation of Social Security organizations.

The structure of this organization was laid down in this agreement between the Mental Health Association of the thirteenth ward and the affiliated administrations. In the administrative council—which has a proportion of elected members—representatives of the Health Ministry are slightly in the majority. This Ministry directly subsidized the building of the mental hospital for adults and supervises the development of the undertaking. Other voting members of the council are representatives of the central Social Security agencies, who consider the thirteenth ward service an experiment, representatives of the preventive psychiatric services of the Préfecture de la Seine, and representatives of the Social Security services directly committed to the experiment (Paris Regional Fund and the local fund for the ward). Other agencies are represented because of the role they play in operating the service (Family Allocation Fund of the Paris Region). Two private foundations that have given aid to the Mental Health Association are also represented on the administrative council. They are the Fraternity of the Children of France, whose child psychiatric clinic in the thirteenth ward has remained one of the Mental Health centers, and the Rothschild Foundation, which founded and is still managing the day hospital for children.

The authorities dealing with national education, vocational guidance, social assistance, and so on, have non-voting members on the administrative council.

It must be emphasized that, because this is a very interesting innovation for Paris, public administrative accommodation has been made available, without charge, to the Mental Health Association for the everyday operation of its outpatient facilities for adults and children.

The Mental Health Association came into full development only in 1960, when the agreement described above was signed. The administrative situation is an unusual one: a private organization is financed by public funds. The idea underlying this organization was to give it, in principle, greater flexibility by permitting it to avoid some of the more rigid administrative edicts applicable to French public services. Admittedly, this hope has only partially been fulfilled, because the supervision exercised by the affiliated organizations that subsidize the operations has often been even more detailed and strict than it would have been had the service been directly subject to regulations for public services. On the other hand, the advantage of the semipublic system adopted has been that it has facilitated, at least in some cases, the engagement of subordinate staff. Unfortunately, salaries and fringe benefits have remained on the scale of the civil service, which in France is considerably below that of private undertakings; in many cases this has impeded recruiting of specialized personnel. At present this statement applies to nursing personnel for the mental hospital for adults and to the specialized social workers in the children's mental health center.

This structure is the source of some particular difficulties, budgetary difficulties that arise each year in preparing the preliminary budget or the budget for the following fiscal year. Every year the administration must, before the month of May, approve the preliminary budget for the next year. It is exceedingly difficult to make correct predictions as to developments, and they are frequently the subject of somewhat dramatic conflicts of opinion, since the authorities concerned must impose limitations in view of other immediate needs of the City of Paris.

INTEGRATION OF SERVICE

In the course of five or six years, the mental health service has gradually taken root; but this has not occurred without various vicissitudes and difficulties.

Consultations for children have always had excellent responses from the school services; that is, the social workers and special welfare workers of the schools, who in some cases also work as trained nurses. Contacts between the psychiatric social workers and the primary school headmasters are similarly being built up.

In the past three years, an attempt has been made to integrate branches of the children's mental health service as psychopedagogic units into the schools; National Education inspectors were approached and have fully associated themselves with the effort. Perhaps we should go into some detail about the trials and tribulations experienced in the relations with the National Education services. Because of their intimate connection with the schools, the children's mental health service and its clinics have for several years received their cases largely from the National Education services. As in all community services, there was at first an abundance of referrals for whom therapy would have been useless; they were generally backward children for whom special classes (as prescribed by law) were not available. It was necessary, then, to educate the school social services as to the function of a service more or less approaching a child guidance center.

The situation was not facilitated when the relationship between the mental health service and the school services became an official one. True, this relationship made it possible to establish what may be described as psychopedagogic branch units: small centers where some children can be examined and where dyslexia and dysorthography can be corrected without referring the children to the center; frequently, with the cooperation of a schoolteacher, workers from the mental health center furnish the special education required.

The existence of these psychopedagogic units also has other advantages; for example, they make it possible to provide expert advice on some difficult school situations, to give special psychotherapeutic treatment, and sometimes to undertake rehabilitation "on the spot," if the parents are not cooperative. This approach is necessary in cases where families are simply not interested in their children's school performance.

These are some of the advantages that have gradually arisen from the cooperation between school inspectors and the children's mental health service. Unfortunately, the official formalization of this cooperation has somewhat exacerbated existing difficulties between the children's mental health service and some of the school social workers and teachers. Now, with the compulsory presence of senior officials, information meetings have lost their informal, spontaneous character; they have become more administrative and the participants often hesitate to express themselves before their superiors.

Considering the difficulties that have marked the implementation of the mental health service for children, we must also mention the relations between this service and the pediatric services of the thirteenth ward. The psychiatrist of the technical teams has gradually become the consultant of mother-and-child protection services—veritable Well Babies Clinics, a number of which exist in the thirteenth ward. The psychiatrist (who is to establish relations with the pediatrician) has decided to concentrate his efforts on two of these clinics, because of their importance, the presence of physicians who in principle desire this collaboration, and the availability of specialized psychologists in the day nurseries associated with these clinics.

The psychiatrist has had great difficulty in limiting his function to that of consultant. Initially, the pediatricians referred enough cases to occupy all his time; these cases would normally have been referred to the children's mental health center. It seemed that the pediatricians were more or less consciously seeking to demonstrate, to the psychiatrist and to themselves, that the psychiatrist was fully occupied when handling only a few cases, and was consequently no great help.

Later, the pediatricians learned to use the psychiatrist, either to attend certain of their consultations and show them the deeper meaning of their attitudes, or to help them train the psychologists working in the day-nurseries, or to assist them in adopting a more clearly dynamic and rational approach. Case discussions were organized, and there were clinical and theoretical discussions to plan specific tasks. The pediatricians thus came to accept their assigned role of valued link in the program of the children's mental health service of this community.

This brief discussion of the relations between the service and the educational and pediatric authorities of the community shows that a dual policy can be adopted in establishing contacts between the children's mental health service and the various community agencies. One approach, in principle functional, takes into account the relations that are established gradually, out of continuity or necessity, a more or less natural development. It has the disadvantage of being loosely planned, but the advantage of complete adaptation to actual practical needs. It avoids bottlenecks in operations that often arise in formal relationships. And it enables the community services to make use of the consulting facilities of the children's mental health center.

The other approach is based on the establishment of organic relations in the official hierarchy. It permits of official interference with the community services and planned studies of requirements and resources. Its disadvantage is that it requires a long time to achieve authenticity and reality; it entails the risk that the service will be submerged in a flood of demands for consultations, more or less consciously motivated by the aggressive wish to demonstrate that the children's mental health service cannot meet the real requirements of the population.

The problems of implementing the adult mental health service can be more readily solved. It requires knowledge of the people's conditions of life, acquired not only by accumulating demographic data but by real ecological penetration on the social, economic, and cultural level. In this respect, the necessary technical experts in France are generally wanting; there are very few cultural anthropologists.

A study of actual resources in the matter of rehabilitation offers few difficulties; careful and patient work makes it possible to interest community leaders, intellectuals and industrialists in efforts to promote mental health.

As will be shown, alongside the children's and the adult mental health services, a central mental hygiene service attempts to coordinate this preventive effort.

☙ DESCRIPTION OF SERVICE ☙

The Mental Health Association of the thirteenth ward has two services: one for children and one for adults. Both have a structure based in principle on the presence of four teams, working in the two respective centers.

So as not to upset the population by using the term "Child Guidance Center," which in this district might be considered an invidious term, the mental health center for children was named the Alfred Binet Center. It has four teams, each including a psychiatrist, a psychologist, two social workers, and a secretary; one team is responsible for each geographic sector of the ward.

The *Alfred Binet Center* operates as a child guidance center, and its intake consists of cases requiring diagnosis and, possibly, treatment.

Rehabilitation and treatment are in the hands of various specialists organized in pools at the disposal of the teams. The pools supply psychotherapists, spoken and written speech specialists, specialists in psychomotor rehabilitation, and psychopedagogues.

It is difficult to do justice in an account such as this to the personnel working at the Alfred Binet Center, the constant development of which is limited by the financial resources.

The personnel working in rehabilitation and treatment, either full time or part time (halftime or less) shows considerable fluctuation.

On the whole, the limitation of number of personnel, caused by the inadequacy of financial resources, limits the therapeutic efforts of the center, which has an annual intake of 400–500 cases.

The team for the geographical area in which the child and its family live remains in charge throughout. The child can however be referred to one of the agencies working on behalf of the Alfred Binet Center, particularly to the *Day Hospital*, which can accommodate twenty-five psychotic or severely neurotic children per day.

For 1965, the Alfred Binet Center planned, in addition to the day hospital, a *school for oligophrenic children* and a *foster family care system,* organized in cooperation with a similar system for adult mental patients.

In the course of the following year, the thirteenth ward hoped to organize a *special boarding-out system* for children who must be temporarily separated from their family because of dramatic conflict situations; these children are to be placed with families of teachers.

In the course of the same year, one of the sections of the Alfred Binet Center hoped to open *two rehabilitation classes* as stepping-stones between the day hospital and the normal school; here, children are able to take special courses. This can be done more effectively than at the day hospital, where the time required for the various treatments sometimes interferes with scholastic activities.

The intention is to establish, in subsequent years, a *neuropsychiatric center for children,* where more severe cases can be hospitalized for observation and treatment.

Plans for the more remote future include extensions of the above-mentioned agencies to *adolescents,* with special emphasis on day services, to be subsequently associated with *night facilities.*

In 1965, a *clinic for adolescents* was opened, in association with *teener clubs* for recreation. Facilities for adolescents are made available to those who wish to seek the advice of their educators without involving their families. When the case seems sufficiently serious to be taken up by the Alfred Binet Center proper, the adolescent is invited to report, with his family, during the regular consulting hours of the center. In many cases, however, diagnosis and treatment can be completed at the special clinic without any contact with the family.

The *mental health center for adults,* too, has four teams and a smaller pool of technical experts. In the next few years it is to be reorganized and extended to include an *auxiliary emergency service* for brief hospitalizations.

As we have seen, the thirteenth ward already has fifty beds at its disposal in a *mental hospital* to be completed within the next two years, in the nearest southern suburb of Paris, on a large plot of land outside the built-up city area. This hospital is not to have more than *160* beds; if this standard is maintained, there will be a deficit according to the standards suggested by the WHO. It will be necessary, therefore, to develop more outpatient facilities. At this time there is the nucleus of a *day hospital,* now operating as a "therapeutic workshop." Associated with this is a second workshop for *effort training* which affords a transition between the therapeutic workshop proper and the normal working environment. Other effort training establishments will have to be set up in the ward, as will after-care agencies for discharged hospital patients.

As regards *the aged,* in addition to studies of this subject that we will discuss later, relations between the mental health service and the services for home assistance and general hospital care make it possible to evaluate the requirements in this respect. The intention has been to receive the aged in need of hospitalization in a foundation which can provide the necessary care and which should be an auxiliary of the mental hospital serving the thirteenth ward.

In the district where the hospital is being built, special foster family care for children as well as for *adult mental patients* is being organized.

Within the hospital there is an *advanced training school for nurses* recruited for the mental hospital of the thirteenth ward; this arrangement ensures that both nurses and technical advisers receive better professional training.

As would be expected, each team, both in the adult and in the children's service, is responsible for the relationships with the community institutions and for the promotion of better mental health.

It has proved necessary to centralize the efforts in this respect in a body embracing the services for adults and children. This *mental hygiene service* stimulates the efforts of the technical teams in the matter of mental health promotion. In particular, it has organized a club for ex-patients; here, they can work or participate in organized leisure activities. There is also a specialized female psychologist for the parent-education program, which consists of discussions held at the schools, with showings of educational films or activities in training groups. The mental hygiene service has also organized what is known in France as a "Ciné-Club": every month, a commercial film is shown in a rented hall; on the basis of this film a discussion is opened on educational problems and, more generally, on problems of personal interrelations in the family.

The mental health service of the thirteenth ward also has a research program for *clinical research* and *epidemiological research,* currently based on the epidemiological study of hospital inmates who are followed up by annual evaluation cards and, on their return home, by discharge cards. Each card bears an evaluation of the case in sociopsychological and in medical terms (diagnosis, prognosis, and treatment).

It is impossible to discuss in this chapter the details of the results of these studies. Let it be sufficient to state that the sociopsychological data on the inmates show that they are not a representative sample of the thirteenth ward population; a study of the socioeconomic conditions of these families shows that the sample corresponds with what in France is known as "petite bourgeoisie" (the English "lower middle class"). It is probable, therefore, that the economically less favored part of the population, which is generally known as asocial, is not reached by psychiatric activities. It can be stated in general that the motives of such activities are misunderstood, and that this group has not attained the level of acculturation to the middle-class norms that include an acceptance of psychiatric notions. This finding suggests the need for new policies in the matter of psychiatric care.

Statistical studies of the case material give some impression of the divergence that gradually occurs between our therapeutic ambitions and the achievements of which we are actually capable. An idea of the real impact of our activity can be gotten, for example, from the number of cases withdrawn from our care by the family. We estimate that one-third of our cases sever their contact with the service in the course of a year. This proportion may not seem excessive, but the finding must play a part in any assessment of the impact of our efforts. We have also had to evaluate the gap between the treatment we could consider ideal and that which the resources of our service make it possible to provide, taking into account our technical facilities (evidently dependent on the financial resources of our undertaking). All these considerations tend to deepen our understanding of our indirect activities.

WORKING PRINCIPLES ADOPTED

The foregoing material has concentrated on the material facts and the general lines of our organization; now, let us consider the principles underlying this community service.

One principle seems essential and must always be maintained: continuity. Many observers have remarked on the fact that difficulties in psychiatric activities arise from discontinuity, from successive ruptures and expensive efforts on the human and financial level involved in the referral of a case to another agency. In the organization described, each case is accepted by a technical team in charge of one of the territories of the thirteenth ward. In the service for adults, this principle is applied as strictly as possible. For example, patients admitted to the psychiatric clinic continue to be treated (while there) by the therapist of the team that accepted them. The hospital doctor has the responsibility for the patient only as long as he is in hospital, and only in terms of supervision and chemotherapeutic prescriptions. He is also in charge of the internal operation of the institute.

This principle is also observed as far as possible at the Alfred Binet Center. In all cases, the special social worker in charge of the patient and his family remains in charge throughout the period during which the subject receives care. For example, children accepted at the day hospital are in the charge of this organization, but the contact with the family is maintained by the social worker who first accepted the case.

The second original feature of the service is its psychoanalytic orientation. The psychiatrists who work here and have worked together for many years all have a psychoanalytic background. It is not the intention to describe the principles by which psychoanalytic practice can be applied in such a service. It is undoubtedly more interesting to give a brief description of the way in which psychoanalysis can work in a community service without altering the form of their psychopathological concepts. The risk entailed is that rigorous courses of psychoanalysis may be instituted in all cases seemingly in need of it, even if technical conditions are unsuitable and while the population is probably not prepared to accept this type of care. This might lead to an adulteration of psychoanalysis, without either the team pyschiatrists or the psychoanalysts who administer these courses of treatment being effectively in charge of the case.

It has seemed to us, however, that our psychoanalytic vocation—although giving us what we consider the best understanding of a case—has led us to an indispensable understanding of the meaning of "taking care" of a case in such a service. Thus the principle of continuity on which we insist would seem to be felicitously applied and extended by the introduction of new responsibilities in the wider sense of psychotherapeutic care. With some cases, both adults and children, it is possible to practice psychoanalysis in the proper sense. In the vast majority of cases, however, outpatient or clinical treatment is more a matter of "psychotherapeutic care," a situation that confronts every specialist working in the center with an awareness of his own responsibilities. The individual responsibility of the specialists for every case—within the scope of continuous action and extension of true care—clearly justifies the many meetings of the teams at case conferences and discussions aimed at improving practice on the basis of a theoretical and critical exchange of ideas.

Our third working principle concerns the need for long-term indirect action. This need arises not only from the number of cases but also from the fact that the case material is not representative of the general population of the thirteenth ward. In the poorest and least psychiatrically accessible layers, we need "relay persons" who could play a significant role in mental health matters. Pediatricians, for example, are more readily accepted by the population in dealings with very young infants. The statistical and epidemiological data disclose the clear relationship between the school services and the mental health service for children, for about 50 per cent of cases are referred to us by the schools, either because of difficulties in scholastic achievement that warrant consultation with the family, or because the family asks the school service for the address of a special care agency. This stresses the importance of psychiatrically oriented education for the teachers and social workers within the school system.

Another example may be found in certain poorly adjusted adolescent groups, on the verge of delinquency, who require immediate psychiatric care. There are clubs, known in France as "prevention clubs," that may give a socializing framework to these predelinquent groups who usually come from the families resettled in the ward after World War I. Special consultant activities on behalf of these clubs have proved very effective, in terms of special training for those who work here (known in France as "educators") and in terms of organizing the clubs. It is in the framework of these clubs that psychiatric activities for adolescents are to be organized, without any need for formal consultation and its associated system of registration.

☙ CONCLUSIONS ❧

The mental health service of the thirteenth ward of Paris is an experiment within the program that must ensure provision of adequate psychiatric care in the capital. A private service, it is subsidized almost entirely by public administrative bodies and, to a small extent, by private funds.

Its special character, apart from the organic links established between the service for adults and that for children, is most apparent in the emphasis on outpatient facilities.

Continuity of care is ensured by a unique system of service teams in which the responsibilities of each member are to institute and maintain specific therapy.

The case material, however, does not seem to be a representative sample of the population, the poorest layer of which has not yet attained the level of contact with psychiatry. This underlines the importance of indirect action: for the children, this indirect action is supplied outside the family in the branch units at school; it is extended to both adults and children by the intermediation of "key persons," to whose training the mental hygiene service contributes.

While the development of the service is limited, if only for financial reasons, to spontaneous consultations that must be prepared by effective education of the community services and the population, and cases incidentally detected at certain times (examination after the first elementary school year, at age seven to eight, and at matriculation time, age thirteen to fourteen; psychiatric studies of certain school groups) it will be gradually replaced by a systematic approach formulated on the basis of a study of requirements.

The intention is to make an epidemiological survey of this type, although we are aware of the difficulty of doing this in the field of child psychiatry where requirements are changeable. It is possible that, in terms not only of its unavoidably limited size, but also with respect to the special character of the child's psychiatric needs, the needs created by the setting up of the service, needs transposed from the scholastic to the psychiatric realm, needs misunderstood by an intolerant environment, and needs ignored in some very poor families— the service described only very imperfectly meets the real requirements of the community.

However this may be, this mental health service has the advantage of ensuring continuity of care and of promoting understanding and assistance in mental health matters within other community services; at the same time, it is carrying out observations that will make it possible to verify the working hypotheses which have led to its foundation.

A London Community Mental Health Service

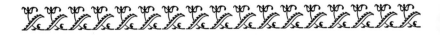

Jack H. Kahn

LOWER ELM LODGE, HAMPSTEAD, ENGLAND

XI

Community mental health services in the United Kingdom are part of the complex National Health Service in what has been called the "Welfare State." We have the paradox of a highly individualistic culture arranging for collective provision of basic needs; and the planning of the various services carries with it the consequences of the fact that each separate provision has its own history and its own statutory and professional framework.

New services, and developments of new ideas, sometimes face a disadvantage in having to fit into, or supplant, pre-existing systems, and the result is an illogical, inconsistent, and irrational pattern. At times one envies countries less well endowed, where each new service is seen as an improvement and not as an encroachment on the rights and responsibilities of workers already in the field.

STRUCTURE AND HISTORY

Some British social services are the direct responsibility of the central government, others come under the local authority, and were developed originally by voluntary bodies and later became absorbed into local or national institutions.

The Health Service has a complexity even within itself. The responsible government department is the Ministry of Health, but general medical practice, the hospital service, and the public health service have separate organizational structure. General practitioners (or family doctors) operate independently, having a direct relationship with their patients, but the service is organized through local executive councils responsible to the Ministry of Health. Inpatient and outpatient hospital services are organized on a regional basis through Regional Hospital Boards, of which there are fifteen. The hospital boards build, provide, and are responsible for the structure of the hospitals and for the organization of the medical, nursing, and ancillary services. Most medical consultants, even if working part of their time outside the hospital system, have contracts of service with the Regional Hospital Board.

The local authority is responsible for public health, including all the systems for the prevention of illness. Much of the medical care of young children falls on the local authority as an extension of the School Health Service, and specialized services (such as orthopedic, ophthalmic, and ear, nose, and throat) are provided at school clinics by joint arrangements with Education Departments, Health Departments, and Regional Hospital Boards. Some of the anomalies of the division of services have been surmounted by informal and ad hoc arrangements.

The community mental health services are the responsibility of Health Departments. The clinical treatment of mental illness is the responsibility first of the family doctor, and next of the hospital system, whether inpatient or outpatient. The local authority is responsible for supporting and rehabilitative services, and for fulfilling the statutory requirements whenever a patient is to be admitted to the hospital under some form of legal compulsion.

Before the passing of the National Health Services Act in 1946, mental illness was almost entirely a local authority concern. Nearly every one of what are now called *psychiatric hospitals* was built by local authorities, acting singly or in conjunction with one another, in order to provide a place where the insane could be safely kept. As with infectious illness, it was the safety of the community that was the first consideration, and ideas of treatment developed subsequently amongst those who had the individuals in their care. The buildings were first called lunatic asylums, later mental hospitals, and in 1959 they became designated psychiatric hospitals.

Local authority services are organized under committees consisting of elected members of the borough, city, or county councils. Some of the services are partly paid for by local rates and partly through government grants, and the services fit into a statutory framework. It would need a separate article to describe the organization of Housing Departments, Health Departments, Children's Departments, and Education Departments, linking their activities with respective ministries and government departments such as the Ministry of Housing and Local Government, Ministry of Health, Home Office, Department of Education and Science.

The health services were reorganized as a result of the National Health Services Act. When hospital management came under Regional Hospital Boards, it was possible to bring mental hospitals into the same administrative pattern as all other special or general hospitals. Advances in the medical treatment of insanity made it possible to alter organizational structure. The local authorities lost their mental hospitals, but retained some of their old responsibilities. It was still necessary to employ "authorized officers" to arrange for the legal process of admission to the hospitals when compulsion was necessary, and these still remain in the service of the local authority. The same officers were given the duty of providing after-care and supervision of patients discharged from hospital.

Present-day local authority responsibilities for mental health represent a further level of progress, which has been recognized by further legislation. The therapeutic role of the staff of psychiatric hospitals has superseded the old custodial function. More patients than ever before recover sufficiently to be discharged and carry on their previous work. Some recover only enough to take some share in community life if given adequate support. The climate of public opinion has become tolerant to the presence within ordinary life of those who are mentally ill. Patients, on their part, are willing, where necessary, to enter psychiatric hospital at an early stage and, at the same time, methods of domiciliary treatment are now available that may obviate the necessity of entering hospital at all.

The diagnosis of mental illness has ceased to be the decision to take an individual from his work and his home and place him in some remote institution. Once again, it needed an act of Parliament to mark the progress that had been made in treatment and in public attitudes. The 1959 Mental Health Act redefined mental illness and abolished some of the nomenclature that had ceased to have a clinical function. It simplified procedures for entering and leaving psychiatric hospitals. It specified the duties of local authorities with regard to making arrangements for the admission of patients to hospital, and for the after-care of those leaving hospital. It laid upon local authorities the duties of providing hostels for those who needed residential care but did not need the kind of medical and nursing care that is the function of the hospital. Here the wheel has turned full circle. Local authorities at one time provided asylums that later became hospitals; now they have to provide hostels that will be asylums for the few for whom these are still appropriate. Local authorities are also responsible for the care and support of mentally subnormal children and adults. Psychiatric services for emotionally disturbed children in the form of child guidance have mostly remained within the School Health Service.

Preventive services are a new function of health departments. Usually we speak of mental *health* and then proceed to describe merely the services for dealing with mental *illness*. Positive mental health services need new concepts, which have to be developed in combination with other social services.

Following the 1959 Mental Health Act, local authorities were called upon by the Minister of Health to set out their proposals for implementing their new responsibilities. Uniformity was not sought. Different local authorities created services with different interpretations or with different emphasis on the various aspects of the services that were required. Some may have been content to do the minimum that would satisfy the regulations, and to do no more than could be enforced. Authorities in other localities have been proud to be pioneers.

WEST HAM SCHEME

I propose to describe a particular scheme inaugurated in 1960 in the County Borough of West Ham and now extending to an enlarged area, the London Borough of Newham, created by the amalgamation of the two previously independent areas of East Ham and West Ham. The amalgamation took place in April 1965 as part of a major reorganization of local government in the London area. Prior to the amalgamation, the community and mental health service in East Ham was less developed than its counterpart, and, at the time of writing, the service for the new borough is the old West Ham service spread a little more thinly than before the amalgamation.

West Ham itself, although part of the great metropolitan area, has had a long tradition and history separate from its neighbors. Although only four square miles in extent, it had a population of over 300,000 before the second World War. This number was reduced to approximately 80,000 by bombing and evacuation, and gradually built up again to 160,000, where it has remained static. The population is regarded as uniformly working class and those who advanced financially and socially tended to move out of the borough. This uniformity has been a twentieth-century phenomenon, and the borough had in the past been composed of separate minor townships, each with its own shopping center and own individuality, including Stratford and Forest Gate, which in the nineteenth century was the residential area of fairly prosperous commercial families. Canning Town, Silvertown, Custom House, and Albert Docks are districts close to the River Thames, and here there are some small residential pockets between the various docks, isolated, except for swing bridges, from the rest of the area. These, and many other parts, have their separate level of social esteem. Many of the nineteenth-century substantial terraced houses have been subdivided without structural alteration into homes for a number of families. Houses, factories, and docks are intermingled.

The southern part of the old borough of West Ham is mainly dockland, and is occupied by families who have lived in the locality for many generations. The northern part, with mixed heavy and light industry, includes a proportion of transient and immigrant population, and an increasing proportion of these are of West Indian origin.

Slum clearance, and rebuilding into flats, has broken up some of the continuity of the older communities in the area. Nevertheless, the inhabitants in general remain conscious and proud of the borough's separate existence. The solid Labour Council has been responsible for many pioneer social projects; and it was part of West Ham that returned Keir Hardie, the first Labour M.P., to Parliament. There is no division between the decisions of the council and the wishes of the population. New modern flats and schools represent a corporate spirit, and are worthy successors to the well-designed public buildings erected at the turn of the century. A long tradition of social progress, and a certain degree of geographical isolation from other parts of the metropolitan area, are expressed, surprisingly, by a conservatism in the culture.

In spite of a vigorous housing program the shortage of accommodation remains acute, and recommendations for favorable treatment in the allocation of a corporation house or flat on grounds of threats to mental health are likely to be met with the uncontrovertible statement that other families on the waiting list are in worse plight.

Newcomers to local authority employment are presented with a stereotype of large families congregated around a surviving grandmother (a West Ham "Mum"), and of neighborhoods each having a cohesion represented by informal support for families in trouble. Voluntary organizations, such as are well represented in middle-class areas, are thin on the ground, since the Borough Council itself is felt to represent the population. There are, however, a number of charitable "Settlements," and, in the past, the area was a practicing ground for many voluntary social workers coming in from outside.

Few of the senior administrative staff of the local authority live in the borough. Even the family doctors mostly live at a distance, in more salubrious areas, and have lock-up surgeries; and very few teachers have homes in the area. In some of the local authority departments, members of the staff (many of whom had risen in the employment of the local authority from the post obtained immediately after leaving school) claimed that they knew the population, having followed families sometimes through two or three generations. It was implied that those who used the local authority services felt either that they were being forced to do something they did not wish to do (and therefore resisted it), or that they wanted something that the local authority did not wish to give them (and therefore insisted upon having it). There was none of the middle-class familiarity with social work, where worker and client accepted a joint aim.

East Ham, with its population of 100,000, is contiguous with West Ham and has a briefer history. Much of its building of houses took place between 1890 and 1910. The streets are neat and regular, and industrial buildings are few.

Although the population is largely working class, there is a significant middle-class element, and the whole area has been considered socially superior to West Ham. Some of the professional people who work in West Ham, but could not consider living there, have found residence in East Ham. Some have moved on to the still more desirable residential areas in the rapidly growing commuter towns in once-rural Essex. Newham suffers, in common with other large working-class metropolitan areas, in having no unbuilt rural fringe in which new suburbs can be developed.

The impressions described above have been found to require considerable correction. All the stereotypes have their embodiment, but the majority of the inhabitants are not represented by them. A school welfare officer, for example, may know a few hundred families intimately and consider that he knows the town. Some surnames are recognized at once by the staff of the Children's Department, which is responsible for children deprived of parental care, and the same names may be familiar to a host of other statutory and voluntary agencies. The health visitors, whose work includes the visiting of homes and families, have a wider range, and meet inhabitants who never come to the notice of services that deal with the materially deprived. Many families, however, are not numbered among the consumers of any of the local authority social services. Some are unknown even to the family doctor on whose list they are registered. There is an invisible middle class, which has only just begun to reveal itself to professional staff, as the image of the local authority service gradually alters.

Most local authorities have based their community mental health service on the existing provisions for the psychotic patient. The "Duly Authorised Officer," (who had remained responsible for the legal processes of emergency admission to mental hospital since the 1946 National Health Services Act came into operation in 1948), was given social work functions with psychiatric and mentally subnormal patients without any formal training for that work. Many new entrants to the renamed posts of "Mental Welfare Officer" are being recruited from those who have taken the (Younghusband) General Social Work Training Course.

For theoretical concepts, many local authorities have turned to psychiatric hospitals. Some consultants who are appointed to psychiatric hospitals have been allowed to devote part of their time to advisory and consultative duties in the local Community Mental Health Service. The contributions vary in the same way as psychiatrists and psychiatric hospitals vary. The primary concern of psychiatric hospitals is the medical treatment of mental illness, and the thinking in clinical categories, which is meaningful in a hospital context, needs to be translated into other terms before it becomes relevant for social care in the community.[1]

Child guidance, in contrast, has developed somewhat differently from adult psychiatry in that its multidisciplinary system[2] is based upon the principle of simultaneous investigation by a team of at least three highly trained professional workers. It is recognized that the identified patient who requires treatment is a *child* who is living and growing *within a family* and *within an educational framework.* If account is taken of the *adult's occupational life,* and his *family and social interaction,* it would follow that a similar multidisciplinary approach to the mentally disturbed adult, also, would have advantages. Moreover, although medical treatment is usually best focused on the individual, there are many instances when the family structure can be looked upon as the unit of pathology, and in these cases treatment is directed to the family interaction rather than to separate individuals. This kind of concept allows intervention into the problem at an earlier stage than when an individual has been singled out as carrying the illness, and could also provide a basis for preventive services.

The Medical Officer of Health for West Ham, Dr. F. R. Dennison, chose the system of child guidance as his model for the community mental health services for the borough. For over three years before any plans were formulated, discussions took place between the Medical Officer of Health and his staff, consultants of the psychiatric and general hospitals in the area, representatives of family doctors, an officer of the Regional Hospital Board, and a consultant from the Tavistock Clinic.

When the principles of the services were agreed, the first step was to construct an appointment jointly between the Regional Hospital Board and the local authority for a psychiatrist who would be both the Medical Director of the Child Guidance Clinic and Consultant Psychiatrist in charge of the community mental health service.

The next step was to find skilled family caseworkers to work in the community service, which was to be integrated with the Child Guidance Clinic. It was decided to try to recruit qualified psychiatric

[1] Querido, A., *The Efficiency of Medical Care,* Leiden: H. E. Stenfert Kroese N. V., 1963, p. 278.

[2] Kahn, J. H., *Unwillingly to School,* London: Pergamon Press, 1964, p. 163.

social workers who would be prepared to accept the statutory duties of mental welfare officers (including the night emergency rota) as well as the more familiar functions in the Child Guidance Clinic. The remaining mental welfare officers who were experienced but untrained, and whose numbers had been reduced by retirement, were to be integrated with the newly appointed psychiatric social workers into a single team and share the title "Mental Health Social Worker." Well before the Health Act of 1959 came into operation, this outline scheme was accepted by the Health Committee of the West Ham Borough Council, and also by the Education Committee, which was concerned with the administration of the existing Child Guidance Clinic. Pilot schemes, including discussion groups with health visitors and medical officers in the Health Department, were introduced, and the first consultant psychiatrist took up his appointment January 1, 1960. How the rapid growth of the service was achieved remains somewhat of a mystery. Planning of the service still continues, and any description of the procedures actually being undertaken becomes rapidly out of date. Conflict, disillusionment, and frustration alternate with pride of achievement.

The first and main obstacle was the unavailability of qualified psychiatric social workers. A trainee scheme was set up under which holders of degrees or diplomas in social science were appointed, and later released, on full salary, to university training courses for the Mental Health Certificate. Four such trainees were appointed in 1960, and the first to become qualified returned to the service in 1962.

Other newly qualified psychiatric social workers were then recruited, and it was discovered that the more a service has, the more it can attract. A surprising number of qualified and experienced psychiatric social workers showed a courageous readiness to expose themselves to the unstructured and uncertain demands that come from professional workers in a variety of services for something called "community care."

There are at present nine qualified psychiatric social workers and two trainees. The establishment at present allows for the number to be increased gradually in stages approved by the committee. The staffing in the other disciplines has not shown the same growth. Psychiatrists, psychologists, and psychotherapists are under-represented in relation to social workers.

⚔ FUNCTIONS ⚔

The obligations of the local authority with regard to mental health were originally discussed in planning under five headings:

(1) *Statutory Obligations* are (a) *Compulsory admission* of mentally ill patients to psychiatric hospitals, and "after-care" of patients discharged from hospital. In this field it was hoped that a continuous process of family casework given in advance of hospitalization might sometimes avert it. (b) *Residential care* of patients discharged from hospital who are not yet able to live unsupported in the community. This was first thought of in terms of hostels for different categories of patients—emotionally disturbed children, mentally handicapped children and adults, elderly patients with minor degrees of psychiatric disturbance, and patients who have had clinically recognized psychiatric illnesses but who do not require hospital treatment at that particular time. This provision is now being thought of on lines of functional need rather than the above categories. (c) *Training centers* for the partly recovered and partly disabled mentally ill adults were also envisaged.

(2) *The Child Guidance Clinic,* which was operated on traditional lines. Its function includes casework with parents, as well as treatment of the children on whose behalf intervention was sought in the first place. Treatment was based upon recognition of family interaction and the co-existing life in school. There was an existing establishment for psychiatrists, psychologists, psychiatric social workers, and a part-time psychotherapist.

(3) *In-service Training Schemes* for health visitors and assistant medical officers of health, to be extended to professional workers in other departments of the local authority.

(4) *A Consultative Service* for many types of local authority staff including health visitors, school medical officers, welfare officers, probation officers, and for voluntary workers in organizations such as the Marriage Guidance Council. This service was designed to help in dealing with mental health problems that became apparent in the course of the work of nonpsychiatric services.

(5) *A Co-ordinating Committee* consisting of workers from different local authority departments and voluntary bodies that had been in existence for a considerable time. This committee discussed

problem families whose social and economic needs called for attention, and whose psychiatric problems might be relevant to their situation.

The original conception was of an all-purpose team of social workers, practising family casework in all the different areas of the service. With the expansion in the size of the team and the extension of its range of activities, a steady increase in specialization became inevitable. However, the principle of one integrated service has been maintained, with each social worker appointed to the service as a whole, and becoming identified with the total service rather than any particular part of it. Specializations are developed but no specialization is exclusive. Each social worker continues to work with the family allocated to him, or her, drawing upon the total resources of the service, however diverse and shifting the areas of need might be.

The starting point, still the central core, was the statutory services that must be provided—the emergency admission of patients to mental hospitals, the social after-care following discharge, and the child guidance service. The aim has been to bring these into a family casework service that has gradually extended its activities as areas of need have been uncovered, and as the special interests and abilities of different members of the social work team have permitted. To a considerable extent the service has been shaped by special interest and abilities.

The psychiatric social workers state that they all feel untrained for much of the work that they do. Their training as psychiatric social workers gives a basis, but is not enough. They have to draw on other resources in themselves. They need replenishment through conferences and discussions within the department and elsewhere and the support of an administrative structure whose growth keeps pace with theirs.

The aim of the integrated service is to provide for a flexible matching of community provision and patient's needs, with a minimum of administrative lets and hindrances. Boundaries between different parts of the service must exist, but they are divisions of convenience rather than barriers to be surmounted. It is hoped to make the service a preventive one by making it a better service, finding that where a disability is seen to be given better provision, it attracts less stigma. Access to the service is made easy, so that families at risk can approach us before the difficulties become acute or become crystallised into some form that is difficult to resolve. Attempts are made to create links with other professional workers in order to find ways of working together in areas of mutual concern, joining resources so that all can extend the range of their work. When the total family situation and the needs of all the family members are considered, the work has a preventive aspect.

The use of qualified psychiatric social workers for statutory duties concerned with admission of patients to hospital is an unusual feature, but it is the essence of the scheme. The aim is to start work with families before admission to hospital of a family member becomes necessary, with the hope that it may be forestalled. Even if hospitalization should occur, the dynamically trained worker may take the drama out of the situation and thereby prevent the family division that leads to alienation of the patient.

The family may be helped to hold its sick member through the acute stage of his illness, and to allow admission to hospital to be arranged later and at leisure. This process has been helped by good communication with psychiatrists at the hospital that serves West Ham. They look upon admission to psychiatric hospital as mainly a medical decision of the family practitioner, and they are ready to visit the homes of patients in consultation with the patient's doctor. Patients themselves learn that it is not necessary to be violent before they can be acknowledged as in need of psychiatric treatment. The mental health social worker is ceasing to be the officer who responds to an emergency call by removing a troublesome individual to a psychiatric hospital in order to oblige the doctor or members of his own family.

The convenience of the emergency service provided by the old D.A.O. (Duly Authorised Officer) is missed by some people. An officer responds to a call on the terms on which it is made. A professional worker redefines the terms, and this redefinition may not always be welcome.

It is necessary to establish a new image of a service in which calls are dealt with in the context of long-term needs of the patient, the family, and the community. All this has to be carried out in association with the psychiatric hospital, family practitioner, ambulance driver, and, sometimes, the police.

A new development is that two mental health social workers are on duty during office hours to respond to emergency calls and to see members of the public who may call in without appointment. This "walk-in" service has been formulated to cater to the increasing number of people who were calling at the office. This was when it was noticed that the type of client and type of problem were becoming more varied. Professional workers, university students and grammar-school dropouts entering employment, not previously thought to be typical of the borough, were coming for help with severe emotional problems.

At this point it becomes possible to realize that all the patients and clients seen previously were also atypical. A common language exists as a ready-made medium of communication between the professional worker and the middle-class client. Even here there are some differences of vocabulary that need translation, but a basis for communication is present. Difficulties of communication are greater with those whose language is restricted by lower levels of intelligence, class barriers, and lack of identification with the educational system. When, however, the range of understanding of the worker increases, so does the range of individuality of his clients!

The *Young People's Consultation Service* was established a year ago to cater for those whose needs are not met by adult psychiatric services, and who would not consider attending a Child Guidance Clinic. Young people are encouraged to approach the service directly, and where, as usually happens, an introduction is in fact made by another worker, the young person is invited to get in touch with the service himself to arrange his first appointment. The age group has not been defined. It could perhaps be looked on as a service for people who have begun to break away from the primary family group but have not yet become identified with an independent adult role. The youngest client was a boy of thirteen years, who was in fact transferred to the Child Guidance Clinic. The oldest person to approach the service was a man of twenty-nine years, who wrote asking for a consultation because of the difficulty he had in making friends, particularly with women. More than one married couple has been referred to the service, and the majority of cases have been concerned with problems of interpersonal relationships.

Special interests of individual psychiatric social workers have provided the service with growing points. One or more have assumed some personal responsibility for the work in the areas described below.

(1) *Psychiatric Hospitals:* Although there is no joint appointment of social workers between local authority and the psychiatric hospital serving the area, three of the social workers are attached respectively to the three medical "firms" in the hospital. They attend ward meetings and the discharge conferences. They have links with the psychiatric outpatient clinics. They are responsible for after-care, which, when it is an extension of the primary relationship, becomes continuing care.

(2) *The Child Guidance Clinic:* Four of the social workers spend a major part of their time in the child guidance clinic. There are no full-time psychiatric social workers in the clinic. Child guidance is brought into relation with other parts of the service by those workers of all disciplines whose duties overlap.

(3) *Liaison with Children's Department and Probation Department* is mainly a function concerned with the child guidance clinic, but other parts of the Community Mental Health Service may be involved. One psychiatric social worker has been allotted special responsibilities where these departments are concerned, and arranges contacts and communications on behalf of, or together with, other members of the staff.

(4) *Maternal & Child Welfare Clinics:* Nine maternal and child welfare clinics spread out strategically over the borough. Each clinic looks to a particular social worker for regular contacts.

(5) *Handicapped Children:* A Development Clinic has existed for some time under the direction of one of the medical officers who works with health visitors and a visiting consultant pediatrician. Mothers of infants with suspected physical, sensory, or mental defect are invited to attend regularly for investigation of their children and for the preparation necessary for the next stage of training or education.

Social workers interested in this field will be introduced in turn, and each will build up a case load for long-term counseling of families.

(6) *Junior Training Courses for the Mentally Subnormal* will be referred to later. One of the social workers attends parent-teacher meetings and also has her own group of parents needing special counseling or casework.

(7) *The National Assistance Board, the Industrial Rehabilitation Units, Housing Departments, Welfare Departments:* The staff of these departments are all confronted with problems of a psychiatric nature in the people they serve. Sometimes this necessitates transferring a client to the community mental health service from the service where the problem is first recognized. At this stage he becomes a patient. This transfer is not always appropriate, and an individual who has

some mental abnormality may not desire nor be responsive to psychiatric procedures.

Many people show symptoms of mental illness, yet live reasonably normal lives and have no wish to receive psychiatric treatment. Others appear to need treatment on account of the damage or distress that they cause to others. They may deny the fact that they are in any way mentally ill and yet their disturbance may not be of a nature that makes them subject to a compulsory order. These individuals may demand (and need) other types of social service, and, in these cases, the nonpsychiatric services may require help in the form of consultations in the absence of the client.

(8) *Adult mentally subnormal individuals* present a special problem that increases in magnitude with the longer expectation of life that some of these individuals may now enjoy. In addition to the severely subnormal, this group includes those who have attended schools for the educationally subnormal. Although in this case the mental handicap is of a moderate degree, they may still have difficulty in fitting into occupational or social life.

The above list by no means exhausts the separate functions that are distributed among the social work staff at present, nor does it include those in preparation.

Reference has been restricted so far almost entirely to the social work function. The service was planned on a multidisciplinary pattern. Growth in function and numbers has, however, been mainly in psychiatric social work staff.

Mentally subnormal adults are not a statutory responsibility of the Health Department under present-day legislation if they and their families can manage their own affairs efficiently, but, at the time of school leaving, a conference of Education and Health Department staff is held and some individuals may be recommended for supervision by the Health Department.

Here the new service seems to fail in comparison with the traditional friendly visiting by the former Duly Authorised Officer. His range of work was somewhat narrower than that expected of the psychiatric social worker, but some areas were dealt with more intensively. Supervision of the adult subnormal ("mentally defectives" in previous terminology) was undertaken in between other duties. He might call at the home and pay a doorstep visit or would be invited into the house. Problems of the "defective's" behavior would be discussed and, at times, he might have even been invited to give the young man or woman "a good talking to." In a paternalistic society such service is valued. Trained social workers are unwilling and, in fact, unable to do this kind of work.

Those who withdraw a previous service must face criticism if they do not provide something that can be seen to be even better. The solution must be a long-term one, which will mean establishing a case-work relationship with the family *at the earliest point of recognition of the handicap* in infancy. On this basis the handicapped member of the family would not be expected merely to conform to some rigid and restricted pattern of behavior, but would continue to receive some encouragement for development of his intellectual and emotional po-tentials, even in his adult life.

The psychological contribution has been mainly the inspira-tion that has come from Dr. Ravenette, the Senior Psychologist, who has duties in the School Health Service in the Child Guidance Clinic, and also has a function directly under the Education Department in the School Psychological Service. He has no formal connection with the Health Department, but has made himself freely available in in-dividual consultations and in the broad planning.

PROBLEMS OF AMALGAMATION OF BOROUGHS

The amalgamation of West Ham with East Ham to form the Borough of Newham has provided a new beginning and an opportu-nity to review the staffing needs and to face shortcomings.

At the time of the reorganization of London local government, Inner London Boroughs had to inaugurate new mental health services to replace what had previously been provided centrally. East Ham and West Ham had previously had their own services. Only one of the four mental welfare officers of East Ham remained to serve Newham. Three found senior posts in new boroughs. The remaining East Ham officer joined the Newham team of mental health social workers with senior status.

The Child Guidance Clinic in East Ham had been entirely separate. The consultant psychiatrist there held a contract with the Regional Hospital Board only and not with the local authority. The combined Child Guidance Service of Newham will be served by this psychiatrist and the two consultants with joint appointments. There are three vacancies for psychologists in the Child Guidance Clinic and School Psychological Service, and one more vacancy has been created for a psychologist to serve specifically the community mental health service. There was no psychiatric social worker in the former East Ham Clinic, and the joint team of mental health social workers will serve the integrated Child Guidance Service. Each of the pre-existing clinics employed a part-time child psychotherapist. Further sessions are now available to include work with the mentally subnormal in the Junior Training Centers.

Fresh recruitment and reappraisal of concepts and techniques have to go hand in hand.

✠ THE COMMUNITY PSYCHIATRIST ✠

The psychiatrist's function in the service as a whole presents difficulties. The function of a medical director of the Child Guidance Clinic has its established pattern. He is the leader of a professional team, which has traditions of separate areas of competence and of shared responsibilities. Conferences are held weekly at the former West Ham Clinic for case discussion and development of diagnostic and therapeutic concepts which provide a common language for the team. The clinic itself provides a base in which the work with patients within the clinic gives its professional members the confidence to go out beyond the clinic walls and meet teachers, nurses, and doctors who are dealing with the child guidance patients at other levels and with other aims.

The community psychiatrist's function in the other sections of the community mental health service is more ambiguous. He has to maintain contact with psychiatrists at whatever hospital is providing clinical treatment for mentally ill patients. The hospital consultant himself carries clinical responsibility for all patients receiving inpatient or outpatient hospital treatment. The psychiatric social worker who is attached to the particular hospital consultant keeps in contact also with the family doctor and may become the focus for unifying the work with the family as a whole.

Formulations of conjoint family therapy are being built up wherein a group of workers (psychiatrist, psychiatric social worker, and psychologist) carries out joint therapeutic interviews, in selected cases, with whole families rather than distribute the therapy of different individuals among the different therapists.

In the community mental health service generally, the psychiatrist leads a conference that was originally designed to deal with the intake of new referrals to the service. The social work team has recently been provided with its own principal, and its own casework supervisor, but the psychiatrist has had to take the lead at times in laying down limits and saying what should *not* be done. The service has sometimes been the victim of its own propaganda and of expectations that have been raised too high.

℞ PSYCHIATRIC SOCIAL WORKERS ℞

A psychiatric social worker is often called upon to act as a pacifier to a person justifiably distressed by unsatisfactory housing conditions, by poverty, or illness. The individual is suffering from emotional disturbance and the psychiatric social worker is therefore expected to make a relationship that will lead the patient to accept casework in lieu of his material necessities. Sometimes the skill of the psychiatric social worker can in fact be directed to the confronting of an individual with realities of his situation, but there are illusions about the ability to make a relationship in order to carry out later some subtle modifications in the attitudes of a patient or his family. Medical specialists sometimes expect a psychiatric social worker to be their eyes and ears, and "take a social history." If the psychiatric social worker does this, it does not save the specialist any time—it opens up new dimensions of the problem to be dealt with; sometimes a psychiatric social worker is expected to be the legs of some other worker and "take a message"; sometimes, to be the heart, and "make a relationship," in order to induce the patient to accept some unpalatable decision.

It sometimes happens that during the process of extending the range of Community Mental Health Service, requests that come from other agencies have to be refused. The refusal should not be made without a redefinition of the problem in a way that enables the original agency to handle the problem at a new level within its own service. The intake conference is sometimes used to discuss a problem with workers from other services, or to decide upon a consultation process in which the psychiatrist and a psychiatric social worker pay a visit to the other agency. Consultation is not always as acceptable as taking a patient off someone else's hands would be, but frequently the psychiatric service is less well equipped to deal with the problem than the referring agency. It seems easier to accept a referral, and fail, than to provide acceptable alternative formulations in conjunction with another profession; to accept an unsuitable referral is the line of least resistance.

There are natural and understandable resistances to the idea that psychiatric personnel have anything to add to existing methods of working or to existing diagnostic formulation by others. All professional workers face the problem of insufficient time to deal with present tasks. They naturally resent any attempts to modify their role. Their acceptance of any addition to the range of their work will depend upon their own perception of some need they cannot fill at present within what they consider to be their own field.

The psychiatrist and psychiatric social worker have their own professional field, and they also have problems with regard to the extension of their role when they go outside that field. They may have attributed to them a claim to a superiority of their methods over those of workers in a different setting.

People believe that the psychiatrist is itching to take over the work of other professions or to tell them how to do their work. The psychiatrist or the psychiatric social worker may frequently be invited to enter into the field of work of others who are confronted with problems of behavior. They face criticism when they accept the invitation, and criticism when they refuse. They are asked to take responsibility for altering the behavior of some individual and then to hand him back, or to keep him secluded even when the law does not allow this to be done.

The psychiatric contribution to other fields can never be a higher level of knowledge of someone else's work, but it is a method of approach to problems that includes an examination of the basic assumptions used when dealing with the problems.

PROFESSIONAL BOUNDARIES

The exploration and examination of basic assumptions and of personal attitudes is always accompanied by the release of hostility, whether it be in the clinical setting with patients, or in the professional setting with colleagues. Hostility can be tolerated when there is clarity about respective roles. Hostility is, however, damaging to the recipient and the one who expresses it, if it finds expression outside the boundaries of defined relationships.

In the clinical setting, any psychiatric worker has the protection of professional traditions, the knowledge of the role boundary on both sides, and the support of the clinical team. The clinical base is the support to the psychiatric workers in community care when going out into other professional fields. It is also the setting in which professional and personal development and progress in the psychiatric worker take place after initial training.

The spread in the range of work with patients and other professional workers should be expected to increase the degree of tensions the worker experiences.

The consultant psychiatrist has been expected to provide some continuity of clinical and theoretical concepts of psychiatry throughout the process of building up a practical working system of community psychiatric social work. His task is to develop and communicate the medical or psychiatric contribution to the treatment of social problems, and to make himself familiar with the thinking of other professional workers sharing this field.

The main difficulty in this role is the absence of relevant formulations. The classical medical model is that of investigation leading to a diagnosis, and the prescription of some treatment appropriate to the category of disorder that has been diagnosed. This system has been responsible for the tremendous progress in the treatment of physical illness in the last hundred years, and the extension of this progress into the field of mental illness has resulted in recent years in what has been described as a therapeutic explosion. The treatment of established psychosis remains the main contribution of the medical man to the field of mental illness, and the psychiatrist is first and foremost a clinician. When the psychiatrist enters the field of social services, and becomes involved with the creation of systems of prevention, he needs new levels of thinking. Medical treatment depends upon diagnosis; prevention is based upon etiology—we must know the cause of what we try to prevent. In social medicine, however, the clinical diagnostic categories seem irrelevant, and the etiological concepts of psychiatry are not sufficiently well established for them to become the basis of large-scale preventive measures.

The making of a diagnosis of schizophrenia, for example, is an essential preliminary to the provision of medical treatment. How relevant, however, is the same label to the industrial procedures used in rehabilitation, or to the consideration of the way in which a partly recovered mentally ill parent will affect the emotional stability of children? Additional dimensions of diagnosis are required in terms of function, and in these considerations other individuals are going to be involved. Employers want information about men and women returning to work. Health visitors ask about the effect that the discharged patient is going to have on the marital partner or the children. Child care officers are concerned about the way children move in and out "of care" as mothers enter and leave psychiatric hospital. National Assistance Board and National Insurance Officials want to know whether pressure should be applied to compel some former mental hospital patient to return to work, when he appears unwilling, or to return to hospital in order to become cured. They all believe that the answer is in the possession of the psychiatrist, and that it can be transmitted by the psychiatric social worker. The psychiatric worker has to confess that it is the nonpsychiatric field worker who has access to most of the knowledge of the way the mentally ill patient fits into family, occupational, and social life. We need this knowledge to add new dimensions to the clinical diagnosis.

The social diagnosis is the dimension in which is described the competence of an individual to deal with his external affairs; the family diagnosis in terms of family interaction; an occupational diagnosis is in terms of his limitations, capacities, and the resources available in the community for them to be used and developed. These other dimensions of diagnosis are not at present within the orbit of psychiatric training—which is for clinical work—although many psychiatrists have made contributions to the knowledge of these factors. Some psychiatrists have, for example, developed ideas of the therapeutic community within the hospital. Others have developed industrial units up to a level of importance at which the wards serve merely as a dormitory for patients whose therapy takes place in the workshops and who begin their rehabilitation at the moment of admission to hospital.

These processes have not yet been professionalized within psychiatry, and in many cases they do not survive the transfer of some pioneer worker to another post.

We need new formulations in which to relate the clinical findings with the standards by which we prescribe some of the present-day procedures, such as industrial therapy, social clubs, and group discussions. It may sometimes seem that we prescribe them merely because someone has developed a unit in which these facilities exist. Many such processes are at present quite fortuitously under the direction of medical men of different specialist training, or of nonmedical personnel from any one of a variety of professions.

Multidisciplinary Processes. It would seem that the professionalization of social and industrial techniques will need the kind of multidisciplinary approach that exists in the Child Guidance Clinic, where psychiatrist, psychologist, and psychiatric social worker represent three areas of the child's life, each with the maximum competence in just one area, but with some knowledge of the other two. Within the community mental health field, the psychologist could contribute to both the diagnostic assessment and the therapeutic process, with occupational factors forming the counterpart of the educational factors in which he is the expert as regards the child.

The psychologist's role has not been adequately represented in the developments in West Ham, nor in Newham, and the multidisciplinary nature of the scheme is incomplete, except insofar as the Child Guidance Clinic provides a clinical base.

Intra-Departmental Communication. The Medical Officer of Health, Dr. Dennison, in addition to being the originator and chief designer of the scheme, has remained an active participant in the conceptualizations of methods of professional work, and in the providing of administrative machinery to make the work possible. He has made himself available to members of professional and administrative staff at all times. He holds weekly sessions with each of the senior staff separately to discuss problems, and the different sections of the department have their own consultation committees which meet regularly. Joint meetings are held at regular intervals and whenever one of the frequent crises occurs.

The John F. Kennedy Center. Planning of each new development is always a joint affair. One example is the Junior Training Center for Mentally Handicapped Children—now called the John F. Kennedy Center. For some years, this center was housed in prefabricated buildings that were disused army huts. Good work was being carried out in unsuitable premises. Before plans for the new buildings were drawn up, a number of conferences were held with the Borough Architect's staff, and these were attended by the Medical Officer of Health, his deputy, the principal of the center, a health visitor, and the consultant psychiatrist. A member of the architect's staff visited the existing center, watching the activities and asking members of the staff what they would like in the new premises. They were ready to give answers once they knew that they were being taken seriously. At the conferences, an attempt was made to see how the building could be adapted to the kind of activities that were intended to take place. The assumption was made that the defect in mentally handicapped children is not static. The children are all subject to emotional disturbance as a result of failure to fit in with inappropriate expectations. They may deteriorate intellectually if given insufficient stimulus, and they have a capacity for intellectual growth if given a level of education appropriate to their developmental stages. This requires all the usual nursery school equipment,[3] adapted to children older than the usual nursery school age. They can also accustom themselves to domestic equipment such as electric washing machines, cookers, sewing machines, and all the fittings of a modern home; and to craft work, using machinery for making articles in wood, metal, and ceramic materials. They can acquire social skills, recognize the words in public notices, go on outings to shops, cafes, cinemas, and clubs. Above all they can learn to play and enjoy themselves alone and with one another. They also need psychotherapy.

The model for a building for all these purposes could not be taken from any existing institution, and something had to be abstracted from the concepts of a home, a school, a workshop, a social center, and a child guidance clinic. The architect took note of the activities that were to take place and provided a structure that has an artistry of its own.

The building contains its assembly hall, classrooms, work rooms, playground, indoor swimming pool, and a special care unit for the emotionally disturbed, with built-in sand and water pits and space in which over-activity can be legitimized. The classrooms have cranked walls to allow nooks for dividing a small class into still smaller groups.

[3] Tizard, J., *Community Services for the Mentally Handicapped,* London: Oxford Medical Publications, 1964, p. 62.

The plans captured the imagination of the committee, who authorized an expenditure greater than was first contemplated, and when the building was approaching completion at the time of the assassination of John F. Kennedy, it was decided to give the center his name.

The move to the new building provided a challenge to the staff that was undertaken with mixed feelings. Would they miss the homely atmosphere of the old building? Would they be equal to the opportunities offered by the new one?

The challenge came from an unexpected quarter. The new building attracted many professional visitors from this country and abroad. The staff found themselves faced with questions about their work to which there was no ready answer, and with compliments that were difficult to live up to. Visitors did not hesitate to ask about their salaries and about their private lives. Some questioned whether mentally defective children would appreciate, or merited, such a fine building or such devoted work. The justification for the building came from the parents who are proud that their children are thought worthy of facilities that help them to develop. The children are dressed better, look prettier, and seem more intelligent than before. Even mentally handicapped children don't look "silly" when carrying out activities that interest them.

Sometimes visitors say, "But of course you don't have those of lower level of intelligence," sometimes, "Of course, this is a *show-place*." The answer to these statements was first that it was the *only* provision, and therefore it is the *standard* provision and not a show-place, and next, that the children were not specially selected but covered the whole range of those children in West Ham who are severely subnormal. The Education Department provides a special school within the educational system for those with less severe handicaps who are designated educationally subnormal.

Adult Centers. A shortcoming in the provision is made apparent when the children leave the center. The adult provision for mentally handicapped and for those with chronic mental or physical illness is still in the process of reorganization. Two adult centers exist at present in the part of Newham that was formerly West Ham, and a combined center (children and adults) in former East Ham. A comprehensive scheme for the borough is being worked out in order to provide several different kinds of center to serve different functional needs.

℀ ADAPTATION TO CHANGING PATTERNS ℀

Dissatisfactions, frustrations, and disappointments with the performance of the Community Mental Health Service have been experienced by the staff of other departments. Those who alter traditional methods of working have to justify the changes by successful results, and these are not always obtainable. Change is not always seen as an improvement and is not acceptable unless some dissatisfaction has been felt with previous methods. The professional and lay population of the West Ham part of the new Borough has made its contribution to the development of the service, and has given expression to its own brand of resistances to the new image of community mental health. There was no reason to expect that a ready-made system would be acceptable to the East Ham part, which had no share in the preliminary thinking and re-thinking.

Much heartburning among the senior administrative staff had been experienced throughout the local government services in the greater London area when the corresponding departments of two or more separate boroughs became united into single departments. The amalgamation of East Ham and West Ham was seen as a take-over, one way or the other. West Ham was the larger of the pre-existing units, but not always the leader. In the mental health field, it was the West Ham pattern that would prevail, and that would therefore remain suspect in the eastern part of the new borough.

Difficulties within the staff of the mental health team exist and have increased when new members are recruited who have not had to survive previous turmoil and disappointments. The service as a whole is one that is much visited by professional workers from many parts of the world. The staff develop a patter that is a mixture of accounts of actual practice and of aspirations. We sometimes deceive ourselves by our own patter. Prospective recruits to the service are encouraged to pay visits before making a formal application for an advertised post. They are warned about the deficiencies in the service, but they pick up the enthusiasm and the excitement of those working in the field. The enthusiasm frequently wanes in old and new staff alike. A staff that is larger and more highly qualified than that of many other similar areas finds itself, nevertheless, stretched beyond its capacity by demands that grow faster than the number of its personnel.

Many short term and long term visits of observation have been made to the service. During the academic year 1964/5, a Fulbright Professor was placed with us. We were fortunate in that the one chosen was Henry Maier, Professor of Sociology at the University of Washington, Seattle. He had had experience of studying the helping process in social work, particularly with families that had handicapped children. He participated in case conferences, staff discussions, and planning meetings. He conducted seminars with the staff of the community mental health service, and with the staff of other departments. He proved a source of strength at times when the reorganization of a rapidly growing service was creating tensions within the department.

The latest phase has been the provision, in December 1965, of a building to act as Community Care Center for the whole Borough of Newham. Up to this time, the social workers had used offices in one wing of the administrative office block that housed the West Ham Health Department. There was insufficient accommodation for the social work staff, and interviews with patients were apt to be interrupted by office routine. The new Community Care Center is an old-fashioned building, with bare steel girders across a large central hall, and industrial glazed bricks lining the inner walls. With very little redecoration it has acquired a welcoming appearance, and there are a number of small rooms in which interviews can be held comfortably.

It is intended that it will provide experience on which to plan a purpose-built center sometime in the future. Individual and group therapy and social club activities can take place there, and it will be the home for the young people's consultation service. It is hoped that diagnostic assessments for comprehensive and integrated treatment will be carried out there, including those for the consideration of placement in one or other of the specialized training centers. This will have advantages over the present practice of holding interviews at the center at which placement is being requested, as the interview then appears to be for the purpose of acceptance or rejection, rather than for choosing the most suitable placement. It will also allow for a diagnostic conference of all the different professional contributors to the diagnosis—which is a decision for action.

The Community Care Center will also provide facilities for

group meetings and group discussions with professional workers from the Health Department and other services.

☙ INTEGRATION OR FRAGMENTATION ❧

An integrated, comprehensive, or multidisciplinary approach need not become an ideology. The purpose of diagnosis is to separate off the relevant aspects of a problem, and no diagnosis can ever be total. In many cases, intervention in just one area of living is sufficient, and one should not uncover more of a patient's life than is necessary to cope adequately with his needs.

Each professional service has its limited aim defined by legislation or professional ethics, but problems of living cannot always be divided along these artificial lines. In some instances, the clinical medical treatment takes the patient back to his former good health. In others, financial assistance man be all that is necessary to meet a social need. Others again need counseling or casework to help restore disturbed relationships. A single one of these processes may be enough. If several people are working at the same time and on the same problem without adequate communication with one another, and without having some common aim, the result may be damaging.

Fragmentation of problems and of work sometimes is apparent at the time when some aspect is referred to the community mental health service. There are occasions when, despite our claims to be an integrated service, some fragmentation continues after a case has been referred to the local authority, and two departments of the same service may be approached at the same time.

The following case will illustrate a number of points.

An unmarried woman, twenty-eight years old, living with her widowed mother, had recently left the psychiatric wards of a Central London Teaching Hospital. A letter from the psychiatric social worker of the hospital was sent to the Principal Mental Health Social Worker of the Newham service giving the history, which was briefly as follows.

The girl had attended an ordinary school, had been employed for two or three years, and then for some ten years had remained at home with her mother. No one had complained until about eighteen months ago. She then became irritable with her mother, and had begun to suffer from a feeling of strangeness and of depression. She had been referred by her family doctor to the local psychiatric out-patient department, and from there a placement had been obtained for her at the Teaching Hospital. She responded to medical treatment and was placed in an occupational therapy unit where she began to work adequately. When attempts were made to help her find outside employment in anticipation of her discharge, she left hospital immediately against advice. The psychiatric social worker of the hospital had been in touch with the mother and had felt that an over-close and possessive attitude was a factor in the pathology. The letter stated that the psychiatrist in charge of the case would write simultaneously to the Medical Officer attached to the Adult Training Center of the Newham authority. A recommendation was to be made that the girl should attend that Center, and it was requested that visits should be paid by one of the Newham psychiatric social workers to the home in order to "attempt to modify the attitude of the mother."

Later a copy of the psychiatrist's letter was made available to the intake conference of the Community Mental Health Service, but placement of the young woman at the center was apparently being dealt with as a separate process.

The psychiatrist's letter referred to the clinical diagnosis of "Depression and Depersonalization," and ended with the opinion that the prognosis was likely to be bad, as a good deal of the social work that had been done with the mother had been unsuccessful.

It was evident that some coordination of the treatment of mother and daughter would be necessary. Coordination of the processes needs a key figure, and it was thought that this should be the family doctor. One of the psychiatric social workers therefore telephoned the family doctor asking whether he would like to discuss the problem of this family with those who were going to take the next steps to help them. He demurred a little, saying that he did not have much time, and he would need to see the patient first. Would the psychiatric social worker go and visit the young woman and tell her to come to see him, and, after that, he would get in touch with us? He sensed some hesitation, and repeated his request for the psychiatric social worker to go to the patient, saying that he himself could not visit without being asked, and also that he had not much time for consultations with other services. The psychiatric social worker asked if it would help if she and the consultant psychiatrist visited him at his surgery at the same time as the patient. The doctor's tone changed immediately. "Would he do that?" he asked. "In that case, I will go and visit the patient this afternoon, and I shall arrange for us to meet," and he suggested a time two days later.

The story is perhaps spoiled by the sequel, which was that when the doctor visited the home, the daughter and mother together told him that they wanted no medical help, no psychiatric help, nor any attendance at the training center. The young woman would herself get a job when she wanted one.

The staff at the training center still felt that if only the girl could have been separated from her mother in some way, and had attended the center, all would have been well. Had she not worked adequately in the occupational therapy unit of the hospital? The mother was no concern of theirs, if only she would let the daughter free. She needed to be told that she was not acting in the daughter's best interests.

The family doctor was prepared to accept the position that he would offer and arrange any help that was possible when this family felt they needed it. Incidentally, it is never true that doctors have no time for psychiatric patients or those who need to talk about some problem. It is just that they have no time for what seems to have no purpose or end product, or for anything that seems unimportant.

There were a number of diagnoses applicable to this case. There was the clinical one of depression with depersonalization, but the patient was supposed to have recovered from this. The depersonalization syndrome could have been expressed in terms of psychopathology according to particular schools. At this level of diagnosis the correct treatment would have been to provide psychotherapy—if this process was available, was within the resources of a hospital or local authority service, and was acceptable to the patient. We could think of the situation in cultural terms recognizing that scarcely a generation ago it would not have been thought unusual for a single young woman to continue to live with her widowed mother without going out to work. This seems abnormal in the present age, and medical attendants and officers of the various social services are inclined to apply pressures to fit individuals into a pattern that is acceptable to the culture of this age. At the same time, while considering this dimension, it might be conjectured that the patient's original symptoms were associated with an attempt to break out from the outmoded culture within her home.

The next level of diagnosis is that of family interaction. Here the treatment would aim at dealing with the family process and would involve joint interviews of the mother and daughter. The attempt to deal with clinical and occupational treatment of the daughter as a separate process from social casework with the mother has failed. One should have expected such failure. The assignment offered to the Community Mental Health Service was to visit the mother in order to induce her to adopt a more socially acceptable attitude to her daughter and to the outside world. There is no reason to expect that any individual who is conscious of being right will accept the need to question the standards of a lifetime.

So far this case has been unsuccessful, but lessons can be learned from it, and even in this particular case the ground has been prepared for an integrated approach, through the family doctor, when the next crisis occurs. It is to be expected that the conflicts of dependence and independence, separation and union,[4] will have their vicissitudes; and the time will arise when mother and daughter together will feel the need of help. That will be the time for therapy on a family basis.

Among the levels of diagnosis we should not neglect the insights given us by great poets and dramatists. Several months after the discussions on this case, there arose, from the recesses of memory, recollections of Tennyson's "Lady of Shalott." Here a house-bound (or castle-bound) woman who could not face the busy world, except in the reflection of a mirror, made an attempt to release herself and to enter into the ordinary community.

> She has heard a whisper say,
> A curse is on her if she stay
>   To look down to Camelot.
> She knows not what the curse may be,
> And so she weaveth steadily,
> And little other care hath she,
>   The Lady of Shalott.

Seeing her knight in the distance, she ventured to break away.

> She left the web, she left the loom,
> She made three paces thro' the room,
> She saw the water-lily bloom,
> She saw the helmet and the plume,
>   She look'd down to Camelot.

---

[4] Kahn, J. H., *Human Growth and Development of Personality*, London: Pergamon Press, 1965, p. 203.

> Out flew the web and floated wide;
> The mirror crack'd from side to side;
> "The curse is come upon me," cried
> The Lady of Shalott.

The poem goes on to say how she floated downstream to her death.

What was the whisper? In whose voice was it expressed? Many times in the individual therapy of patients, I have been confronted with self-recriminations of patients who accuse themselves of badness at the slightest attempt to find any independence, to assert themselves, or express themselves with vigor. The recriminations are their own, but when pressed, they reveal that the voice in which they are expressed is that of the mother.

In a figurative way the syndrome of depersonalization could be expressed as the shattering of a mold that had been applied to the personality. When the mold is broken (the mirror cracked from side to side), there is no alternative image the individual can recognize as representing the self. The personality has acquired no shape of its own. Cure is sometimes sought in a way that either attempts to fit the individual back into the old mold, or alternatively, there are always other individuals ready to find a new shape in which to compress the patient. Such a patient seldom has the resources, or the opportunity, to achieve an identity that is satisfactory. The pull of family (sometimes even after the death of parents) is too strong. These are the cases where family therapy needs to be a conjoint affair. They are most successful when they are multiprofessional. Many visits have been paid to homes by a combined team of psychiatrist, psychiatric social worker, and a therapist or instructor from one of the training centers.

RANGE OF CHILD GUIDANCE

The Child Guidance Clinic, at the beginning, provided the inspiration for the multidisciplinary nature of the community mental health service. It is now receiving, in return, the benefit of the experience of communication with other services. There had already been a background of integrated investigation and diagnosis. The child psychiatrist in the Child Guidance Clinic carries a responsibility for clinical diagnosis, but he does not make his diagnosis alone on the basis of his own observations and written reports from colleagues. The relevant diagnosis is arrived at in joint personal discussion of the three participants. When communication has to be made with schools, with children's departments, and with probation departments, it is equally necessary to recognize that a relevant diagnosis is not one that is made in the Child Guidance Clinic and conveyed in writing to the other agency—if it is going to acquire meaning for other people who are working with the problem, they, also, need to share in the making of the diagnosis. This means that wherever the problem is one in which a number of people have to share the work, they have to share the making of decisions.

The Child Guidance Clinic carries out a considerable amount of work in the traditional pattern, but wherever it is thought necessary, visits are paid to schools and other departments in order to discuss problems.

Such visits are becoming increasingly welcome. At first, as was mentioned previously, it seemed that other agencies were more anxious to get rid of a problem than to understand it. Schools, naturally, look for help with the problem of children whose behavior is unsatisfactory. The hope is that the undesirable behavior is the equivalent of illness. Sometimes this is so, but it is not invariably the case. Undesirable behavior may be a way of expressing emotional disturbance. It may be a reaction to an unsatisfactory environment, or it may be the failure to acquire normal standards of behavior. It has to be emphasized that a Child Guidance Clinic has not got a stock of "treatment" that will convert bad behavior into good behavior.

Visits to the schools are undertaken in order to discuss problems of particular children, and sometimes it is possible to find explanations that leave the problem within the educational field. These visits, too, are usually multiprofessional. The educational psychologist is the essential member; a psychiatrist and psychiatric social worker may accompany him.

JOINT INTERVIEWS WITH PATIENTS

Health visitors and medical officers often come for help with regard to families with whom they have been working for a long time. Sometimes it is only to discuss the problem. At other times it is because one or more members of the family are thought to be in need of some kind of further assessment or of psychiatric treatment.

Many of these cases are inappropriate to the psychiatric hospital inpatient or outpatient investigation, and many of them, although exhibiting some psychiatric symptoms, can well continue within the field of work of the health visitor or medical officer at the Maternal and Child Welfare Clinic. In such cases it is considered to be better that the psychiatrist's and psychiatric social worker's interview with the family should take place in the presence of the original worker. More and more joint interviews of this kind are being undertaken. The original professional worker is not a silent observer but a participant, and the problem is neither taken over nor competed for.

℀ PLANNING FOR HOSTELS ℀

There is one field of work in which Newham has made no progress at all, although it is a statutory obligation. This is the provision of hostel accommodation for mentally disturbed and mentally handicapped children and adults. None has been built so far because we do not know what to build.

The first thoughts were that different hostels would be built for children and adults with different categories of disturbances or defect, but we do not know how to translate the needs from a clinical diagnosis to a shape of living space. A good many types of residential accommodation already exist in the hospital and social services of the country. There are different kinds of hospitals for those who need medical and nursing care. There are residential schools for children needing special education; remand homes and approved schools for delinquents; children's homes for those deprived of parental care, and these may be institutions, cottage homes, or there may be boarding-out arrangements.

There is a lack of knowledge of how the residential part of any provision is related to the total requirements of some particular category of person or problem.

We shall be driven to experimenting with a number of different kinds of accommodation—for example, small flatlets in the ordinary housing provision for the area; bedroom-sitting rooms in units that may have common dining or recreational facilities; and possibly adaptations of old houses if these can be found in an area where there are very few houses of the larger type. Supervised lodgings in ordinary homes might be obtained. What we hope to do is to introduce, as the criterion for types of accommodation, the concept of functional diagnosis rather than of clinical categories. We shall have to ask "What is the type of residential need for some particular person?" rather than "What kind of hostel is necessary for a mentally defective person or a schizophrenic patient?" The question of supervision, and of clinical and social casework support, will be as essential as the type of accommodation, and many local authorities have already experienced residential staffing difficulties in some of the few cases where hostel provision has been made. When we make our first experiments it will be with considerable trepidation.

℀ CONCLUSIONS ℀

Developments of community mental health services have been found necessary for the following reasons:

(1) Progress in clinical treatment of mental illness has been so great that many patients are able to be discharged from psychiatric hospitals after a fairly short stay. Many of these patients need continued treatment, or supportive services, while living in their own homes. Many other mentally ill patients are able to remain in their own homes and in the community throughout the duration of the illness. Domiciliary treatment is possible only when supportive services are available and when the community is tolerant to the presence of the mentally ill within its midst.

(2) Mental illness is recognized as having expression in forms other than the symptoms that fit into categories of disease. Disturbances of thoughts, feelings, and behavior and of interpersonal relationships have psychiatric implications, but the persons in whom the disturbances appear may continue to be the concern of a variety of professions who have to work in coordination with one another.

(3) Notwithstanding the therapeutic advances referred to, mental illness remains a heavy burden on medical and social services and on the community as a whole. The prevalence of mental illness is so high that the total range of the services that are available is never likely to cover the total needs. There is, therefore, a demand for preventive services.

Prevention is largely a nonpsychiatric process and is a product of the work of every professional and nonprofessional worker who has any responsibility for nurturing, educating, training, or curing human beings.

The theoretical basis is an extension from psychiatry, and community mental health services carry the medical principles of prevention into other services.

The community mental health service provides a working model for coordination of professional practice, which is involved with the many different areas of living activities. The problems are multidimensional, and the service is multidisciplinary.

The service is professionalised on the medical model of the successive processes of (1) investigation, (2) diagnosis, and (3) treatment.

(1) The multidimensional nature of the problems requires that each aspect of the investigation be carried out by a professional worker who has had training and has acquired skill in his particular field. The Child Guidance Clinic system of working with a team of psychiatrist, psychologist, and psychiatric social worker can provide a prototype for a Community Mental Health Service.

(2) It is only for the purpose of medical treatment that diagnosis in terms of clinical categories is useful. Other dimensions of diagnosis are relevant when action has to be taken by nonmedical personnel, and these may be expressed in terms of disorder, function, or relationships, or in levels of maturity. Thus, a diagnosis in terms of educational disabilities and capacities leads to decisions on special educational provision. An occupational diagnosis leads to rehabilitative procedures. A social diagnosis may include descriptions of the ability to use material resources, or may be expressed in interpersonal relationships and is the basis of social casework. None of these diagnoses is ever complete in itself, and a comprehensive diagnosis is necessary for integrated action, which is the treatment.

(3) Treatment is the action that follows from the investigation and diagnosis. It has been customary to confine the word "treatment" to medical procedures, but phrases like "occupational therapy," "remedial teaching," and "special educational treatment" now give recognition to the possibility of a variety of structured therapeutic procedures which follow the making of precise diagnoses.

A community mental health service needs to have a range of therapeutic activities that may be carried out within its own boundaries, or in coordination with other professions.

🌿 *TYPES OF TREATMENT* 🌿

Clinical psychiatric treatment has not been mentioned here as it is the responsibility of the hospital services, but all community mental health services depend ultimately upon the existence of the hospital medical service, which deals with the clinical aspects of mental illness at inpatient or outpatient level, and on the family practitioner, who maintains responsibility for the patient at all times.

The community mental health service supplies the *rehabilitative, supportive and preventive services*. These latter services, applied either to a patient or his family, may have to be coordinated with clinical treatment.

Psychiatric theory and practice make a contribution to the nonclinical services such as occupational therapy and casework dealing with a patient and with the members of the family.

The wide range of services needs a coordinator who becomes a key figure. The key figure may be the family doctor, psychiatrist, psychiatric social worker, or a member of another profession, such as a health visitor or child care officer. The selection of the key figure may depend upon the way the problem is first presented, and frequently it is a diagnostic assessment made by the community mental health service that enables some other service to retain, or resume, the primary relationship with some individual or family. Some professional service has to accept a continuing responsibility during the time that various other services take up and relinquish their specialist rules.

🌿 *INTERPROFESSIONAL CONSULTATIONS* 🌿

Interprofessional consultations may be a part of investigation, diagnosis, and treatment. When a problem is referred by one service to another, the procedure may take any of the following basic courses: (1) complete transfer of the responsibility; (2) examination and reporting back to the original agency; (3) conjoint examinations and treatment (this procedure depends upon the development of common aims and a common language and requires mutual confidence between services); or (4) the mental health consultation (this process takes place in the absence of the client or patient—in discussions with other professions on specific problems, general principles are derived).

Finally, it is necessary to emphasize that all the processes that are at present being undertaken by a community mental health service need conceptualization and formulation. Phrases like "giving support" or "making a relationship" are applied indiscriminately to organized professional work and to the unorganized interpersonal processes that exist among lay members of the community. Professionalization involves a disciplined use of relationships and a study of the nature of the interaction between therapist and patient. Professional work must be capable of being taught in order that the work not die with its originator.

Systems of community mental health are new. Comparisons might be made between the development of the services and the life history of an individual. Referring to the integrative processes that take place in the life of a child between the ages of nine and twelve, Henry Maier[5] states:

> The child brings into several systems the standards he has acquired and practiced in the past. He also incorporates his elders' comments, standards, and expectations. Basically, he relates fragmentary practices, hearsay, and knowledge into one related, practical system, although the theoretical implications of the system will not be comprehended until later.

If, in the above passage, we substitute the phrase *community mental health worker* for the word *child,* we would have a fair representation of the present level of community mental health work. Much progress has yet to be made before even its adolescence is reached.

---

[5] Maier, H., *Three Theories of Child Development,* New York: Harper and Row, 1965.

Mental Health Services in a Canadian Province

M. N. Beck

DEPARTMENT OF HEALTH
CHARLOTTETOWN, PRINCE EDWARD ISLAND

XII

Historical interpretation is not a field to be blithely invaded by one with a basically scientific background; furthermore, natural candor makes it necessary to point out that when one has been closely involved in the working out of the events described, and either highly encouraged or discouraged by their occurrence, complete objectivity in their interpretation is an almost impossible ambition. It is therefore recommended that the following account of the development of a psychiatric service in a small rural province of Canada be taken for exactly what it is—the humble attempt by a passionately involved participant to describe his assessment of the factors important in the development of this service.

Located in the Gulf of St. Lawrence in the crescent formed by New Brunswick and Nova Scotia, Prince Edward Island is roughly 150 miles long, fifty miles wide at its widest point and four miles wide at its narrowest point. Its rich agricultural land was originally settled by the French in the early 1700's but, following the exile of the Acadians (the Louisiana "Cajuns") in 1755, it was populated by predominantly Scotch and English peoples, along with some Irish stock. A few pockets of French-speaking peoples remained or returned following the expulsion, and their descendants now represent some 15 per cent of our population.

The total population now numbers about 100,000, a nice round figure, which incidentally makes us the theoretically ideal population entity for maximal development of community psychiatric services.

By virtue of historical accident—and of our strategic location for the defense of the St. Lawrence River from hostile attack by our then not-so-friendly neighbors to the south—the founders of Canada decreed this island a separate province. Thus, our 100,000 persons have become encumbered or blessed, depending on one's viewpoint, with all the accoutrements of provincial government, the Canadian equivalent of state government. We have the complete issue: lieutenant governor, premier, legislative assembly, an executive council with eight ministers of the various departments of governments, our own courts, and our own civil service.

This heavy concentration of governmental functions for a small population creates an intimate and often personal relationship between the population at large and its agents, be they politicians or civil servants. This relationship is a two-edged sword, offering unusually easy access, with its attendant advantages and disadvantages. Not only is it relatively easy for professional service groups to contact those in positions of power and for the powers themselves to contact and be aware of the usefulness of the various services provided: but also it is much easier for these various groups to get in one another's hair. Personal idiosyncrasies in a small setting such as this have maximal potential for both good and harm.

As one political scientist aptly expressed it, "Prince Edward Island is a microcosm of all that is good, and all that is evil, in democracy."

Yet this intimate political scene offers a situation that permits us to see and to describe some of the pertinent forces and principles at work in the development of comprehensive psychiatric services within our kind of democratic system in either a large or a small state.

This small political unit permits the various private and governmental helping professions an ease of communication that is more difficult to achieve in larger population groupings. A close and often personal relationship has developed between the personnel of the Division of Mental Health, the Departments of Health, Education, and

Welfare, the private agencies, and such individual professional practitioners as physicians.

The early history of the development of our psychiatric services presents nothing unusual, or, if anything unusual, then unusually bad. Our mental hospital evolved from the usual dismal North American combination of poorhouse and jail, later moving toward the more humanitarian, but still dismal, concept of asylum in the late 1800's, and undergoing, during the early decades of this century, the all-too-common regression to the mechanical, demoralized institution of incarceration.

The evolution of our present program from those days is most easily described in two phases. The first phase was initiated in the late twenties and early thirties by the dedicated concern of the late Dr. W. J. P. MacMillan, our first Minister of Health. He had through the years worked on the staff of Falconwood Hospital and with this first-hand knowledge initiated two most significant steps.

First, he ordered a survey of Falconwood Hospital to be carried out by the then Canadian National Committee for Mental Hygiene. This was done by Dr. Clarence M. Hincks, the founder of the Canadian Mental Health Association, whose far-seeing report contains many recommendations implemented only in very recent years, as well as some not yet fulfilled. Second, Dr. MacMillan arranged for, and encouraged and supported, Dr. A. J. Murchison to take specialized training in psychiatry and to take on the post of Superintendent of Falconwood Hospital.

Dr. MacMillan assumed the leadership of the provincial Conservative party prior to the election of 1932. It is not without significance to this report that in that election not one seat in the house was won by a Conservative, and Dr. MacMillan himself was defeated. I am reliably informed that one of the most potent weapons wielded against him in this campaign was "the time and money he was wasting on the nuts at Falconwood."

Dr. Murchison became Superintendent in 1934 and continued as Superintendent and Director of Mental Health until his death in 1961. Because of his persistent and dedicated efforts against heavy odds, the lot of the mentally ill on Prince Edward Island has been a continually improving one since 1934. Providing even the basic essentials of reasonable levels of physical care for his charges required herculean efforts. For example, he spent ten years of intensive effort and attention before he was able to accomplish the installation of a fire protection system in our frame buildings. But his role was much larger than this: he introduced high standards of excellence of care on the scientific level, imbued the attendant and nursing staff with a profound sense of concern and kindliness toward their patients, and, by his continuing efforts for better community services in the late thirties and early forties, laid the groundwork for the developments of the fifties, which now show promise of continuing through the sixties.

In 1946, the administration of Falconwood Hospital was transferred from the Department of Public Works to the Department of Health.

The real cornerstone in the building of psychiatric services was laid in 1948 when the federal government initiated a series of mental health grants. The matter of health care under the British North America Act is the responsibility of the provinces. These grants from the federal level were necessarily administrated by the provinces and were designed as seed moneys for the development of mental health services by the provinces. That they succeeded so well in this latter objective must be attributed to the wise planning for their utilization by the then Minister of Health and later Premier, the Honorable A. W. Matheson, our Deputy Minister of Health, Dr. O. H. Curtis, and his assistant, Dr. J. H. Shaw. Since that time our psychiatric services have developed rapidly both within our mental hospital and in the community. As expected, the expenditure of provincial funds for the development of "new" services now far exceeds that of the original federal grants.

𝕏 INSTITUTION OF PRESENT SERVICES 𝕏

1950: Two psychiatrists start in training for work in our division.

1951: We engage our first clinical psychologist.

1952: Two psychiatrists are added to the staff. Initially, they divided their time equally between Falconwood Hospital and the newly opened Mental Health Clinic in Charlottetown, our capital, a city with a population of eighteen thousand. They introduced the modern therapeutic modalities, intensive psychotherapy, ECT, insulin, and so on, to our services.

1953: We engage a psychiatric social worker.

1954: (1) A program of guidance consultants is instituted into our school system. It is unusual that this program should have been successfully developed by the mental health clinic, and this can only be attributed to the ease of establishing good communication between the Departments of Health and Education in this small province. At present the mental health clinic employs four teachers in this role. (2) Psychology department is stabilized. (3) Occupational therapy and recreational therapy programs are instituted at Falconwood.

1955: (1) Two psychiatrists are added to the staff. (2) A child psychiatry program is initiated. (3) Traveling clinics are started in Summerside (a population center of 8,000 people) offering adult services, child services, and psychology services.

1956: (1) The first day training class for trainable retarded children is started. This program has now been expanded to serve approximately 65 per cent of our population, with classes located in some towns with a population of only three to four hundred. (2) An active program providing diagnostic and counseling services for the retarded and their families is initiated. This, in retrospect, was in direct response to pressure generated by the local branch of the Association for Retarded Children.

1957: Active treatment center of seventy beds is opened at Falconwood Hospital.

1958: (1) By political fiat, the name of Falconwood Hospital is changed to Riverside Hospital, this on the pretext of administrative advantage, but in reality in response to a widespread wish on the part of the public for the change. (2) One psychiatrist leaves full-time civil service for part-time private practice and part-time government employment. At issue is the matter of salary.

1959: (1) The first resignation by one of our psychiatrists is handed in. This follows a private confrontation between the psychiatric staff and the politicians. It is by no means our first encounter on this level, but it is one of the more acrimonious ones. This is soon followed by the resignation of a second psychiatrist. (2) Services are retrenched.

1960: (1) We institute a "boarding out" or "foster home" program for ex-hospital and chronic care patients. (2) A Prince Edward Island Division of The Canadian Mental Health Association is formed.

1961: (1) All the remaining psychiatrists and the director of psychology resign *en masse* from the staff of the mental hospital (the child psychiatrist does not resign from his mental health clinic role). This time the encounter between the staff of the Division of Mental Health and the powers-that-be remains private for a couple of months, but then is conducted in the public forum of the press. Controversy over the issue of mental health services occupies the front page of our leading local newspapers for the best part of two weeks and is the object of much editorial discussion.

This dispute differs from previous ones in several important ways. (A) The issue becomes public. (B) The thinking of the staff matures and we are finally able to define the issues. As an illustration of this, we scrupulously avoid the subject of salaries (when psychiatrists don't talk money, then maturity must be coming close). (C) On our side, we focus on administrative problems, most of which are a legacy from our historical development. Our position again centers on the fact that we remain administratively responsible to three departments of government—Health, Public Works, and Agriculture. (D) Although our Canadian Mental Health Association is a relatively new organization, it joins the battle and helps to mobilize vocal expression of public support.

Predictably, we lose the battle—psychiatrists in the public arena are no match for politicians—but I think we win the war. Our ranks are decimated and, temporarily at least, our services to patients are virtually paralyzed. But from the crucible of conflict there emerges a clearer delineation of the problems inherent in establishing an adequate government-sponsored psychiatric service, an open demonstration of widespread public and professional interest and concern with these services, and a demonstration of the depth of the commitment of professional staff to the interests of their patients.

(2) "Home Strengthening Service" for the retarded is instituted. A full-time social worker is employed for counseling and assistance to the retarded and their families.

1962: (1) Dr. A. J. Murchison, for many years the Director of Mental Health, dies. (2) Sherwood Hospital, a twenty-one-bed residential type institution for the inpatient care of retarded children, opens. (3) Administrative rearrangements are worked out whereby the Division of Mental Health becomes responsible to a Board of Governors, with representation from the citizenry, the Department of Health, the government, the opposition, and the Mental Health Association.

This arrangement, while it has its weaknesses, gives us something of a buffer between the professional staff and the political powers in this snug little island, and also provides a meeting place where we can arrive at decisions without being snowed under by paper. (4) A strong volunteer program is instituted by the Mental Health Association. (5) Four social workers are added to the staff of our division. With this increase in staff, it becomes possible to expand child guidance services to three smaller centers in the province.

1963: (1) The top-level staff of the division is restabilized. Our first psychiatrist to resign is re-engaged as Director of Mental Health despite the fact that he, during his vacation, actively participated in our 1961 affray. Another of our casualties who resigned at that time to go into private practice is re-engaged and gives us four sessions a week while continuing his private practice. Two other psychiatrists are on our staff and two more are expected by June 1964. (2) Three individual advancement classes for educable retarded children open. (3) A sheltered workshop for the adult retarded is started by the Canadian Association for Retarded Children.

PRESENT STATUS

It has been said that mankind lives on hopes; I am no exception to this rule. There is certainly good reason, however, to feel that we have finally arrived at a position where a truly effective and clinically centered program can be developed. To a large extent we have released ourselves from those dead-end traditions stemming from our historical development that so often became our main area of concern in the past decade. Our staff resources are apparently adequate to staff our presently well-developed services, and administration has been stabilized on a workable basis. Much remains to be done, and will be discussed below, but one senses that it can now be accomplished.

That our present services are so close to adequate is in itself remarkable. The fact that we could build these services in a deeply conservative rural culture and in a province that is truly an economically depressed area deserves some analysis of the factors that we think have made this development possible. Although many important influences and persons are undoubtedly overlooked in this discussion, we would draw attention to points in the following paragraphs.

Public Education. Since 1952, all our upper echelon staff have been most active in efforts to educate the public to the pressing needs of the mentally disordered. In turn, the public has shown continued interest in having us present our case. We have presented numberless addresses to Parent-Teacher Associations, church groups, professional bodies, service clubs, youth groups, and so on.

It is almost impossible to evaluate the quantitative effectiveness of this approach, but it is our impression that it has materially helped in establishing a broad base of public support and interest in our programs. The local press has consistently reported such activities. In recent years, the Prince Edward Island Division of the Canadian Mental Health Association has provided yeoman assistance to this effort. Their program of volunteers has been most effective in organizing a goodly sized group whose interest in our services is a personal one.

Our most effective promotion has, of course, been provided by satisfied patients and their relatives. The cliché that nothing succeeds like success certainly applies here. On the basis of our experience, we can confidently state that a reasonably adequate service sells itself to the public. Of course the stigma associated with psychiatric treatment still remains, but one can sense its strength diminishing year by year, and it certainly is not the barrier to people seeking our treatment that it was even as recently as five years ago.

The Medical Society. From the start of our modern era, the psychiatric staff have closely identified themselves with the provincial medical society. On our part, this required ready involvement in Medical Society functions and responsibilities, regular attendance at meetings, and participation in committee work and other activities. In turn we have run into little or none of the commonly reported rejection of psychiatry by our medical confreres, or lack of interest on their part in our efforts to provide adequate services. On the contrary, they have through the years steadily supported our efforts to strengthen and maintain our services, or to improve our personal lot in such matters as salaries. Indeed, in the public confrontation between the psychiatric staff and the government in 1961, the Medical Society fired the opening round on our behalf.

Our early decision to accept patients only on referral from physicians in both hospital and clinical services undoubtedly was a factor in the establishment of this mutually beneficial relationship, although the policy is now being slightly modified.

Voluntary Health Agencies. Over the past ten years, we have had experience in living professionally both without and with voluntary health agencies. Our experience in both situations convinces us that active voluntary agencies are an absolute necessity in the development of adequate psychiatric services. Because of unsatisfactory experiences on the part of our psychiatric staff with the Mental Health Association of another province during our residency, we were loath to encourage the growth of a similar organization in this province. By 1958 and 1959, we began to feel the consequences of this strategic mistake. We came face to face with the frustration of working for services that we knew had widespread public support, when there was no organization or mechanism for either mobilizing this support or making it articulate. With our encouragement, then, the Prince Edward Island Division of the Canadian Mental Health Association came into being in 1960—about twenty-five years postmature.

Since then they have really made their presence felt: public education has been intensified, their Scientific Advisory Committee has prepared an excellent study of the Mental Health needs of our province, and they inaugurated a program of providing Mental Hospital patients with various services in which their corps of volunteer workers have been most helpful.

Our experience with the Canadian Association for Retarded Children has been entirely different. As elsewhere, this group grew up as a grass-roots movement motivated primarily by the parents of retarded children themselves. Our psychiatrists were no more cognizant of the various needs of the retarded than psychiatrists trained elsewhere, and our initial efforts to provide services for the retarded were, in essence, a defensive move to get this highly vocal and emotional group off our backs. Fortunately, we did not resist them too long and our initial professional efforts in this field (our abysmal ignorance could be counteracted only by the application of common sense and skills learned for other problems) were accepted as being of much more value than their true worth. Very quickly, a close working relationship developed between the Child Guidance staff and this voluntary organization.

In the space of some five years, this small but dedicated group had created a profound interest and sympathy in the citizenry for their cause, and this interest was soon reflected by the politicians. The organization's willingness to work on their own projects and, further-more, to back their objectives with their own money greatly increased their impact on the community and on the government.

In the provision of services for the retarded, then, the profes-sional often found himself in the position of having to catch up to projects initiated by the Association and having to implement govern-ment suggestions as to how to provide services for the retarded. This, though rough at times, is a much happier position to be in than the situation we have sometimes faced in developing the more traditional psychiatric services.

The Political System. In the establishment of a state-sponsored program of psychiatric services, it is inevitable that the professionals involved become subject to our politicians and to the various pres-sures of our political system. This is a mystifying world to the profes-sional, and one where the logical, sequential reasoning of professional training ranks very low on the scale of practical usefulness.

The scale of values changes. In this realm, one has to be ready to recognize that one and one do not always make two, and that often, even if they do, it does not make much difference anyway. The basic yardstick becomes votes. The operational yardstick becomes the ebb and flow of power, and the primary resistance to progress is often the threat to the free exercise of power by the politician. With the value system pivoting around the garnering of votes, vote-catching programs become those most desired by government: buildings become more im-portant than staff to operate the program (staffing does not offer either jobs for numbers of potential voters or a convenient corner in which to lay a stone duly inscribed with outstanding names); a program on paper becomes more important than a program with true professional integrity: the presence of almost any person in a position is as good for pragmatic political purposes as the best professional. The political world is indeed a wonderful one, and you ignore it at your peril and the peril of the program you hope to see develop.

Although this might seem strongly phrased, don't conclude that I am casting aspersions on the individual politician. I describe but a single aspect of the reality in which he lives, a reality basically alien to the one in which we as professionals must operate. (Parenthetically, I saw a dramatic example of this question of different orientations when a medical confrere, who had run for election and been defeated, was undecided as to whether to "offer" again or not, The problem, he told me—and I have no reason to doubt his judgment—was whether he could change his way of thinking enough to become successful in politics. The epigram, "If a lady says no she means maybe, if she says maybe she means yes, and if she says yes she's no lady," applies here in reverse: "If a politician says maybe he means no, if he says yes he means maybe, and if he says no he's no politician.")

The wonder is not that we professionals at times are at odds with the politician, but that so often the politician can or will support a good cause in the face of the pressing realities of his own occupation.

Beyond this difference in viewpoint, one must recognize that government faces demands on its resources from all quarters, and that the needs of the mentally ill are a long way from having first-class political appeal.

The question remaining before us is, how can we as professionals best function in promoting the welfare of our patients within our democratic political system?

The ultimate answer lies in a concerned and informed public, and, where this public is present, a mechanism whereby its concern may find overt expression. To be truly effective, this concern must be forcibly and continuously expressed at all levels of government—administrative, departmental, and political—and our objectives must be interpreted to legislators in politically meaningful forms.

On the professionals' side, we must rank public education high on our list of responsibilities. In turn, we must be willing to invest ourselves by actively placing our efforts behind, and with, those of the public in expressing the needs of the mentally disordered or handicapped to all levels of government. Our experience on Prince Edward Island indicates that, in order to make this effort effective, we will sometimes have to become vociferous, and not infrequently an issue will depend upon our willingness to fight or fail.

Finally, all this effort will be ineffective unless the professional is ready to back up his stand by resignation. As one who has not resigned, I can be somewhat objective and state from observation that the resignations of my confreres from their positions has been the single most productive instrument for change in our local situation.

In the civil service, the professional assumes a role for which his professional training and ideals ill equip him. The professional concepts of individual responsibility, responsiveness to personal need, and attention to quality of service often conflict with the bureaucratic values of stability and quiet competence on the one hand, and an attitude of reverence for the written over the spoken word, for evolution over revolution, and for discretion rather than aggression on the other hand.

This is a conflict of interest that both threatens and is threatened by the professional. It is also a job situation that can seduce the professional and subtly neutralize his worthwhile attributes. Diabolical ingenuity could scarcely design an instrument more effective for the lulling of the professional conscience than the security offered in the tenure-related civil service pension, a device which becomes more coercive as year passes year, and as the individual rises in the administrative hierarchy, where his professional value system should become increasingly beneficial.

It is not easy for the professional to be in this system without becoming of it; nor for him to maintain his objectivity while being subject to both the third-party pressures of bureaucracy and the direct pressures of professional responsibility and concern for his patients.

A perhaps unusual facet in the development of psychiatric services on Prince Edward Island is the identification of the community psychiatrist with the conservative element of the community. Certainly the popular image of the psychiatrist is that of a radical, if not indeed a leftist, and at the very least a nonconformist.

That our identification does lie with the conservative element of the community is objectively illustrated by the fact that last fall over 50 per cent of all our clergymen attended, at their own expense, a two-day workshop on mental health.

It is the writer's opinion that this type of identification is one of our real sources of strength, although its coming about has been much more the result of fortuitous accident than deliberate design.

In a province as small as ours, it was perhaps inevitable that our staff should become personally acquainted with and closely related to the staffs of the Departments of Education and Welfare, and of the private health and social agencies.

This has been a most gratifying aspect of our work here, and experience has shown this close integration with other disciplines to be mutually beneficial. We have as often been the grateful recipients of their help as they have of ours.

An interesting development from this integration has been the carrying of the load of guidance services for our school system by staff operating from the mental health clinic. This has been an invaluable aspect of our child psychiatric service in early case finding and other preventive roles, and also has enabled us to provide real assistance to our educational services. Plans are now laid for transfer of this program to the Department of Education, where its further development can more readily take place, but we are confident that its close relationship to the mental health services will continue.

𝕏 THE FUTURE 𝕏

Even in this very small community, with a relatively adequate psychiatric staff, experience has shown too much shuffling of patients from one psychiatrist to another, both within the hospital itself and between the hospital and the clinic. Added to this discontinuity within our services is the emergent pattern of disengagement by the family physician in the treatment of patients when they come into our care. This presents a multifaceted problem which can be solved only by diligent efforts on several levels.

We have found one clue on this problem. The expansion of our Child Guidance Services to the smaller communities (populations of 750 to 1500 persons) has greatly expanded our ability to provide psychotherapeutic services for all our population. It is now apparent that our people will undertake a prolonged program of weekly therapeutic sessions when this program is made available for them in their local shopping area, where before we had much difficulty persuading them to undertake therapy in our larger centers. The problem of resistance to therapy must be remembered here, but we are satisfied that most of this reluctance in the past has been centered on the reality problems involved in the disruption of the life pattern by weekly visits to a center other than the one in which the potential patient usually does business.

This being so, we are now wondering if it is possible to establish an administrative system in which the psychiatric and social work personnel involved in the care of the patient in the community facility could not also become the persons responsible for the care of the patient while in hospital. We wonder too if it would not be wiser to establish a permanent team in Summerside rather than continue our present pattern of serving the western end of the island by traveling clinics.

Our current major problem in relationship to the general practitioners may be an unusual one—at least one not commonly reported. It goes like this: Once the G.P. refers a case to us, some change takes place. The responsibility for the patient's care somehow or other becomes transferred to our governmental service. It is as if the G.P. now says, "This patient is yours." If we discharge the patient from our hospital, the G.P. resists taking him back under his care, and recently we find more and more referrals from our colleagues that read: "This patient was seen by Dr. Theriault (staff psychiatrist) two years ago. Would you ask him to reassess his case and give whatever treatment is necessary?"

The paradox here is that in following this pattern, the family physician is espousing and promoting that which he most actively and vocally disavows—state medicine. Yet the fact remains that, as regards psychiatric services, this apparently is what he wishes to do. We fear that as the adequacy of our staff improves this practice will increase, and we could eventually find ourselves solely responsible for treating the psychiatric ills of our population. This would obviously be an impossible burden.

We have no solution to this dilemma, but we are beginning to face up to it. Would psychiatric units in general hospitals help? Can the general practitioners be persuaded to follow the care of their patients into mental hospitals as they do into general hospitals? Experiments in Saskatchewan indicate that the G.P. can be actively involved in hospital care of the psychiatrically ill. Can our liaison with the G.P. while the patient is undergoing psychotherapy in our clinics be improved, and would this ameliorate this situation?

Like other governments, ours derives a very substantial income from the sale of alcohol; yet it has accepted no responsibility for alleviating the personal and social ravages associated with its abuse. Because of our mental hospital's liberal admission policy, our alcoholism service has been literally swamped. (We have the highest admission rate of any mental hospital in Canada.)

This admission rate has made us acutely aware of the size of this problem, and prompted us into an effort to do something about it.

Again we do not know what to do, but are satisfied that our

present anarchistic approach is of little use, and also that the mental health service cannot tackle the problem on its own. This problem is now under active study.

We have been gratified by the apparent success of our community-oriented programs for the retarded. For three years now we have had one well-trained social worker devoting full time to what we call our "Home Strengthening Program." With this program we are attempting to provide the families of the retarded with the kind of help they need to meet the crisis imposed on them by their retarded child, whether this help be psychotherapy, counseling, direction to the various sources of help available, such as diagnostic clinics, Associations for Retarded Children and so on, or the finding of specialized equipment for the child. This program has proven its worth and shows real potential for becoming the coordinating arm for the many community services involved in the care of the retarded. With the backing of the National Canadian Association for Retarded Children, plans have now been laid to increase the staffing of this program in the hope that we will be able to establish a "Demonstration Project for Community Care of the Retarded in a Rural Area." Such a project, together with the natural evolution of other community services for the retarded, could become an exciting program to watch.

We have always been aware of the fact that the mental hospital traditionally has been a repository for all kinds of community problems other than those due primarily to mental illness. Even so, we were surprised when a recent survey of our mental hospital population disclosed the fact that 40.4 per cent of our patients did not require psychiatric care.

This makes it mandatory that we make a basic change in our pattern of providing services. We are now considering two approaches to this problem: (1) turning over part of our physical plant to the Department of Welfare for the provision of custodial care, and (2) broadening our foster home or boarding-out program.

Our division of Child Welfare is presently legally responsible for the supervision of the care of some 350 children. With a staff of only two trained social workers and some untrained assistants, it is apparent that they cannot adequately discharge this responsibility. It is also apparent that the inadequate care they are able to provide for these children constitutes a hothouse for the development of psychological and social disorders, and that a golden opportunity is lost to provide a truly effective program for preventive psychiatry. This service sees families in the midst of crisis and at a time when help is most needed and should be most effective.

The Canadian Mental Health Association has recently appointed a study group to look into this problem, and hopefully this will bear fruit in the future.

Under the auspices of the Canadian Association for Retarded Children, a small sheltered workshop was opened for retarded adults in the fall of 1963. This program has gotten off to a good start and shows promise of doing big things for us in the future.

At least, this community facility will enable us to keep many of the adult retarded out of hospital who otherwise would have become institutionalized. It should enable us to broaden the base of our boarding out program. Many persons, partially disabled either from social or psychological factors, could become at least partially productive in such a setting. There appears to be no real reason why the one sheltered workshop cannot serve the partially disabled mental hospital patients, the retarded, and those with physical disability.

We are now mentally preparing ourselves for this program involving some 500, and likely more, patients. To keep this operating in a rural area will be no mean feat.

Through the years our staff has been actively engaged in presenting lectures and workshops to teachers on the field. This, while usually well accepted by the teachers, has been in our opinion an exercise of doubtful merit.

Teachers are in a strategic position for early case finding and other preventive roles in the mental health field. One senses that, with their present lack of information, lack of orientation to mental health principles, and indeed often negative approach to the many problems of children, instead of being a tremendous force for furthering mental health in our people, they are often a source of downright harm.

We have, therefore, considered this a matter of some urgency, and arrangements are now well under way for the staff of our teachers-in-training in the normal schools.

It has been recognized for many years that with our small, easily accessible population, Prince Edward Island presents an unusual natural laboratory for research into many aspects of psychiatric disorders. With the present improved staffing of our Division of Mental Health, this field has become even more fertile for research purposes.

University facilities are reasonably accessible. The provincial government has been approached on this matter and has already demonstrated its interest by limited financial backing. Our administrative staff are all anxious to see progress in this respect.

The problem is now one of how to find financial support and personnel to conduct worthwhile research here. It is certain that we are ripe for rewarding research in incidence and epidemiology, genetics, evaluation of treatment, long term follow-up, and other types of studies of our manifold problems.

Plans are now laid to have knowledgeable research people look at our situation and guide us along the way. This is too good an opportunity to pass by and we would welcome further assistance in developing research here from any or all sources.

CONCLUSION

As stated earlier, this account represents the viewpoint of one very biased observer of the development of the psychiatric services in this island province. Undoubtedly, we yet have many problems before us, but it now appears that we are over the worst hurdles, that our groundwork is well and truly laid, that we are in a good position from which to tackle future problems, and that we can now anticipate a stable service with continuing progress in the years ahead.

Psychiatric Care and the Public Offender

Leon N. Shapiro

TUFTS UNIVERSITY SCHOOL OF MEDICINE

XIII

*E*ach age projects its philosophy and assumptions about man into its treatment of criminals. Since World War II and the development of means for universal destruction, there has been an increasing sense of urgency to understand man's relationship to himself. An important element in this understanding is examining his impulses toward others.

Since the early thirties, "efforts to understand" criminality have been essentially sociological in approach, seeing the criminal as the product of a pathogenic environment. Rehabilitation then meant a hopeful reordering of his environment, one aspect of the liberal fantasy of the infinite perfectibility of man and the elimination of poverty, disease, and so on, through social manipulation.

The psychoanalytic position, in contrast, views behavior as the product of the interaction of biological unfolding and ongoing experience. As the attendant concept of unconscious conflict as a central determinant in neurotic symptom formation proved useful in the treatment of the neuroses, it was inevitable that efforts would be made to apply these concepts to the treatment of the psychoses and the major character disorders.

287

This has had little impact, however, on the lot of the average prisoner. He is treated humanely, given a variety of rehabilitation opportunities, and with few exceptions, returns to prison with the same predictable regularity as his ancestors who lived in the more religious age of the original penitentiaries where silence prevailed. On the other hand, a great deal has changed in the kind of thinking we as a society are beginning to do about prisoners and about ourselves.

The "understanding" of a chronic criminal is an enormous task. To feel the panic, the urgency, and the fury of the mildest frustration, to be unaware of the experience that there is someone to trust, to be unable to wait with the reasonable expectation that one won't be disappointed—these are just some of the chronic criminal's moment-to-moment experiences. They are outside the lives of those of us who don't go through the "revolving doors" of the correction system.

Increasing numbers of professional people with clinical experiences in the actual treatment of prisoners are moving into positions of authority in various systems. We seem to be groping our way toward a more rational approach to the management of the criminal, more difficult to achieve because of the depth of his impact on us. Described as a martyr, a scapegoat for our guilt, he is also the reasonable object of our anger. We can get some sense of the difficulty in treating criminals reasonably if we put ourselves in the emotional position of a victim of assault or robbery, or ask ourselves how we would deal with a man who attacks us. Yet it is obvious that our primitive retaliatory response can hardly be the basis on which effective handling of the criminal can rest. But we can try, and we do come up with some steps toward understanding.

This chapter is an account of the formulation of a few such steps, and their practical application by psychiatrists and others, within one state's prison and correctional system. What follows is (1) a historical description of the development of the Division of Legal Medicine, a part of the Massachusetts Department of Mental Health concerned with the treatment of public offenders in the courts and prisons, (2) an attempt to formulate our understanding of the most serious criminal problems, and (3) a brief assessment of the implications of this work.

LEGAL MEDICINE AND THE
CORRECTIONAL SYSTEM

Between 1954 and 1959, we developed in Massachusetts an agency providing psychiatric diagnosis and treatment for 10 per cent of our state prison population, clinics covering 25 per cent of the state's district courts, parole treatment services, consultation, diagnostic, and treatment services in a half dozen juvenile institutions, several extended research programs, and training services for prison guards, probation, and parole officers as well as for psychiatric social workers, psychologists, and psychiatrists with special interests in this area. This section is an effort to describe the major elements in the development of this program. A part of this history is in the form of a personal narrative; this is done deliberately because it seems that the internal experiences are at least as important as the formal history, and some data about the interaction between them may be helpful to someone developing similar programs elsewhere.

The narrative history presents (1) a description of the structure of the correction system, (2) the special place of the sex offender law as the impetus for services, (3) problems of initiating the services and their stage-by-stage development, (4) description of the court clinics, (5) the prison clinics, (6) training problems, (7) paroles, and (8) the Youth Service Board.

Our courts and correctional systems are elaborate structures with wise and powerful traditions evolved to meet the needs of the community. It is important at the outset to stress how well this system works, since there will be much implied and open criticism in what follows. Changes in the system (for example, the moves toward indeterminate sentencing) that have evolved or will evolve through the increased application of psychological principles and techniques will of necessity be gradual, and be built on what is essentially a sound structure necessary for the functioning of the kind of society we have. The prison population is small (about .1 per cent of the whole population) and drawn from the ranks of the emotionally, culturally, educationally, and financially impoverished. Most recent studies point to developmental failures in the earliest years, which become character problems requiring lifelong management rather than "cure." The potential con-

tribution the mental health field can make is largely in the more sophisticated application of external controls, classification, and the clarification of problem research areas.

The Massachusetts correction system is organized like those of
most other states. A review of a typical criminal career segment will
familiarize the reader with the main cast of characters and institutions
concerned with criminal care. John Doe (the legal jargon equivalent
to patient A) commits a crime, is apprehended by the police, brought
to the police station where he is charged, and brought before the clerk
of the court who makes arrangement for the man's case to be heard
at the next sitting of the district judge. At the hearing the judge ac-
cepts the man's plea—guilty or not guilty—and may dispose of the
case by dismissing it or fining or jailing the accused. He may decide
that the case is too serious for a district court and refer it to a grand
jury, which then decides whether sufficient evidence exists to try the
man in a superior court. Finally, the judge may decide he needs more
information, in which case he may allow the man to be at large or
to post bond while the case is postponed.

If the case comes to trial in either the district or superior court,
the presence of a jury may be waived by the defendant, in which case
the judge alone hears the case. If the defendant is found not guilty,
the case is closed. If he is found guilty, the judge then has to decide
on a sentence, the limits of which are prescribed by statute: for such
and such crime, he may be sentenced to not less than so many days
or years, and to not more than so many days or years. The sentence
may be suspended or combined with a fine (also prescribed by statute),
or the man may be placed on probation. In cases where probation or
suspended sentence is ordered, the man is assigned a probation officer
who is to oversee the man's behavior in the community for a specified
period of time.

If he is sentenced to prison, he may be paroled after a certain
portion of his time is served; this is under the jurisdiction of the Parole
Board. The board, through its parole officers, oversees his behavior
in the community. While he is in prison, he is the responsibility of the
Department of Correction; while he is on parole, he is the responsibility
of the Parole Board. Both are in the executive branch of the government, responsible to the governor.

The system for women is identical in structure. The system for children is similar, except for the fact that the courts sentence a child to the Youth Service Board, which then determines disposition. The board runs the juvenile institutions and also decides on time of release and supervises juvenile parole.

In addition to this state system, each of our counties has its own jails, houses of correction and parole system. Whether a man goes to a county or a state institution usually depends on the length of his sentence; in general, sentences of one year or more are served in state institutions. A man may go to a county house of correction one time, and to a state prison the next, depending on the seriousness of his crime.

The personnel who run the correction machinery are (1) the various police agencies, (2) the judges and probation officers, (3) the prison officials and guards, (4) the Parole Board and parole officers, (5) the Youth Service Board and its professional and nonprofessional personnel. These people, plus a few interested legislators, make up the "correction community" with interests, expertise, and organizations (like the Massachusetts Corrections Conference and the Probation and Parole Association) developed around the problems of care and custody of criminals. There are also lay organizations, small special-interest groups, and individuals in the legal community who concern themselves with problems of "correction." Although there is interest from many quarters, the total number of persons in the community who know or care about correction problems is small.

Traditionally, it has been extremely difficult for the correction community to get much action on any reforms, be they new physical facilities, higher pay for personnel, or increased training requirements. Both local and national organizations repeatedly call for action and for new ideas for the management and rehabilitation of the criminal population. Most of these groups have been intrigued with the possibility of introducing some of the newer psychological disciplines into correction work. Generally, however, each change in the field has been intimately tied to some current crisis; an exposure of corruption or incompetence, a series of frightening crimes or a riot usually brings an outcry for action and the "correction community" is presented an opportunity for a leap forward.

In Massachusetts, the traditional relationship of psychiatry to the courts and prisons until 1954 had been through the use of court alienists[1] and the state mental hospitals. The alienists provided a diagnostic service for the courts when questions of competence or responsibility were raised. Rarely was a relationship developed between a psychiatrist and a judge or probation officer that permitted a more fruitful interchange and dialogue about the management of offenders. The state hospitals receiving court cases for thirty days observation limited their reports generally to the finding of psychosis.

Before 1954, private funds had started a few clinics. Some limited county funds had provided part-time court clinic services in two or three communities. The likelihood of direct state support, however, appeared remote without a major demonstration of an effective and useful court clinic. Even though a Massachusetts Bar Association group had been meeting for several years and had done much of the preparatory groundwork for a state-sponsored clinic, they lacked funds to get such a clinic started. A dramatic confrontation of the public and the legislature was needed. It was provided in the early summer of 1954 by a series of sexual crimes, which were covered in exquisite detail by the press and radio.

During an earlier outburst of public indignation, a "sex offender" law had been passed, but for lack of interest and funds had remained inoperative. The law, which was modeled after similar legislation in other states, attempts (1) to define a sex offender, or sexually dangerous person, as someone who is likely to commit a sex crime by reason of some mental disorder as evidenced in part by his past behavior, (2) to establish a center for the care and custody of the sex offender who will be committed under this law, and (3) to set up standards for release of the prisoner to the community.

Spurred by the 1954 crimes, the legislature demanded that the Commissioner of Mental Health implement the existing law by developing a system for eliminating the sex offender from the free population before he committed his crime. This was an interesting request and one that the legislature kept returning to, no matter how often its unrealistic nature was pointed out. Many violent sexual crimes were committed by persons who had been described previously as potentially dangerous; the idea of a law that would "get these people off the

[1] The "alienist" has been an official court designation for psychiatrists qualified by the court to certify commitments and perform a variety of diagnostic services.

streets" was very attractive. The commissioner made a counterproposal: a request for $50,000 to begin the clinical study of some sex offenders in the prisons and the courts so that the Department of Mental Health might find out what population it was dealing with. How many were there? What were they like? What were the treatment possibilities? The legislature then resolved the issue by appropriating money for research "as a step toward a center."

Although we accepted the money for development of services, we in the Division of Legal Medicine deliberately delayed the organization of a special center. We argued that a single center for sex offenders made no sense. There were psychotic sex offenders, mentally retarded sex offenders, those requiring maximum security, and those requiring little or none. We already had a variety of facilities in the state for the care and supervision of criminals, the mentally ill, and the retarded. Sex offenders, we argued, did not constitute a special category. Our hope was to establish court clinics for sex offenders who could be managed on probation, prison services for sex offenders who needed more security, services for the retarded sex offender, and so on.

The arguments went on. There were repeated legislative demands that we open a center. We stalled, hoping to develop general services for all types of offenders, which would make a special sex offender center unnecessary. We managed to proceed unhampered until a new series of sex crimes in 1957 triggered court hearings in which we were told that the law required us to establish a single center with all deliberate speed. Later that year, a "center" was established, but a practical compromise was worked out in which prisoners, probationers, and parolees were in most instances handled by the court and prison clinics, while a minimum number were officially tagged as sex offenders and sent to the center at Bridgewater.

The Director of the Division of Legal Medicine of the Department of Mental Health of the Commonwealth of Massachusetts was a job originally held by a pathologist, vacant in 1954. Like many government jobs, the salary was inversely proportional to the length of the title. I had finished my residency only the year before and was not yet enmeshed in private practice when the commissioner asked if I had a "couple of hours a week" to organize and supervise a few psychiatrists who would do some research in therapy with sex offenders. I agreed to "explore" the problem. I was to be paid one-quarter time and could put in my time any way I liked. This very "part-time" work began in September of 1954.[2]

At first I had absolutely nothing to do. The office facilities at the department were primitive. There was a secretary who would take dictation, if I had anything to dictate. In the time I had, I looked around the department and got to know various division heads and administrative personnel whose friendship and tolerance later proved most valuable in bending department policies. I also read the sex offender legislation, which I didn't understand. While still somewhat confused about what I was to do and where I was to begin, I was invited to lunch by a Bar Association Medical Society Group, which had been meeting for two years in an effort to establish a demonstration clinic in the Cambridge court. They explained that the Third District Court of Eastern Middlesex County (Cambridge) was centrally located, and could be staffed easily, and had a large case load. The chief probation officer ran the best probation office in the state and was determined to get more psychiatric help. The court alienist was willing to stay, continuing to do diagnostic work while a court clinic built a treatment service. They had everything but money and someone to do the work. It became clear at the first meeting that they expected to use the funds for the sex offender research to get a court clinic set up in Cambridge and that they expected me to run it. Even if I weren't the impressionable and somewhat gullible and green psychiatrist that I was, I would have been moved by this eloquent and distinguished group who talked about the "historical import," the "grand pioneering traditions," and the Sacco-Vanzetti case.

The rationalization was to set up a court clinic so that "sex offenders could be seen and evaluated." The first problem was to get a functioning clinic. I recall this period as one of increasing discomfort, as I realized how different this clinic was from the usual medically-centered operation. The clinic was, and has remained, peripheral rather than central to the court as an institution. As far as the court was concerned, 95 per cent of court cases were none of the clinic's

[2] Several devices were used to get around the problem of low salaries which plagued the development of division services. The first of these was the "part-time" lure used by the commissioner in hiring me. Other techniques were (1) allowing wide flexibility in how professionals put in their time, for example, nights, weekends, (2) considering all related activity to be in their work time, for example, time off for personal treatment, training, reading, writing reports, and so on.

business. The chief demands in the other 5 per cent were for diagnostic services. Several steps taken with the establishment of this clinic made it unique and opened the possibilities of a far-reaching impact on our judicial system. They were:

(1) The clinic was located *in the court building,* minimizing the natural tendencies of court and clinic, each with its own special expertise and problems, to withdraw from each other.

(2) The clinic belonged to the court, was established primarily for court problems, and did not handle court cases as an unwelcome addition to other clinical work.

(3) The clinic was established as an extension of the probation idea, to bring increased clinical skills to the management of probationers in the community.

The quality of probation supervision itself varied from worker to worker, but was generally limited by case loads to fifty to eighty cases per worker. The clinic then provided an opportunity for more intensive treatment of a small number of probation cases. Occasionally, a case would be handled almost exclusively by the clinic, but the most productive were handled by the clinic and the probation officer working together. We decided early that we would resist the pressure to become a diagnostic "mill"; that we were interested in understanding something about the dynamics of criminal behavior in general and the sex offender in particular. That meant getting involved in therapeutic relationships.

At first, many referrals were of the type seen by the alienist— diagnostic problems, questions of psychosis, and the like. The court alienist saved the clinic from being swamped with these, but we saw some, often preventing a thirty-day diagnostic admission to a state hospital. This type of direct savings was always welcome ammunition at budget time.

The purely voluntary clinic case was rare. All referrals were made with the authority of the court in the background. Though we were concerned at first with the problem of motivation, we quickly found that it was possible to "force" probationers who were "poorly motivated" into a treatment relationship within four or five sessions by using the probation officers' police powers and the implied threat of jail. Where clinic treatment was made a condition of probation, we reached a segment of the delinquent population otherwise unmanageable. Many of these patients, struggling with overwhelming dependent wishes, were able to deny these wishes in the form of "I don't want to be here—the court is making me," while at the same time gratifying unconscious wishes for closeness.

The issue of confidentiality of material—a pseudo-legal problem with major psychological dimensions—was one of the first to confront us in the development of services. The problem for us, trained to observe in scrupulous detail the privacy of our patients' communications, was painful. The general solution (many individual exceptions are made) throughout the prison and court clinics has been that all communications from a patient are private unless (1) the patient is being seen specifically for evaluation for a correction agency—*and knows it;* (2) the patient in treatment communicates information that in the therapist's judgment requires action to prevent damage or injury to the patient or someone else. Patients generally are told this; actually, the implied relationship is no different from that with any other type of patient. (The doctor has an obligation to protect his patient from suicide by commitment without the patient's consent, for example, and the patient has legal recourses against improper interference.) The issue of confidentiality was not settled until work in the prisons had gone on for some time. It then appeared that the question, "Is what I'm telling you confidential?" was only the most superficial expression of the basic problem, "Can I trust you?" and the sooner this was brought up in the treatment relationship, the better. In other words, the *legal problem* of "confidentiality" merged into the psychological technical problem of establishing a therapeutic alliance with an ego defective individual.

The probationer's problems in trusting the probation officer or the clinic were repeated in a minor key in the clinic's distrust of the court and the court's of the clinic. The mutual suspicion showed itself in many ways. Often the clinic would be treated as an intruder. Decisions would be made on clinic cases without the clinic participating. The clinic would be unduly secretive about clinical material on the theory that we didn't know what the court would do with the material. As director of the clinic, I had to get used to the idea that I couldn't make decisions on disposition and management of cases as I could in a medical setting—that this was the court's responsibility, not mine. The probation office was jealous of the small case loads (twenty patients) in the clinic. The judges jealously guarded their power and prerogatives. Every other week some problem occurred that threatened the clinic's end.

Our early treatment techniques were naive and ineffective. We had difficulty maintaining a continuing treatment relationship. We hadn't learned how to go after patients and their families, how to conduct interviews in the back of taxis, how to present ourselves as real people in therapy in contrast to the shadowy role one plays in the treatment of the neuroses. We felt that the probation office was uncooperative, that the court didn't deserve us. They thought we were "in the clouds." They withheld cases or made referrals in such a way that the patients never got to the clinic. In time, however, court and clinic became friends. Aside from the personal commitment of both clinic and probation staff, it was clear that there was a need for these services in the court and that this was a challenging and interesting group of patients.

A method of operation was worked out along the following lines:

(1) If the probation office wanted the clinic to see a patient, it would obtain a continuance from the court. (A continuance is a postponement of court action for a specified time and can be repeated indefinitely. If the accused is willing, it can be a method of keeping him under the control of the court without any judicial finding of guilt and thus no court record. It has the additional advantage of being completely indeterminate.) In almost all cases where prolonged continuances were obtained, the charges were eventually dropped.

(2) The clinic would then undertake a diagnostic evaluation, attempting to assess (a) the degree of psychological disturbance, (b) the immediate dynamics of the current episode, and (c) the range of problems in the school, work, or family situation.

(3) We would then confer with the probation office, pooling our information and deciding whether the case would be managed primarily by the clinic or the probation office, and to what extent each had to be involved. (Periodic reevaluation conferences were also arranged as needed.)

(4) The probation officer would then present the combined recommendations to the judge, who would either continue the case or make other disposition.

(5) If the case had already been adjudicated and placed on

probation, a similar series of diagnostic and disposition conferences would be held, but the material in this case would not usually be presented to the judge unless he had some special interest in following the case.

It took two years before this system worked at all smoothly, but by the end of that period: (a) the clinic was seeing about 5 per cent of the court cases; (b) there was no waiting for diagnostic evaluation, although several months would sometimes be required for an intensive treatment disposition; (c) probation officers were bringing their cases to the clinic for consultation in casework techniques; (d) clinic workers and probation officers were communicating freely the essential information each needed in his work with cases; (e) the judge was able to keep in the community cases that might otherwise have to be imprisoned or hospitalized.

As the Cambridge clinic proved useful, requests for services began to come in from other district courts. Each court reflected the special problems of its community, and the type of services varied with the judge and probation office. Over the next seven years, a dozen court clinics were developed in both urban and rural areas with growing awareness on the part of the legislature that it was appropriating money for more than the treatment of sex offenders. Let me remind the reader that some courts had other sources of psychiatric help from various clinics and hospitals in the commonwealth. What the court clinics offered in addition to increased service were those special functions associated with being inside the court, having daily contact with probation officers and judges, functioning as a part of the judicial process. It is clear that this close physical relationship allowed the clinics to reach a segment of the probation group that can be touched by neither an outside clinic nor a probation office alone.

In spite of the many problems of the type described in Cambridge, in spite of each community's peculiarities, in spite of occasional pompous judges, ill-trained probation officers, and tactless psychiatrists (and others), only one of the court clinics was closed. I am not sure we understand this failure, but I will set down the essential facts.

This court had had a small consultation service supported by the county since 1950. It was one of the rare instances where a dialogue about the management of court problems had developed among the psychiatrist, the probation officer, and the judge. A limited part-time service, it had worked well. First, we hired this court's psychiatrist (using the traditional part-time seduction) to head the division's growing court clinic program. We were careful to select an intelligent, well-trained, tactful replacement for him at that court and at the same time we expanded the part-time service into a full-time court clinic. (The expanded services were introduced gradually and were well tolerated by the court, except that in retrospect a joking remark by one of the judges to the effect, "Are we running a court or a hospital here?" seems significant.) Next the division borrowed the court's chief probation officer to help prepare new courts for clinic services. Within six months the presiding judge asked the clinic to leave the court building. Since we had made being *in the court building* a condition of providing services, that ended the clinic. It seems clear that a successful court clinic rests on an adequate probation office and the probation officers' good relationship to the judges. Most judges, in dealing with petty offenses, lean heavily on the probation work-up and recommendations in making disposition. A good court clinic enriches this process, and the continuing demand for increased clinic services is a testimony to their usefulness.

In the fall of 1954, at the same time that the court clinic program was starting, we began to investigate the possibility of seeing some sex offenders in the prisons. The principal officer (warden) of the Concord Reformatory was willing to have us see any prisoners who would see us. An immediate problem arose: What sort of feelings would there be about seeing psychiatrists when it became known that only sex offenders were being seen? We decided that we had to see all kinds of cases not only to minimize the "stigma," but to broaden the range of treatment experience and make comparison studies possible. Again, the sex offender was the wedge for new services.

Initially, we had no idea where to start. The prison had five hundred inmates in their late teens and early twenties, 20 per cent of whom had a history of some sex offense. We began reading prison records and met the prison social workers and some of the officer personnel. We hired psychiatrists in their third, fourth, or fifth year of training to work one night a week. We told the prison personnel that we would see anyone for evaluation—not just sex offenders. The first referrals included some sex offenders and some other problems for psychiatric diagnosis.

At first, three out of four prisoners refused further contact after initial evaluation. Within six months this figure was reversed, as the image of the psychiatrist in the prison improved. Before the introduction of a treatment service in the prison, the only reason a man saw a psychiatrist was for transfer to Bridgewater—a hospital for the criminally insane and a relatively neglected, understaffed institution that most prisoners dreaded. Once a psychotherapy program began, the self-referrals increased to the point where there was always a waiting list.

The first year of the division's existence was one of organization, getting some experience in work with prisoners, getting some "feel" of the field. We had a going court clinic in Cambridge and a small treatment service at Concord. For the time being that was enough, but things didn't stay quiet for long.

In 1955, a group of prisoners at the Charlestown Prison barricaded themselves with hostages in what was called the Cherry Hill (maximum security) section of the institution. It took a couple of days and some National Guard tanks to get them out. All of the prisoners were soon to be transferred to the new prison at Walpole. The riot temporarily focused public attention on the prison problems in general, and a series of investigations of the corrections system was held. The resulting recommendations, calling for progressive changes in all phases of corrections, became a blueprint for gradual change and reform.

One of the more immediate results was the hiring of a career professional from another state as Commissioner of Corrections. His appointment marked the end of gross political interference with the upper echelons of the Department of Corrections. Both he and his successor (who is also a trained criminologist) actively pushed for an extension of the prisoner-treatment program into all of the state penal institutions. Each of the programs was different. No set plan was used. Much depended on the sophistication of the institution and the available correction staff. The amount of integration into the working of the prison varied; at the women's prison in Framingham, for example, the division was involved in every major phase of prison activity, from initial evaluation to rehabilitation programs, to release and post-release planning, while at Concord, the psychiatric treatment service was as limited and isolated as, say, the dental service. We found that each of the prisons had a unique character, and like the courts, each acquired a unique service.

Our psychiatrists for staffing both the court and prison clinics were drawn from the various residency programs in the Boston area. Helping out some difficult financial situations for many residents by providing part-time evening work was an incidental benefit of the prison program and a key to recruitment. Social workers and psychologists were attracted by the exciting possibilities of the new program with its flexible emphasis on research, training, and treatment.

Supervision of part-time people in training has developed into a major continuing activity. At first, we had monthly informal group discussions on prison problems. Within a year, these group discussions had developed into formal individual supervision. At present, to mention just one case, the suitability of the prison experience as a training opportunity has been formally recognized by the Massachusetts Mental Health Center, which assigns up to ten of its psychiatric residents to this program each year. Individual supervision is provided and a continuing seminar explores the special problems of work with ego-defective individuals. The prison, by the imposition of external physical controls, allows the trainee an opportunity to study in detail major character disorders that cannot be managed in any other setting. It is this aspect of the work that lends itself so well to training purposes. Most psychiatric residents, social workers, and psychologists are trained in a setting where patients or clients come with complaints (physical or psychological) and ask for help. That aspect of the patient's wish for help and trust in the therapist as a helping figure grows into the "therapeutic alliance." Since prisoners, especially the chronic offenders, come to treatment lacking the capacity for basic trust, the specific problems of alliance formation stand out clearly.

It is clear that the protective and shadowy anonymity of the therapist in the analytic model requires great modification for work with ego-defective characters. Since the therapist must function in many ways like the primary object, the kind of person he is takes on greater significance. He will be a model for identification, and thus have greater responsibilities toward his patient than in the treatment of the neuroses.

We have felt it was important for residents and others to have had at least a year of experience before going into the prisons and have been careful to select only those who seem to have reasonable capacities to "be themselves" and to be comfortably in control of their own impulses.

Training programs for correctional personnel and various parole projects grew directly from the work with the prisoners. Increasing numbers of mental health personnel, psychiatrists, social workers, and psychologists in the prisons provoked requests for conferences, discussion groups and teaching sessions. Regular lectures in criminal psychology were added to the officers' training program, with variable responses from the officers. At one of the institutions, a case seminar was developed to which officers would bring various disciplinary problems, and an effort would be made to understand the behavior from the institution record and clinical evaluation.

This was a mutual exchange. The guards know much more than the psychiatrists about the prison, its culture, and the relationships among inmates and between inmates and guards. A widespread feeling among correctional personnel at all levels that the problems are immense and that no one else cares is quickly shared by the mental health professionals and tends to bring all workers in the field closer together. After a lecture to a group of guards, in which I was attempting to bring the "light of scientific psychology into the darkness of the correction night," an older guard stood up and said, "What you say is very interesting, doctor. There were a bunch of those Rockefeller people around here in the '30's who talked much like you do. They were here a year, wrote a book and left us with the same problems we always had." In the eight years since that lecture, the division—rather than leaving—has become more involved. The guard probably still has the same problems, but he hasn't been left alone with them. In each of the state penal institutions, there are now full-time correction and mental health personnel concerned with treatment services. Approximately 10 per cent of the male prison population is seen in some form of psychotherapy. The figure is 20 per cent for women.

The problem of continued treatment on parole arose as soon as significant numbers of treatment cases came to the end of their sentences. The Parole Board had asked us to see parole cases as early as 1956. Every effort to establish a long-term relationship with a parolee seemed to fail unless a prior relationship had been established during at least six months of prison treatment. If this relationship could be established in prison, more than half would continue treatment with the same therapist after release.

A five-member Parole Board, once a part of the Department of Correction, is a separate agency. The chairman of the Parole Board is the chief administrator, and twenty-four parole agents cover the state by geographical district. (In the Parole Board and its functions, one can see the precursor of a sentencing authority. Some states are experimenting with an indeterminate sentencing system in which the court's function is reduced to the determination of guilt; the prisoner is sentenced to an adult sentencing board, which determines where he goes, how he is treated, and when he is ready for release. Steps toward this system have been taken here and elsewhere by increasing the maximum and lowering the minimum sentence, so that the Parole Board has a wider range of discretion.)

The division and the Parole Board have not yet worked out a satisfactory relationship. The members of the Parole Board want as much information as they can get in trying to make release decisions. Thus, when they know we are seeing a prisoner, they ask for a report. If we give regular reports to the Parole Board with recommendations, it would violate the contract we have with the prisoners. If we refuse any and all requests for information, our professional situation becomes untenable. How to write a report that would be useful to the board and at the same time not destroy our position with the prisoners? A tentative solution was finally worked out and hedged with many exceptions: a brief note is sent to the board describing the major general issues in treatment. It contains treatment but not parole recommendations and is written with the knowledge and participation of the prisoner. This method gives the Parole Board some information but, more importantly, helps focus on the issue of trust in the relationship between prisoner and therapist.

To help interpret the increased amount of psychological material coming from the prisons, we assigned a psychiatrist to the Parole Board. As the position developed, he was also available for consultation on parole problems and would advise on referrals to the new follow-up Parole Clinic, where we were providing continued contact for prisoners in treatment who were released on parole. Like many of our projects, this opened with much promise. The need was acute, the board members cooperative, but our experience with them was quite uneven. The first psychiatrist we assigned managed to antagonize the board enough so that referrals to the parole clinic stopped. His replacement, on the other hand, got so chummy with the parole people that productive work with parole problems stopped. Another attempt is being made currently. The problem in parole has special complications. The board itself consists of appointees of uneven talents. The releasing functions of the board require careful case study if reasonably accurate predictions of parole success are to be made. The board does not deal with petty offenders. A "mistake" usually means headlines. The board is open to pressure from relatives, friends, congressmen, and others. They also know that refusing to parole a man means that when he is released, he goes into the community without supervision.

The individual parole officers are drawn from experienced correction personnel, but are generally without specific psychological training. Efforts to bring minimal educational standards to both parole and probation officers have been only partially successful. Our tactics here have been to support the healthy moves that the agencies themselves made, for example, hiring a research director, making a college degree a requirement for appointment, increasing salaries (to attract better people), and giving time off for training. We are a long way, however, from having a politically independent, well-trained and staffed parole system that could justify the establishment of a sentencing authority.

Even though the same criticisms can be leveled at the Youth Service Board, it already has sentencing authority. The court can find a child delinquent but cannot decide to which institution or for how long he should be sent. The Board does that and, in addition, runs the juvenile institutions. The entire orientation to juveniles is different, and services developed for the Board and its institutions have reflected these differences. Since the Youth Service Board already had "treatment" personnel, our contribution has been more in terms of consultation, training of personnel, and diagnostic or brief treatment services for juveniles. A major contribution has been made in terms of increased facilities for work with the families of delinquents. In Massachusetts, these efforts have been only a small part of a widespread interest in juvenile offenders on the part of several private children's agencies. The division's role in part has been the financial support of promising programs often instigated elsewhere.

𝕏 CONCLUSIONS—AND WARNINGS 𝕏

Opportunities for the establishment of services for public offenders will differ in every state. Sponsoring agencies may be private, state, county, or city. The settings, individual problems and personalities will vary. The initiating circumstances and types of services it is possible to develop will depend on the traditions and past history of the locale and the types of personnel available for recruitment. Few areas, for example, can match the reservoir of training personnel in the Boston area, which we used for staffing our court and prison services throughout the state.

Nevertheless, there are certain general difficulties and opportunities that one can expect.

1. Logical and orderly development will be rare. The final structure of services will be the resultant of many special interests and forces in the community rather than the consequence of rational planning. The psychiatrist will find himself in the position of guiding rather than leading, minimizing the catastrophes rather than starting revolutions.

2. The major day-to-day problems will be with his own peculiar and wonderful mental health personnel and their opposite numbers in the host institutions. He will have to deal with jealousy, rivalry, and pettiness in situations where it is not "analyzable," and at the same time, keep his own matching feelings under reasonable control.

3. He will have to bend and stretch most of the rules and regulations if his project is to get started.

4. The closer he stays to his basic clinical formulations and the treatment of patients, leaving the grand plan for "reorganization of the system" to wiser men, the more effective he will be.

5. He will find among these "difficult" people many lasting friendships. Once involved in the correction field, he will find it very hard to leave.

Planning for a Community Mental Health Center

Robert L. Leopold

UNIVERSITY OF PENNSYLVANIA AND
WEST PHILADELPHIA MENTAL HEALTH CONSORTIUM

XIV

Community mental health center planning must first of all develop, by way of administrative procedures, techniques for eliciting and maintaining community sanction and support and for solving or at least ameliorating power conflicts as they arise.[1] And ultimately, of course, any administrative structure must be tested by how adequately it provides comprehensive mental health facilities to that segment of the population most in need—enabling it both to recognize its own need and to cope with many of its daily problems—so that the center can move toward a real reaching out and a gathering in of *all* community members to provide access to an integrated network of service.[2] The

---

[1] This chapter is adapted from "The West Philadelphia Mental Health Consortium: Administrative Planning in a Multihospital Catchment Area," a paper read at the 123rd annual meeting of the American Psychiatric Association, Detroit, Michigan, May 8–12, 1967, and published in the American Psychiatric Journal, V. 124, No. 4, October 1967, in a special supplement on Community Psychiatry, pp. 69–76. The paper has been enlarged to encompass pertinent developments since the West Philadelphia Community Mental Health Consortium, which was projected at the time the paper was delivered, began operations on July 1, 1967.

[2] To qualify for federal construction funds, a community mental health

issues are urgent. Yet the problems concerned with creating administrative planning structures appear to have been the subject of somewhat less discussion than have problems directly concerned with specific service development and delivery.

The developing community mental health centers are often
organized around one university center, around one hospital, which
may or may not be a university hospital, or around one ongoing facility, such as a psychiatric outpatient clinic. In many areas of the
United States, however, there are no suitable institutions available to
act as sponsors and organizers of community mental health centers
and the local or state government has had to help organize appropriate support.

The situation in the western part of the city of Philadelphia
is another kind entirely. This section is the home of three major educational institutions (the University of Pennsylvania, Drexel Institute
of Technology, and the Philadelphia College of Pharmacy and Science), six hospitals, and one department of psychiatry in a large
medical school—that of the University of Pennsylvania. These lie in
Region VII, Catchment Area 3,[3] which covers the southern half of
West Philadelphia.

Of the six hospitals, five have their own psychiatric departments. Two of these are fully affiliated with the Department of Psychiatry of the University of Pennsylvania as major teaching facilities,
one is partially affiliated, and two are not affiliated but have representation on the university faculty. Despite the presence of these major
medical facilities, however, care is not necessarily provided specifically
for the area just described; rather, the hospitals draw patients on a
citywide and even multistate basis. Until the recent upsurge of interest
in community psychiatry, none of these institutions had indicated any

---

center must provide at least five *essential elements* of comprehensive mental
health services: (a) inpatient services; (b) outpatient services; (c) partial hospitalization services, including at least day care; (d) emergency services provided 24 hours per day within at least one of the three services above; and (e)
consultation and education services available to community agencies and professional personnel. *Adequate services* are defined as consisting of the five essential
elements plus five other components: (a) diagnostic services; (b) rehabilitative
services, including vocational and educational programs; (c) pre-care and after-
care services in the community, including foster home placement, home visiting,
and halfway houses; (d) training; and (e) research and evaluation.

[3] The Catchment Area designated #3 by Pennsylvania in its Comprehensive Mental Health Plan has a population of approximately 204,000.

particular interest in or responsibility for providing mental health services in their particular geographic communities. As each hospital became aware of community mental health legislation and its funding opportunities, several began to make individual plans for establishing community mental health centers. But this kind of planning, because it is not concerned with coordinating efforts, fails to take advantage of the potential force for integrating services that rests in consideration of the needs of the total community.

Not long after the 1963 Community Mental Health Centers legislation was enacted, the University of Pennsylvania began to examine its existing mental health facilities because of major changes in university thinking first articulated in the 1950's and continuing in this decade, and at least in part because of developments growing out of the 1963 legislation.

The University of Pennsylvania, like other universities, is moving from traditional academic isolation to closer identification with the community. Its participation in the work of the West Philadelphia Corporation is only one indication, but a particularly pertinent one here, of its growing sense of responsibility for what goes on in the community. Meanwhile, its Department of Psychiatry has become more acutely aware of the changing face of psychiatry—specifically, with respect to community action for mental health and the necessity to participate in such action if the department is to continue as an active force in the profession. A reflection of the direction of its thinking was the decision to establish a Division of Community Psychiatry within the department, and early in 1965 I was assigned the task of establishing this division.

These trends led the university inevitably to a sense of responsibility for some participation in planning and operating a community mental health center. Meanwhile, I had decided that the Division of Community Psychiatry would have to start from a base of existing mental health services under university auspices. The necessary survey of these services gave us an opportunity to collect data that would enable the university to conceptualize its potential role in developing a center.

This examination, carried out in the fall of 1965, made it plain that the university's mental health facilities did not, in most instances, offer true community services. They provided little direct access to persons living in the community other than through the traditional means: the private practitioner for the well-to-do, overloaded clinic services for the less well-to-do. There was little relationship among the services and between the services and the outside community; and little knowledge within university facilities about other pertinent facilities under the university's sponsorship, to say nothing of other caretaking agencies in the surrounding community.

The findings of this survey strengthened university feeling in favor of participation in developing a center, a feeling that grew even stronger when the state Office of Mental Health urged participation and when it became increasingly apparent that various other agencies in the area were eager to proceed with plans of their own. If the university was to retain a leadership position in the community, it could hardly avoid the decision it finally made in the spring of 1966 to seek an active role in the development of a center for West Philadelphia.

But the idea of establishing a center of its own was soon rejected because such a move would waste the very considerable resources of other community agencies and arouse the hostility of many people who had spent much time and effort in planning services under their sponsorship. However, the varying degrees of affiliation between the university's Department of Psychiatry and the psychiatric departments of the hospitals seemed to present impossible obstacles to working out arrangements whereby the separate hospital facilities could be used economically and effectively by a university-directed center. Even if such arrangements could be worked out, the university would inevitably look like a power-hungry monolith.

Alternatively, the university might have planned a program in which it would become a pivotal point for a loose union of center services developed independently by the other agencies. The university would simply supply certain resources not otherwise available to the agencies (for example, various research and administrative facilities), and also consultative services. Although the university might thus be relieved of much work and worry, this course of action would bear little relation to its policy of assuming increasing responsibility for what happens in the community. The university could see as the outcome of such a course only duplication of effort, waste of resources, and, ultimately, chaos; and it too was soon discarded.

Meanwhile, the state, in consultation with the hospitals in the area, was urging cooperative measures, a fact that gave impetus to the university's effort to find a better choice of action. A series of informal exploratory conferences followed, involving representatives of all six hospitals and of the Health and Welfare Council of Philadelphia, through its West Philadelphia office, as well as the university. Cooperative planning was soon seen as a necessity, but how to go about it without sacrificing any one agency's autonomy was a serious problem. Finally, it was agreed that sponsorship was needed from an outside agency, one with no vested interest in mental health.

The West Philadelphia Corporation had been formed in 1959 by the four major academic institutions in West Philadelphia, one of its six major hospitals, and the community itself to provide for orderly physical and social planning in that section. Thus it seemed the agency most nearly representing the interests of the entire community, and the most appropriate for facilitating community cooperation. After some negotiations with interested parties, the corporation called a meeting, early in July 1966, in which many institutions and individuals having a concern with mental health were invited to participate. The stated purpose was to explore the feasibility of joint planning for a community mental health center in West Philadelphia.

At this meeting, all interested agencies agreed that a group to facilitate cooperative effort and joint planning should be organized. The name *Consortium* was selected because this term is derived from the world of finance rather than of mental health, and therefore carried no emotional charge. The Consortium was conceived as a partnership or association of the six hospitals committed to planning and developing the West Philadelphia Community Mental Health Center. Its structure would permit each hospital to retain its own autonomy, and it was devised with sufficient openness to permit participation in its activities by other interested agencies. Although the Consortium was to be directly responsible to the West Philadelphia Corporation, it was to have its own chairman and its own directors, who would be the Presidents of the Boards of Managers of each of the member hospitals (or their designates). The Vice-President for Medical Affairs of the University of Pennsylvania agreed to serve as its chairman. We think this use of a Consortium is an unusual, and perhaps unique, administrative arrangement for planning and developing a community mental health center.

The first action of the Consortium was the formation of an ad hoc planning committee; as Director of the Division of Community Psychiatry of the Department of Psychiatry of the University of Pennsylvania, I was asked to serve as chairman. The ad hoc planning committee consisted of representatives of the psychiatric departments of the member hospitals, a representative of the School of Social Work of the University of Pennsylvania, and the Director of the West Area office of the Health and Welfare Council of Philadelphia. During the life of the committee, informal discussions were held with the president and the members of the board of the West Philadelphia Corporation, and with the District Supervisor for our area of the School District of Philadelphia.

The Consortium idea offers extraordinary opportunities for creative planning and integration of services and for conceptualization and research, but it obviously increases the complexities of the planning process itself. As elsewhere, the particular needs of the community must be understood and met; but also, the special needs of each member institution must be negotiated and settled within the framework of the partnership agreement that the Consortium represents. Such negotiations are arduous and, at times, anxiety-ridden and unpleasant. Nonetheless, when problems are worked out in this way, the ultimate effect on the Consortium's planning is wholesome and integrating.

Soon after the initial meetings we realized that a center operated jointly by a number of agencies could function effectively only if it developed an overall administrative planning and evaluative structure, which of itself would have to be attached to an organization with many resources. The committee proposed to the Consortium, and received its approval for, a plan whereby such a structure would be attached to the university's Department of Psychiatry in order to utilize both the university's considerable resources and the relationships already established between the university's Department of Psychiatry and some of the member hospitals and various other highly relevant social agencies.

An organizational structure finally emerged as the product of many hours of work by the committee alone and of its many working conferences with the full Consortium, the West Philadelphia Corporation, university officers and other interested university personnel, and representatives of the Health and Welfare Council.

The Consortium derives both its program and its administrative structure from the following postulates:

1. The program must reach out into the community and ac-

tively encourage the participation and involvement of all its members, and particularly those who heretofore have not had direct access to mental health services. The fact that certain services have been technically available for many years but have been under-utilized is here taken into account.

2. Each member institution expects and is expected to maintain administrative control and authority over its own facilities. The Consortium is to function as a confederation of peers responsible for making these facilities component parts of a community mental health center for use by all residents of Catchment Area 3.

3. The Consortium must create and operate facilities *additional* to those of the member institutions wherever necessary—to provide eventually a full range of services, both essential and additional, under the terms of current national and state community mental health center legislation.

4. The Consortium must provide for an orderly flow of patients through the complex system of services it offers.

5. This responsibility implies the obligation to provide for an orderly flow of *information* about the patients who come into the system and their families as well. Thus the Consortium must establish a central computerized record-keeping and information-dispensing system as quickly as possible.

6. The binding element in this loosely structured organization is to be the Department of Psychiatry of the University of Pennsylvania. It is charged especially with the responsibility for those aspects of the Consortium's program concerned with training, research and evaluation, and coordination with other community programs; and it is to have the full cooperation of the School of Social Work of the university in carrying out this responsibility.

Turning now to the organizational chart: the responsible agency for the center is the West Philadelphia Corporation and its Board of Directors, which, in effect, created the West Philadelphia Community Mental Health Consortium. The Consortium appointed me as its director. I was already Director of the Division of Community Psychiatry at the university. It was felt that only by way of this joint appointment could the resources of the university be utilized most effectively with respect to service development, staffing, training, research and evaluation, and community organization. The Associate Director for Research similarly is the Assistant Director of the Division of Community Psychiatry; the Associate Director for Training likewise holds appointments in the university's medical school; and the Associate Director for Program Planning, a social worker, is a member of faculty of the University's School of Social Work. An Associate Director for Mental Retardation has been added to the Consortium staff, and serves on the university faculty.

The Director and the Associate Directors will meet with the psychiatrists responsible for the program in the member institutions of the Consortium on a regular basis in order that patient flow, record information flow, and other programs can be integrated. This community mental health center is not a geographical reality but rather a planning and operative entity. One hospital has an inpatient service, another provides outpatient services, still another will develop a diagnostic service, and so on. From an administrative standpoint, there are obvious problems with this kind of geographical dispersion, but it may well turn out from the standpoint of the community that the dispersion of services is appropriate.

It is clear, however, that such dispersion can be feasible only if adequate administrative support is provided for a free flow of information through the caretaking network. It is imperative, for example, that information developed by community organization workers in specific geographical localities flow upward through the Coordinator of the Community Organization Program to the Associate Director for Planning and then flow smoothly back to the community organization workers. This process is complicated by the necessary input of information from other agencies (schools, social service agencies, city welfare department) and by the relationship to these agencies of the community consultation teams to be developed by the Consortium. The problem of providing information for use throughout the structure of the Consortium is certainly not unique, but because of the geographical dispersion of facilities, special consideration will have to be paid to it. It is here that the Department of Psychiatry and the School of Social Work should play pivotal roles, since the collection, integration, and exposition of social and behavioral information lie within their fields of competence.

Let us now return to the planning process from which the organizational structure resulted. At the initial meeting of the planning committee, each hospital was asked to submit a proposal as to which service or services it felt most competent to provide and most inter-

ested in providing for the Consortium. These proposals were submitted to the planning committee; they were then discussed, and, with
the consent of the hospitals, often revised; and finally they were given
to the chairman of the Consortium in draft form. The chairman was
then empowered to incorporate all plans received into a proposal for
one community mental health center. Members of the Department of
Public Welfare, Division of Mental Health (both in the Philadelphia
region and in Harrisburg) gave ongoing consultative help to the Consortium during this planning process.

In mid-January 1967, the West Philadelphia Community Mental Health Consortium submitted an application for a staffing grant
to the National Institute of Mental Health. It had been approved by
the Consortium's Board of Directors and by the Executive Committee
of the West Philadelphia Corporation. Since a city hospital was among
those involved in this endeavor, individual approval had also been
sought and granted from the Health Commissioner of Philadelphia.

Despite approval by all concerned in submitting the application, it was recognized that because of the rapidity of the planning
process, several problems remain to be worked out during the implementation of services. Nonetheless, we felt that sufficient agreement
had been reached on the principles involved to make the clarification
of details easily manageable.

The community, both professional and lay, responded enthusiastically to our plans. The Consortium was literally flooded with applications for staff positions, before any promise of funding had been
received. The interest generated in the catchment area by the application remains active and work with the Health and Welfare Council
agencies is continuing. A school consultation program started in the
fall of 1966 by volunteers from the university's Department of Psychiatry has been exceedingly well received and is creating considerable
excitement in the school system, which views it as a forerunner of the
Community Mental Health Center's work. Conversations have been
held with the Marriage Council of Philadelphia, and it is hoped that
in the near future programs can be initiated to integrate its work and
the work of its Division of Family Study (that is, its academic arm)
with that of the Consortium and of the Department of Psychiatry.

The continuing exchange of ideas made possible by these la-
borious months of negotiation and joint planning and the consequent
involvement of many sectors of the professional and nonprofessional

community in West Philadelphia have resulted in an ongoing cooperative planning process, which we hope will continue into the indefinite future.

The West Philadelphia Community Mental Health Consortium received its federal grant in May 1967 and started operation on July 1, 1967. At the time of the writing of this addition (late October 1967) many programs have been started and planning is advancing in other areas. Despite the hectic pace of the initial months, several critical questions are emerging. These are related less to day-to-day operations than to overall strategies of conceptualization and long-range planning. These questions, different in form from questions raised elsewhere in this book, are, nonetheless, the same generic problems of community process and of the psychiatric dilemmas concerning social interaction.

At this time we have begun to bring some order into the chaotic discontinuity of care for the mentally ill patient. The catchment area's major inpatient unit, under the direction of the University of Pennsylvania service at Philadelphia General Hospital, is receiving patients referred by the Emergency and Intake Service and by other Consortium facilities. The partial hospitalization and outpatient services are being linked with the inpatient service. The absence of facilities for children has been met by the establishment of a Children's Coping Clinic situated at the City Health Center District Office. A service for adolescents has been initiated. Special services for narcotics addicts (in a Methadone maintenance program) and for young alcoholics are in operation. Planning for the care of mental retardates is progressing well. The Education and Consultation Service is moving, albeit slowly. A staff of close to 100 persons has been recruited, inservice training established, and an excellent demographic data bank compiled.

As we proceed, different categories of problems arise. The relationship between two of the major Consortium members, the university and the city, is still tenuous, although Consortium functioning has not been compromised. The demands of the community for consultation services are still largely unmet, partly by reason of needs for staff training and partly because of the caution of the Director of that unit.

Several serious current areas of difficulty presage even more trouble in the future. The lack of coherent community organization in our catchment area compelled us to apply for, and receive, a number of community organization workers in our federal grant. Despite this, the state has taken the position that the community organizer has little place in a mental health center, so that continuing state financial participation is questionable. In order to comply with the state's stance, it has been necessary to add clear mental health responsibilities to the community organization teams, particularly in pre-care and after-care of patients. This distorts somewhat the philosophy of needed community participation, and, if extended, could undermine a substantial conceptual base of the Consortium.

Our financial situation is a most complicated one. In those mental health centers sponsored by a single administrative unit, a budget can be prepared with realistic estimates of both costs and revenues, including third-party payments such as Medicare and Medicaid. An accounting system for separation of receipts and income is operating, and the mental health system can be added without undue complexity. In the Consortium structure, the several hospitals and especially the City hospital feel it is impossible to segregate either Consortium costs or income. Accordingly, the Consortium Board felt that a different fiscal policy must be devised.

At present, each hospital collects its own fees and places them in its general funds. Those fees collected by personnel and programs not clearly affiliated with a member hospital are billed by the administrative unit of the Consortium and fees collected are placed in the Consortium account. To date, these are negligible and will probably continue to be insignificant since the philosophy of the Consortium is one of decentralization. A formula has been established whereby each member hospital contributes to the total expenses of the Consortium in proportion to its pro rata share of the staffing moneys it receives. For the current fiscal year, a Consortium budget of $50,000 has been approved and members will contribute proportionately this amount. However, we currently are housed in a temporary, rent-free building on city grounds. This building is scheduled for demolition in mid-1968. Moreover, to minimize expenses, we have begged for and received old furniture, have not painted our walls, and have incurred none but the most necessary housekeeping and operating expenses.

This situation cannot be expected to continue indefinitely without compromising the program. One must question whether the financial base outlined above can be expected to continue as our operating budget increases two-, three-, or four-fold. The member institutions of the Consortium will not be able to identify income derived from community mental health services, but the outflow, that is, the contributions to the Consortium, will be a highly visible line item in their respective budgets. Despite these realistic difficulties, we can only hope that the degree of concern and enthusiastic involvement evidenced by each member institution will continue and that we will be able to demonstrate on a continuing basis the value of the concept of the Consortium model in order to maintain our fiscal and other ties with our member institutions.

As a corollary, it should be noted that our present sponsor, The West Philadelphia Corporation, is eager for the Consortium to become independent and form its own nonprofit corporation. The financial, as well as the community, impact of this step is totally unclear, although this direction seems inevitable.

To this point, a number of problems coherent in the Consortium structure have been described. Many problems common to most mental health centers are unasked, and even when posed, may be unanswerable. The most cogent question remains, how do you plan without knowing the range of variables for which you are planning?

Yet, clearly, planning *must* proceed, despite the lack of adequate knowledge of all the variables. This time, we are asking ourselves a series of questions—not for immediate answers, but in order to prepare some response to meet the numerous variables, and to try to make ourselves aware of potential options. It is to be hoped that the questions below will suggest one means of trying to maintain an openness of approach.

1. What are the dimensions of the total health system developing for our community? It is now fragmented and many pieces neither interlock nor even touch each other. How will the city hospital, the university, the private nonprofit hospital, the practicing self-employed physician and other health professionals, the voluntary agency, the public agency, and other health facilities relate to each other and to the community mental health center? How does one plan responsibly for financial solvency in this public-private-voluntary mix, which itself is in marked flux?

2. These questions could be extended. In what ways does the Consortium, a group related to, but not entirely part of, the university complex, develop its relationships with the total university health sys-

tem? As a mental health center we must be concerned with the university-based student health center, the emerging multi-university heart, stroke, and cancer center, the research units of many university departments, the Office of Economic Opportunity and its numerous problems, other federal problems, and with potential centers that can offer us such services as the computer center. The important service-teaching and research polarity of any major university must be faced.

3. How do we, as one community mental health center, relate to the ten or eleven other community mental health centers developing in Philadelphia so that services may be ensured for the entire city? This is especially relevant in view of the membership in our group of the city hospital. In what ways do we, and the other Philadelphia centers, relate to the state in areas of financing, planning, and training? What kinds of superordinate structures must be erected at a city-state level and how do we relate to these?

4. Can we really be free enough to understand and to accept the thrusts of demands from troubled groups of human beings whom we should be serving?

Less comprehensive questions also arise. These are no less relevant and no less puzzling.

1. How do we create our own successor? Today's organization can become tomorrow's rigid institution. How do we prevent this and maintain a self-renewing agency?

2. Are we willing to deal with the current critical manpower shortage? Can we creatively and meaningfully employ and train people with differing backgrounds? Is such training consonant with the goals of our member agencies, including the university? How can such training programs, if found desirable, be funded?

3. What research options should we elect? Some options may be less useful than others, but more easily financed. What, indeed, is the future of research in a community mental health center under a system of cost, effect, and accounting built on the military model?

These questions remain open. By the time this book is published, the questions may have to be posed differently. The attempt to answer one question inevitably opens other questions which are no less baffling. Only one thing is certain: If we could say exactly where we expect this program to be five years hence, and at that time prove correct in our expectations, then the program must be a failure. Such a high success in predicting our outcome would mean that we had opted *not* to become responsible to the demands of the community, *not* to remain flexible in providing openness and continuing responsiveness to the ever changing needs of the community, and had *not* accepted both the challenge and the opportunity of community mental health programs.

Index